Preface

THIS collection, grouped in thirteen sections, offers a wide choice in poetry. The poems were selected because they are readily comprehensible to pupils and therefore more likely to be enjoyed and remembered.

The influence of science in the modern world is emphasized in *Modern Marvels*; the glory of the commonplace and the importance of the common man in *The Workaday World and Its People*; humor in *The Funny Side*; and animals in *All Manner of Creatures*. One further section may be called to the teacher's attention, *Men and Women in Literature and Fable*.

The Introduction, intended for the pupil, sets forth the traditional elements of poetic study in less formidable terms than has hitherto been the case in anthologies of poetry. The pupil who seeks help in creative writing will find it at the end of the Introduction and also in the exercises for each section at the back of the book.

In the study material each section is treated as a separate unit. There is ample material for pupils of different interests, abilities, and needs. In utilizing these study helps the teacher will obviously apply the principle of selection best suited to his purposes. Notes, questions, assignments, and suggestions for creative writing are supplied for each section to satisfy varying demands of taste, capacity, and scholarship. In general, it may be desirable to have all pupils refer to the notes as help is needed and answer at least some of the questions that pertain to each section. The more ambitious pupils may use the special assignments and the supplementary reading.

Differentiated and individualized teaching will help to enrich the course in poetry, with a resultant improvement in the whole tone of the class. To this end every opportunity should be given for exercise in creative writing as well as in appreciation.

The editors have had recourse to the soundest portion of the progressive ideas in the field of English — ideas for which the editors express due acknowledgment, with particular mention of the *Experience Curriculum* and the *Correlated Curriculum* published by the National Council of Teachers of English.

Acknowledgments

Grateful acknowledgment is made to the following publishers and authors for permission to reprint copyrighted material:

D. Appleton-Century Company, for "El Poniente," "Symphony Pathétique," and "The Travel Bureau," from *Collected Poems*, by Ruth Comfort Mitchell. Walter C. Arensberg, for "Out-of-Doors," from *Poems*. Hilaire Belloc, for "The Frog," from *Cautionary Tales*. Stephen Vincent Benét, for "America" (from the "Invocation to *John Brown's Body*"), and "Pickett's Charge," from *John Brown's Body*, copyright, 1927, 1928, by Stephen Vincent Benét; and "The Mountain Whippoorwill," from *Ballads and Poems*, copyright, 1918, 1920, 1923, 1925, 1929, 1930, 1931, by Stephen Vincent Benét. Both these volumes published by Farrar & Rinehart. William R. Benét, for "The Last Ally." The Bobbs-Merrill Company, for "When the Frost is on the Punkin," from *Neighborly Poems*, by James Whitcomb Riley, copyright, 1891, 1919. Used by special permission of the publishers, The Bobbs-Merrill Company. Berton Braley, for "To a Photographer." Copyright by Berton Braley, all rights reserved. Gelett Burgess, for "Cinq Ans Après," "On Digital Extremities," and "The Purple Cow," from *The Burgess Nonsense Book*. Melville Cane, for "Emily Dickinson." Mrs. William Herbert Carruth, for "Each in His Own Tongue," by William Herbert Carruth. Madison Cawein, for his father's poem, "The Old Bayou." Roberta T. Swartz Chalmers, for "To Engineers." Chapman & Grimes, for "The Glory Trail," from *Sun and Saddle Leather*, by Badger Clark; for "The Lineman," and "The Song of the Press," by William H. Hillyer. The Clarendon Press, Oxford, for "London Snow," and "Nightingales," from *The Shorter Poems of Robert Bridges*, Clarendon Press, Oxford (1931), by permission of the publishers. Elizabeth Coatsworth, for "The Circus-Postered Barn." Frances Cornford, for "To a Lady seen from the Train." Covici Friede, Inc., for "Through Streets Where Crooked Wicklow Flows," by Horace Gregory; and for "Say This of Horses," by Minnie Hite Moody. Coward-McCann, Inc., and the author, for "Ceremonial Hunt," "In Walpi," "Navajo," and "The Bad Kittens," from *Compass Rose*, by Elizabeth Coatsworth, copyright, 1929, by Coward-McCann, Inc.; and for "June," from *The Complete Poems of Francis Ledwidge*, reprinted by permission of Coward-McCann, Inc. The *Daily Oklahoma* and the *Kaleidograph Press*, Dallas, for "Tame Duck," by Kenneth Kaufman. Thomas Augustine Daly, for "John Keats." The John Day Company, Inc., for "Home-Coming," by Leonie Adams. Dodd, Mead & Company, Inc., for "Jesse James," from *Golden Fleece*, by William Rose Benét; for "The Dead," and "The Great Lover," from *Collected Poems*, by Rupert Brooke; for "A Vagabond's Song," by Bliss Carman; for "Comrades," and "Love in the Winds," by Richard Hovey; for "Brooklyn Bridge at Dawn," by Richard Le Gallienne; for "A Dream," by Stephen Phillips; for "Alley Cat," and "Immigrants," by Nancy Byrd Turner; and for "One Week," by Carolyn Wells. Used by permission of the publishers, Dodd, Mead & Company, Inc. Doubleday, Doran & Company, Inc., for the following selections all copyrighted by Doubleday, Doran & Company, Inc., "Sim-

POEMS
for Modern Youth

EDITED BY

ADOLPH GILLIS

Principal, Public School 3, Brooklyn, New York
Formerly Head of the English Department, James Madison
High School, Brooklyn, New York

AND

WILLIAM ROSE BENÉT

HOUGHTON MIFFLIN COMPANY

The Riverside Press Cambridge

The Riverside Press

CAMBRIDGE · MASSACHUSETTS

PRINTED IN THE U.S.A.

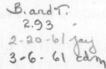

B. and T.
2.93
2-20-61 jay
3-6-61 cdm

plicity," "Persicos Odi," and "The Slump in Sybaris," from *So Much Velvet*, by Franklin P. Adams, copyright, 1924; for "The Hedgehog," from *Basket for a Fair*, by Laura Benét, copyright, 1929, 1934; for "Don Quixote," from *Selected Poems*, by Arthur Davison Ficke, copyright, 1926; for a selection from "The Troubadour of Eze," from *American Song*, by Paul Engle, copyright, 1933, 1934; for "I Shall Not Be Afraid," from *Candles that Burn*, by Aline Kilmer, copyright, 1919; for "Martin," from *Trees and Other Poems*, by Joyce Kilmer, copyright, 1914; for "If," from *Rewards and Fairies*, by Rudyard Kipling, copyright, 1910, and "The Gipsy Trail," from *Rudyard Kipling's Verse, Inclusive Edition*, copyright, 1904, 1934, both selections reprinted with permission from Mrs. Kipling and Doubleday, Doran and Company, Inc.; for "Lindbergh: A Ballad," from *Fool's Errand*, by Alexander Laing, copyright, 1928; for "The Dog," from *Love Sonnets of a Caveman*, copyright, 1928, "The Tom-Cat," from *Poems and Portraits*, copyright, 1922, and "Unrest," from *Dreams and Dust*, copyright, 1915, all by Don Marquis; and for "I Hear America Singing," "Miracles" (from "Song of Myself"), "O Captain! My Captain!" and "Pioneers, O Pioneers," from *Leaves of Grass*, by Walt Whitman, copyright, 1924. E. P. Dutton & Co., Inc., for "The Man Hunt," taken from *The Vale of Tempe*, by Madison Cawein; for "London to Paris, by Air," taken from *Poems: 1904–1936 — By Lord Gorell*; for "Tacking Ship Off Shore," by Walter Mitchell, taken from *Poems of Youth*, edited by William Rose Benét; and for "Craven," by Sir Henry Newbolt, taken from *Poems Old and New*; all published by E. P. Dutton & Co., Inc., New York; for "Hills," taken from *Death & General Putnam & 101 Other Poems*, by Arthur Guiterman; for "Kentucky Mountaineer," taken from *Man With a Bull-Tongue Plow*, by Jesse Stuart; and "The Builder," taken from *Lanterns in Gethsemane*, by Willard Wattles, all published and copyrighted by E. P. Dutton & Co., Inc., New York. C. L. Edson, for "Ravin's of Piute Poet Poe." Paul Eldridge, for "Of China and Her Wisdom," and "Wang Peng, Famous Sociologist." Francis E. Falkenbury, for "South Street." Farrar & Rinehart, Inc., for "Gargantua," from *Earth Moods*, by Hervey Allen, copyright, 1925; and for "Ellen Hanging Clothes," by Lizette Woodworth Reese. Reprinted by permission of Farrar & Rinehart, Inc., publishers. John Gould Fletcher, for "The Swan." Hamlin Garland, for "Do You Fear the Wind," and "Magic." Crosbie Garstin, and Eric S. Pinker and Adrienne Morrison Incorporated, for "Callao," from *The Ballad of the Royal Ann*, by Crosbie Garstin. Arthur Guiterman, for "Messire Geoffrey Chaucer to His Editor." Harcourt, Brace and Company, Inc., for "Between Two Loves," and "Mia Carlotta," from *Selected Poems of T. A. Daly*; for "Caliban in the Coal Mines," "Dog at Night," "In the Subway," and "Swimmers," from *Selected Poems and Parodies of Louis Untermeyer*; and for "The Factories," from *The Factories*, by Margaret Widdemer, all reprinted by permission of Harcourt, Brace and Company, Inc., holders of the copyright. For "Smoke and Steel," from *Smoke and Steel*, by Carl Sandburg, copyright, 1920, by Harcourt, Brace and Company, Inc. Harper and Brothers, for "First Rain," by Zoë Akins; for "Is This the Lark!" "The Riveter," and "Ulysses In Autumn," by Joseph Auslander; for "Fame," from *Guinea Fowl and Other Poultry*, by Leonard Bacon; for "The Sack of Old Panama," from *Poems*, by Dana Burnet; for "The Sycophantic Fox and the Gullible Raven," from *Fables for the Frivolous*, by Guy Wetmore Carryl; for "For a Pessimist," from *Color*, by Countee Cullen; for "Quivira," from *A Ballad Maker's Pack*, "Strictly Germ-Proof" and "The Legend of the First Cam-u-el," from *The Laughing Muse*, and "The Vizier's Apology," from *The Light Guitar*, all by Arthur Guiterman. Henry Holt and Company, Inc., for "The Golf Links," and "Vermont," from *Portraits and Protests*, by Sarah N. Cleghorn; for "All That's Past," "Nod," "Old Susan," "Silver," and "The Listeners," from *Collected Poems, 1901–*

1918, by Walter de la Mare; for "Fireflies in the Garden," "Mending Wall," "Stopping by Woods on a Snowy Evening," "The Sound of Trees," and "To Earthward," from *Collected Poems by Robert Frost*; for "Machines," from *Bright Harbor*, by Daniel Whitehead Hickey; "Loveliest of Trees," "Oh, When I Was in Love with You," "Reveille," "The Merry Guide," and "When I was One-and-Twenty," from *Shropshire Lad*, by A. E. Housman; for "Chicago," "Fog," and "Under a Telephone Pole," from *Chicago Poems*, and "Grass," from *Cornhuskers*, by Carl Sandburg; and for "Four Little Foxes," and "To a Wild Goose Over Decoys," from *Slow Smoke*, by Lew Sarett. Houghton Mifflin Company, for "Identity," and "Memory," by Thomas Bailey Aldrich; for "The Plaint of the Camel," by Charles E. Carryl; for "Old Nürnberg" and "To the Schooner Casco," by Grace Hazard Conkling; for "The Owl-Critic," by James T. Fields; for "Oread," by H. D.; for "Plain Language from Truthful James," by Francis Bret Harte; for "Jim Bludso of the *Prairie Bell*," by John Hay; for "The Kings," by Louise Imogen Guiney; for "A Lady," "A London Thoroughfare Two A.M.," "Lilacs," and "Madonna of the Evening Flowers," by Amy Lowell; for "'Not Marble Nor the Gilded Monuments,'" and "You, Andrew Marvell," by Archibald MacLeish; for "Pandora's Song," and "The Brute," by William Vaughn Moody; for "Love is a Terrible Thing," by Grace Norton; for "The Blind Men and the Elephant," by John Godfrey Saxe; for "Opportunity," by Edward Rowland Sill; and also for selections from the poems of William Cullen Bryant, Ralph Waldo Emerson, Oliver Wendell Holmes, Henry Wadsworth Longfellow, James Russell Lowell, Edgar Allan Poe, and John Greenleaf Whittier. Jonathan Cape Limited, for "I Heard a Soldier," by Herbert Trench. The Johnson Publishing Company, for "At Magnolia Cemetery," and "Quartorzain," from *The Poems of Henry Timrod*, published by The Johnson Publishing Company, Richmond, Virginia. Mitchell Kennerley, for "Shade," by Theodosia Garrison. Alfred A. Knopf, Inc., for "Ghost of Indians," "Grenstone River," "The Chaplet," "To a Phoebe Bird," and "Voices," by Witter Bynner; for "Python," by Grace Hazard Conkling; for "I Saw a Man," and "The Blades of Grass," by Stephen Crane; for "The Grand Canyon," and "Triad," by Adelaide Crapsey; for "The Negro Speaks of Rivers," by Langston Hughes; for "The Tree Toad," by Orrick Johns; for "The Slave," by James Oppenheim; for "Everyday Alchemy," by Genevieve Taggard; for "The Steam Shovel," by Eunice Tietjens; for "Drug Store," by John V. A. Weaver; and for "August," the sonnet "Down to the Puritan marrow of my bones," "The Eagle and the Mole," and "Velvet Shoes," by Elinor Wylie, reprinted by permission of and special arrangement with Alfred A. Knopf, Inc., authorized publishers. Elias Lieberman, for "I Am an American," and "An Abandoned Tow-Path," copyrighted by the author. Therese Lindsey, for "Radio." J. B. Lippincott Company, for "At the Mermaid Cafeteria," "Of a Child that Had a Fever," "On a Portrait of Dr. Johnson," "Reading Aloud," "Smells," and "To a Post-Office Inkwell," by Christopher Morley. Little, Brown & Company, for "Pedigree," "I Like to See It Lap the Miles," and "This Quiet Dust Was Gentlemen and Ladies," from *The Poems of Emily Dickinson*, Centenary Edition, edited by Martha Dickinson Bianchi and Alfred Leete Hampson. Reprinted by permission of Little, Brown & Company. Francis Litz, for "Evolution," by Father Tabb. Liveright Publishing Corporation, for Poems of the Machine Age — "Power House," "Corliss Engine at Rest," and "Reciprocating Engines," by Macknight Black; and for "The White Rooster," by George O'Neil. John A. Lomax, for "The Cowboy's Lament," and "The Dying Cowboy." Longmans, Green & Co., for "Scythe Song," and "The Odyssey," by Andrew Lang; and "Clouds," and "The Flyers," by Frank Ernest Hill. Lothrop, Lee & Shepard Company, for "Shakespeare Reads the King James Version," by

Richard Burton; and for "A Little While I Fain Would Linger Yet," and "In Harbor," from *Selected Poems*, by Paul Hamilton Hayne. The Macmillan Company, for "To a Modern Poet," from *The Poets*, by Joseph Auslander; for "Crystal Moment," and "The Spider," by Robert P. Tristram Coffin; for "Monkeys," by Padraic Colum; for "All Life Moving to One Measure," "Back," "In a Restaurant," "Rupert Brooke," and "The Conscript," by Wilfrid Wilson Gibson; for "The Man He Killed," by Thomas Hardy; for "Eve," "Stupidity Street," "The Gypsy Girl," and "Time, You Old Gipsy Man," by Ralph Hodgson; for "Wild Plum," by Orrick Johns; for "Factory Windows Are Always Broken," "General William Booth Enters into Heaven," "The Congo," "The Eagle that is Forgotten," "The Leaden-Eyed," "The Mouse that Gnawed the Oak-Tree Down"; and "The Santa Fé Trail — A Humoresque," by Vachel Lindsay; for "The Automobile," and "Goethals, the Prophet-Engineer," by Percy MacKaye; for sonnets, "Are we neither Heaven nor Earth," "O little self," "Man has his unseen friend," and "What am I, Life? a thing of watery salt," and for "A Wanderer's Song," "Cargoes," "Sea-Fever," and "The Kings Go By," by John Masefield; for "Radio," and "The Man of Science Speaks," by Harriet Monroe; for "Cry of the People," by John C. Neihardt; for "New England," by Edwin Arlington Robinson; for "Hare," "Little Things," "The Road," and "The Shell," by James Stephens; for "Wood Song," by Sara Teasdale; for "The Son," by Ridgely Torrence; for "Chipmunk," by Marie de L. Welch; and for "Fallen Majesty," by William Butler Yeats. Edwin Markham, for "Lincoln, the Man of the People," "Outwitted," "Preparedness," "The Man with the Hoe," and "Victory in Defeat," copyrighted by the author and used by his permission. Marshall Jones Company, for "Sky-Signs," from *New York and Other Verse*, by Frederick Mortimer Clapp. Edna St. Vincent Millay, for "Elaine," "Lament," and "Prayer to Persephone," from *Second April*, published by Harper & Brothers, copyright, 1921, by Edna St. Vincent Millay. Nolan Miller, The Lotus Press, Detroit, for "be still," by Closson Emory. Abbie and Juanita Miller, for "Columbus," and "Charity," from the *Bear Edition* of the Works of Joaquin Miller, copyright, 1909. Mrs. Harold Monro, Cobden Sanderson, and The Macmillan Company, for "Man Carrying Bale," by Harold Monro. Thomas B. Mosher, for "Tears," from *A Wayside Lute*, by Lizette Woodworth Reese; and for "After a Dolmetsch Concert," by Arthur Upson. John Murray, for "Lines Written after the Discovery by the Author of the Germ of Yellow Fever," from *Philosophies*, by Ronald Ross. *The Nation*, and the author, for "Winter Revery," by Sara Bard Field. Oxford University Press, for "Leisure," and "The Sleepers," by W. H. Davies; and "The Old Houses of Flanders," by Ford Madox Ford. Random House, for "I think continually of those," from *Poems*, by Stephen Spender. Reprinted by permission of Random House, Inc., New York. Siegfried Sassoon, for "Aftermath," "Does It Matter?" and "Dreamers." Charles Scribner's Sons, for "Music I Heard," by Conrad Aiken; for "Medusa," by Louise Bogan; for "A Pitcher of Mignonette," by H. C. Bunner; for "Little Boy Blue," and "Wynken, Blynken, and Nod," by Eugene Field; for "Margaritae Sorori" (excerpt), "Invictus," and "The Blackbird," by W. E. Henley; for "A Ballad of Trees and the Master," "Evening Song," and "Song of the Chattahoochee," by Sidney Lanier; for "November Blue," by Alice Meynell; for "Faith," by George Santayana; for "I Have a Rendezvous with Death," by Alan Seeger; for "Aes Triplex" (excerpt), "Requiem," "Romance," and "The Vagabond," by Robert Louis Stevenson; for "To a Snow-Flake," by Francis Thompson; for "For a Dead Lady," and "Uncle Ananias," by E. A. Robinson; for "The Fish-Hawk," by John Hall Wheelock; and for "Work," by Henry van Dyke. Scripps-Howard Newspapers and the author, for "And Yet Fools Say," by George Sanford Holmes.   Martin Secker and Warburg, Ltd., for "The Old Ships," by James Elroy Flecker.   Thomas Seltzer, Inc., for "Caesar Remembers," by William Kean Seymour; for "Adelstrop," and "Cock-Crow," by Edward Thomas; and for "Immortal," by Mark Van Doren.   Leonora Speyer, for "Sardinia from a Liner."   Arthur B. Spingarn, for "Pittsburgh," by James Oppenheim.   Frederick A. Stokes Company, for "The Barrel Organ," and "The Highwayman," reprinted by permission from *Collected Poems*, volume I, by Alfred Noyes.   Copyright, 1906, by Frederick A. Stokes Company.   *The Sun*, for "Remembering," by Alice Hartich.   Turner Company, for "Courage," from *Dreamers on Horseback*, by Karl Wilson Baker.   Emma Taylor, for "Post Impressionism," by Bert Leston Taylor.   The Viking Press, Inc., for "Go Down, Death," from *God's Trombones*, by James Weldon Johnson, copyright, 1927; for "Anthem for Doomed Youth," from *Poems*, by Wilfred Owen; for "Portrait of the Artist," and "Résumé," from *Not So Deep as a Well*, by Dorothy Parker, copyright, 1926, 1928, 1931, and 1936; for "Wind Rising in the Alleys," from *Sun-Up*, by Lola Ridge, copyright, 1920; for "Horse," "The Hens," and "The Worm," from *Under the Tree*, by Elizabeth Madox Roberts, copyright, 1922 and 1930; for "On Reading the War Diary of a Defunct Ambassador," from *Satirical Poems*, by Siegfried Sassoon; for "Climb," and "School," from *The Hesitant Heart*, copyright, 1919, and "Nosegay for a Young Goat," and "River Skater," from *Blossoming Antlers*, copyright, 1933, by Winifred Welles.   Published by The Viking Press, Inc., New York.   Carolyn Wells, for the limericks, "A Canner, exceedingly canny," and "There was a young fellow named Tait."   Yale University Press, for "The Falconer of God," by William Rose Benét.

Contents

THE WORKADAY WORLD AND ITS PEOPLE

THE FUNNY SIDE

All Manner of Creatures

Challenge to Courage

MAN AND WARFARE

REMARKABLE SONNETS

LOVE AND MEMORY

FOOTLOOSE FOR FAR PLACES

Men and Women in Literature and Fable

Introduction

WHY READ POETRY?

Many pupils have asked themselves this question. They enjoy literature written in prose. They respond eagerly enough to the charms of the novel, short story, drama, and essay. But, when they turn to works of poetry, they seem to grow uncomfortable; sometimes, indeed, bored.

And yet, when you think the matter over, you find that poetry is very much like prose. Poetry can, like the prose novel, develop a long narrative; it can spin a brief yarn like the short story; it can, as effectively as the prose drama, unfold a tale of human destiny. There is nothing in the realm of thought or feeling that the writer cannot express in poetry. Why should the average pupil, none the less, like prose better?

The answer comes: "The language in prose does not interfere with our pleasure. In poetry, it often does."

Let us examine this objection as carefully as we can. Take the following passage written in prose:

"The changes wrought by death are in themselves so sharp and final, and so terrible and melancholy in their consequences, that the thing stands alone in man's experience, and has no parallel upon earth. It outdoes all other accidents because it is the last of them. Sometimes it leaps suddenly upon its victims like a Thug; sometimes it lays a regular siege and creeps upon their citadel during a score of years. And when the business is done, there is sore havoc made in other people's lives, and a pin knocked out by which many subsidiary friendships hung together. There are empty chairs, solitary walks, and single beds at night."

Now let us read the following stanzas:

I have had playmates, I have had companions,
In my days of childhood, in my joyful schooldays;
All, all are gone, the old familiar faces.

I have been laughing, I have been carousing,
Drinking late, sitting late, with my bosom cronies;
All, all are gone, the old familiar faces.

I loved a Love once, fairest among women:
Closed are her doors on me, I must not see her —
All, all are gone, the old familiar faces.

I have a friend, a kinder friend has no man;
Like an ingrate, I left my friend abruptly;
Left him, to muse on the old familiar faces.

Ghostlike I paced round the haunts of my childhood,
Earth seemed a desert I was bound to traverse,
Seeking to find the old familiar faces.

Friend of my bosom, thou more than a brother,
Why wert thou not born in my father's dwelling?
So might we talk of the old familiar faces,

How some they have died, and some they have left me,
And some are taken from me; all are departed;
All, all are gone, the old familiar faces.

The prose passage is good literature, you will admit; in fact, masterly. It represents the opening sentences of *Aes Triplex*, one of the best essays by that great writer, Robert Louis Stevenson. The poem, too, is well known; it is *The Old Familiar Faces* by that beloved author, Charles Lamb.

Of course, it is quite impossible to weigh the two selections, to determine their merits point for point. But surely it is possible to consider them with respect to their theme. Both deal with the subject of death. Each describes the losses which this great catastrophe produces.

Which, do you suppose, conveys the sense of loss more poignantly?   Which gives *you* a deeper feeling of loss? Which carries you back more swiftly to your own memories? Which would you like to read aloud?   Which, in short, has stirred you more profoundly?

The answer is, in all likelihood, *The Old Familiar Faces*.

But, you will protest, not all poetry is so simply constructed as *The Old Familiar Faces*, nor so easy to grasp. You may even go so far as to confess: "I like poems that I can understand.   I like *A Psalm of Life* by Longfellow and *Barbara Frietchie* by Whittier, and *The Highwayman* by Noyes, and *Gunga Din* by Kipling.   I like them because I do not have to puzzle out the meaning.   But that is not the kind of poetry I am given to study in class.   My assignment for today, for instance, is the *Ode on a Grecian Urn* by Keats:

> Thou still unravished bride of quietness,
> Thou foster-child of Silence and slow Time,
> Sylvan historian, who canst thus express
> A flowery tale more sweetly than our rhyme:
> What leaf-fringed legend haunts about thy shape
> Of deities or mortals, or of both,
> In Tempe or the dales of Arcady?
> What men or gods are these?   What maidens loth?
> What mad pursuit?   What struggle to escape?
> What pipes and timbrels?   What wild ecstasy?

The pupil may say, "We have been told that those lines introduce one of the most magnificent odes in the language. But I find that its thought is deeply hidden; it deals with a subject remote from my daily life; it is filled with allusions that I cannot understand unless I consult the notes.   That is why I don't enjoy poetry, especially great poetry.   It takes so much time and trouble to understand what it is all about."

Let the pupil, however, ask himself this question: Did I ever achieve anything worth while without an effort?   The

finest and most discriminating minds have found the effort
of studying poetry amply repaid; and millions of average
mentality have found poetry saying things that have not
been so well said in prose. Poetry has said them beautifully
and memorably; above all, personally. It is the closest to us
of all the arts, intent on the meaning and salvation of life
and of the mysteries we can never solve with the brain. Are
pupils interested in such matters? Are they not, as sorely as
their elders, perplexed by the problems of life? If grown men
and women have gained much from poetry, is there not some
gain available for youth?

Read aloud this poem by Alfred Lord Tennyson:

BREAK, BREAK, BREAK

Break, break, break,
 On thy cold gray stones, O Sea!
And I would that my tongue could utter
 The thoughts that arise in me.

O, well for the fisherman's boy,
 That he shouts with his sister at play!
O, well for the sailor lad,
 That he sings in his boat on the bay!

And the stately ships go on
 To their haven under the hill;
But O for the touch of a vanish'd hand,
 And the sound of a voice that is still!

Break, break, break,
 At the foot of thy crags, O Sea!
But the tender grace of a day that is dead
 Will never come back to me.

Do you notice the tender melancholy of the verses? Do you
feel the *sound* of the lines filling your ears in much the same
way that Massenet's or Chopin's *Elegy* does? This resemblance

between poetry and music is readily apparent. Tennyson's poem is pure music; its melody is as important as its idea.

This quality of poetry, its music, cannot be overemphasized. There is not a thought or mood known to man for which the poet cannot find the appropriate harmony in words. Does he wish to convey the sense of joy? Listen to Milton in *L'Allegro*:

> Come and trip it as you go
> On the light fantastic toe.

He pours out his ecstasy as does Shelley in *To a Skylark*:

> Higher still and higher
>   From the earth thou springest,
> Like a cloud of fire,
>   The blue deep thou wingest,
> And singing still dost soar, and soaring ever singest.

And when Gray writes of weariness, his lines drag in tempo and pitch:

> The curfew tolls the knell of parting day,
> The lowing herd wind slowly o'er the lea,
> The plowman homeward plods his weary way,
> And leaves the world to darkness and to me.

Study these three brief selections somewhat more closely. Is it not true that the *sound* of gaiety, the *sound* of ecstasy, the *sound* of weariness may be heard from the lines as they are read aloud? So emphatic are these sounds that they may be heard, or at least sensed, even by a silent reader. It is not too much to maintain, therefore, that music is fundamentally important in the craft of the poet.

In a strict sense, the poet has less in common with the painter or the sculptor. The poet does not use pigment to fill his canvases; he does not hammer marble or melt bronze. His medium is words. But with these words he can make

you see objects in the world as vividly as the artist can paint
or draw them for you, and he can do this because he knows
how to put a spell upon you under whose influence things rise
before the eye as if they actually existed.   Such is his power.
Words become trees, clouds, people; the poet's imagination
has brought this miracle about.   Read these lines, for example, from Coleridge's famous *Ancient Mariner*:

> All in a hot and copper sky,
> The bloody Sun, at noon,
> Right up above the mast did stand,
> No bigger than the moon.

Note the following verse from the same poem:

> About, about, in reel and rout,
> The death-fires danced at night;
> The water, like a witch's oils,
> Burnt green and blue and white.

Close your eyes after reading these lines.   Can you not
picture the sun and the water in your fancy, or as Shakespeare
phrased it, in your mind's eye?   Can you not visualize them
as well as you might after looking at paintings portraying
these very scenes?   You can if you use your imagination.
    The poet, as we have shown, appeals to all our senses.
He does so because he knows that through them he stimulates
our imagination.   Nothing is more important to the poet
than imagination; it is this quality of his mind which makes
his verses seem real and alive.   Good poets possess this
quality in high degree.   And because they wish so earnestly
to communicate their thought or feeling to us, they try to
find words that will quicken *our* imagination to its highest
activity.   Hence it is that they employ *figures of speech*.
    Pupils sometimes find it difficult to understand figures of
speech.   They are the poet's way of enabling us to see, hear,
smell, taste, and touch the universe in which we live.   But

human beings do not go through life using their eyes, ears, noses, tongues, and fingers alone; they are not mere animal machines. They do not see only with their eyes. They see with their feelings, their memories, their imaginations. Before an abandoned house, they *feel* the cold hand of death. Before a blazing fireside, they *remember* the faces of their parents long years ago. They *imagine* these things, of course; they are constantly finding comparisons and resemblances throughout their waking hours. That is why figures of speech are so necessary. They help us to discover these similarities and contrasts in the world. They enable us to discern meanings and truths that would otherwise remain hidden. Vivid and beautiful in themselves, these figures show us the amazing vividness and beauty of the earth.

THE SIMILE

When we say that a man is as strong *as an ox*, is as thin *as a rail*, runs *like the wind*, fights *like a tiger*, snarls *like a dog*, we are using similes. We are indicating a resemblance in some respect between the man and the ox, the man and the rail, the man and the wind, the man and the tiger, the man and the dog, respectively. By making such associations, we perceive the man more clearly. These, of course, are common similes, heard in everyday speech. They have lost some of their effect by constant use. The good poet, however, creates similes that have not been staled by repetition, as may be seen in the following lines:

> And the muscles of his brawny arms
> Are strong *as iron bands*.

> A feeling of sadness and longing
> That is not akin to pain,
> And resembles sorrow only
> *As the mist resembles the rain.*

Forlorn! the very word is *like a bell*
  To toll me back from thee to my sole self!

Art is long, and Time is fleeting,
  And our hearts, though stout and brave,
Still, *like muffled drums*, are beating
  Funeral marches to the grave.

Fear at my heart, *as at a cup*,
My life-blood seemed to sip!

With these illustrations before you, you should find it simple to define the simile. It is an expressed comparison, usually containing the words "like" or "as." You must remember, however, that not all comparisons with "like" or "as" are similes. *Like his brother* in the sentence, *He swims like his brother*, is not a simile. Neither is there a simile in *He was better as a student than as an athlete*. There must be an element of *difference* in the comparison. When the poet writes that the blacksmith's muscles are like iron bands or that the word "forlorn" is like a bell, he is in each case stating a resemblance between two *different* things. In each case, too, you will note, the simile is original and appropriate. The more original and appropriate it is, the more it pleases us. *He is as red as a beet, he was as white as a sheet* do not show an effective use of the simile. The comparison is too commonplace, the language too trite. A really artistic simile adds power and beauty to the poet's work.

THE METAPHOR

You have often heard the term, *metaphor*. This, too, is a common figure of speech. Since you have mastered the simile, it will not be difficult to understand the metaphor. You have perhaps seen an infant looking up at the sun and crying out with joy: "Ball! Pretty ball!" The child's imagination is active. It transforms the weeds in the marshes into beautiful golden hair; in the waves breaking against a cliff, it sees an enraged and frustrated primitive beast. Are you not very often like the child yourself, especially in moments of deep feeling or understanding? When love or fear or joy sweeps over you, or when your mind is most discerning, do you not find yourself recreating the world after this fashion?

When you do so in words, you are most likely using metaphors. We saw, a moment ago, in the case of the simile, that by the use of *like* or *as* we can compare two things that are really very different. In the metaphor we do not employ *like* or *as*; we substitute one thing for the other. When I say: "He was *like* a lion in the battle," I am framing a simile; when I say, however, "He *was* a lion in the battle," I am framing a metaphor. A metaphor, therefore, is an *implied comparison*, unlike the simile in which the comparison is explicit.

In the following illustrative lines, the metaphors are italicized:

I like the German fir-woods *in green battalions* drilled —

I want a ship that's westward bound *to plow the rolling sea*

And up around the apple-earth they come
Blasting *the whispers of the morning dumb*

Seventeen hundred and fifty-five
Georgius Secundus was then alive —
Snuffy old drone from the German hive

But the wind without was eager and sharp,
Of Sir Launfal's gray hair it made a harp

PERSONIFICATION

We do not have to be deeply read in poetry to realize how often poets, when carried away by their feelings, invest the world with heightened life. In moments of deep emotion it is not difficult for us to imagine that all external things share our moods. We ordinary people are exactly like the poets in this respect; for us, even inanimate objects in the world seem extraordinarily alive. When our spirits are low, all Nature is in tune: the *wind howls* savagely, the *clouds charge* menacingly across the sky. When we pass into a happier mood, Nature is still alive for us: the *sun smiles*, the *flowers dance* in the breeze, the *waves frolic* on the sand. We have seen such phrases many a time before; they represent what we think or say *when*, with a little imagination, *we give personal life to what actually has no such life*. It is then we are using the figure of speech known as personification.

What is the effect of the following examples of personification (in italics)? It is not enough to say they add beauty to the lines. They also add vividness and naturalness.

Yet e'en these bones from insult to protect
Some frail *memorial* still erected nigh,
With uncouth rhymes and shapeless sculpture deck'd
Implores the passing tribute of a sigh.

Can *storied urn or animated bust*
Back to its mansion *call* the *fleeting breath*
Can Honour's voice provoke the *silent dust*
Or *Flattery soothe* the dull cold *ear of Death*?

For *the faint east quickens, the wan west shivers,*
Round the *feet of the day* and the *feet of the night.*

A late lark twitters from the quiet skies
And from the west,

Where the sun, his day's work ended,
Lingers as in content,
There falls on the old, gray city
An influence luminous and serene,
A shining peace.

THE APOSTROPHE

From these examples it is very easy to see how the poet, carried away by his emotions, is able by sheer force of imagination to make even inanimate objects pulse with life. Suppose him now thinking of some person far away or long since dead; is it not natural for him in his longing to see once more the distant or vanished face, to touch the hand so dear to him, to speak as though the friend or beloved were actually within hearing? We ourselves, one and all, have known moments when our desires have brought such dreams as real as life itself, sometimes even more poignant or more beautiful. It is the privilege of the poet to avail himself of the figure of speech known as *the apostrophe,* by *addressing an absent person as though he were indeed present or by calling some departed being back to life*:

Milton! thou shouldst be living at this hour:
England hath need of thee.

And chiefly Thou, O Spirit, that dost prefer
Before all temples the upright heart and pure,
Instruct me, for Thou know'st.

Wee, sleekit, cowrin, tim'rous beastie,
O, what a panic's in thy breastie!

O Mary! dear departed shade!
Where is thy bliss of blissful rest?

See'st thou thy lover lowly laid?
Hear'st thou the groans that rend his breast?

Stern Daughter of the Voice of God!
O Duty! If that name thou love
Who art a light to guide, a rod
To check the erring, and reprove!

THE ALLEGORY

We come now to a very interesting figure of speech, the allegory. This last is an extended metaphor, generally found in narrative poetry, in which the characters and incidents do not exist solely for their own sake but stand as personified traits or moral symbols. The following example of the allegory may help to make the meaning clear:

Then Gareth, "An ye hold me yet for child,
Hear yet once more the story of the child.
For, mother, there was once a King, like ours.
The prince, his heir, when tall and marriageable,
Ask'd for a bride; and thereupon the King
Set two before him. One was fair, strong, arm'd —
But to be won by force — and many men
Desired her; one, good lack, no man desired.
And these were the conditions of the King:
That save he won the first by force, he needs
Must wed that other, whom no man desired,
A red-faced bride who knew herself so vile,
That evermore she long'd to hide herself,
Nor fronted man or woman, eye to eye —
Yea — some she cleaved to, but they died of her.
And one — they called her Fame; and one, — O mother,
How can ye keep me tether'd to you? — Shame.

In this story of Gareth you can readily understand the working out of the allegory. Fame and Shame, two abstractions, are given the parts of real characters.

Sometimes, however, the significance of the allegory does not emerge at a first reading. Closer study is necessary to extract the hidden parable. Take, for example, the famous description of the gate farther on in the same idyll of *Gareth and Lynette*:

> And there was no gate like it under heaven
> For barefoot on the keystone, which was lined
> And rippled like an ever-fleeting wave,
> The Lady of the Lake stood: all her dress
> Wept from her sides as water flowing away;
> But like the cross her great and goodly arms
> Stretch'd under all the cornice and upheld:
> And drops of water fell from either hand;
> And down from one a sword was hung, from one
> A censer, either worn with wind and storm;
> And o'er her breast floated the sacred fish.

Tennyson, you will note, describes the gate in great detail, but each of these details has allegorical value. The sword, for instance, is the symbol of justice; the censer, of holiness; the fish, of Christianity. The poet was clearly making use of Gareth's adventure to hint at some truth about the matter of faith. Whenever a poet invents a story in which the characters are abstract virtues (or vices), we know that the moral message is important. This is the chief characteristic of the allegory.

HYPERBOLE

Another figure of speech in which a degree of imagination is found is *hyperbole*. Poets resort to it *when they seek an effect by exaggerated statement*. This is a figure of speech, therefore, that must be used discreetly for the exaggeration may appear incredible or even downright silly. Effectively employed, hyperbole has always a basis of truth in reality.

Note these examples of hyperbole:

> So fair art thou, my bonnie lass,
>   So deep in love am I:
> And I will love thee still, my dear,
>   *Till a' the seas gang dry.*

> The forests *with their myriad tongues*
>   Shouted of liberty.

> Flashed all their sabres bare,
> Flashed as they turned in air
> Sabring the gunners there,
> Charging an army, while
>   *All the world wondered.*

> And when thy sons to fetters are consign'd,
> To fetters, and the damp vault's dayless gloom,
> Their country conquers with their martyrdom,
> *And Freedom's fame finds wings on every wind.*

IRONY

Another interesting figure of speech is irony. This, we are told, is "ridicule in the guise of compliment or praise: a mode of speech meaning the opposite of what is said." It is often employed in daily speech, the tone of voice betraying the true intent of the words. If, for example, you should say, "Noble work!" to a person who has just beaten a dog, you would be using irony. Your voice would unmistakably reveal how exactly the reverse of noble you felt

the act to be.   In poetry it is necessary to infer both the
tone and the thought from the context:

> Yet Brutus says he was ambitious;
> And sure he is an honorable man.

You know that Mark Antony, delivering the funeral ora-
tion over Caesar's body, considers Brutus *dis*honorable.

ALLITERATION

To the figures of speech described above should be added
two devices of the poet to enrich the meaning through the
sound of the words.   They are *Alliteration* and *Onomatopoeia*.

Alliteration is present when the initial letter is repeated in
two or more closely associated words.   Coleridge's *Ancient
Mariner* affords several examples in point:

> The *fair* breeze blew, the white *foam flew*,
> The *furrow followed free*;
> We were the first that ever burst
> Into that silent sea.

> O sleep! it is a gentle thing,
> Beloved from pole to pole!
> To Mary Queen the praise be given!
> *She sent* the gentle *sleep* from Heaven,
> That *slid* into my *soul*.

Indeed, the whole range of English poetry is rich in al-
literative phrases:

> For in the days we know not of
>   Did fate begin
> *Weaving* the *web* of days that *wove*
>   Your doom.

(Swinburne, Faustine)

In the fell clutch of circumstance
I have not winced nor cried aloud.
Under the *bludgeonings* of chance
My head is *bloody, but unbowed.*
(Henley, *Invictus*)

Alliteration, like hyperbole, should be used cautiously. It should never be used, of course, for the sole sake of hearing the initial letter repeated, as it sometimes is in the case of the familiar "tongue-twister." Alliteration reaches a very low level indeed in such specimens as:

"She sells sea shells on the sea shore,"

or:

"The ragged rascal ran around the rugged rock."

The objection to these examples is that they do not *add* to the *beauty* or the *meaning* of the context. Alliteration, in the practice of the best poets, seeks the perfect harmony between the sense and sound of the verse. In the case of *Invictus*, do you not hear the dull blow of the bludgeon bearing down upon the head of the sufferer? The repetition of the letter *b* deepens your emotional appreciation of the poem.

It is important that you understand the very great effect which various consonants and vowels have upon the ear and also upon the mind of the reader. Consider, for example, the letter *s* in the following stanza by Andrew Lang. Does it not vividly convey the sound of the scythe cutting the grass?

Hush, ah, hush, the Scythes are saying,
Hush, and heed not, and fall asleep;
Hush, they say to the grasses swaying;
Hush, they sing to the clover deep!

Hush — 'tis the lullaby Time is singing —
Hush, and heed not, for all things pass;
Hush, ah, hush! and the Scythes are swinging
Over the clover, over the grass!

ONOMATOPOEIA

Similarly, *onomatopoeia* (ŏn'ŏmătōpē'yà), in the hands of
a skillful poet, contributes much to the suggestiveness and
power of his work. The term comes from the Greek meaning *the forming of words to imitate natural sounds.* In this
limited sense, expressions like *splash, whizz, crash, hiss* are
examples of onomatopoeia. Illustrations are found in great
variety among poets, ancient and modern. We shall confine ourselves to Tennyson:

Wailing, wailing, wailing, the wind over land and sea.

The *moan* of doves in immemorial elms,
And *murmurings* of innumerable bees.

And ever and anon with host to host
Shocks, and the splintering spear, the hard mail hewn,
Shield-breakings, and the *clash* of brands, the *crash*
Of battleaxes on *shatter'd* helms, and *shrieks*
After the Christ, of those who falling down
Look'd up for heaven, and only saw the mist.

The words italicized tend to reveal their meaning by their
very sound. But onomatopoeia does not have to confine
itself to the mere imitation of sound; it may function in less
obvious ways. We have noticed before (see *Alliteration*,
page xxxiv) that the poet may by artistic arrangement of
consonants and vowels produce tonal effects of extraordinary
quality.

Let us study this matter more closely. Take the con-

sonants *b* and *d*.   There is something dull and heavy about
the sound of words dominated by these letters:

> Un*d*er the *b*lu*d*geonings of chance
> My hea*d* is *b*loo*d*y *b*ut un*b*owe*d*.

> An*d* each slow *d*usk a *d*rawing-*d*own of *b*lin*d*s.

Other consonants, of course, start happier echoes.   The
liquid consonants *l* and *r* suggest calm, sometimes passing
into more active joy:

> When the me*rr*y bells *r*ing *r*ound,
> And the jocund *r*ebecks sound.

> S*l*eep; and high p*l*aces; footprints in the dew;
> And oaks; and brown horse-chestnuts, g*l*ossy new;
> And new-pee*l*ed sticks; and shining poo*l*s on grass; —
> A*ll* these have been my *l*oves.

> Over earth and ocean, with gent*l*e motion,
>   This pi*l*ot is guiding me,
> *L*ured by the *l*ove of the genii that move
>   In the depths of the purp*l*e sea;
> Over the ri*ll*s, and the crags, and the hi*ll*s,
>   Over the *l*akes and the p*l*ains.

The nasal consonants *m* and *n* also tend to soften the mood
of the verse:

> That orbéd *m*aide*n*, with white fire lade*n*,
>   Who*m* *m*ortals call the *m*oo*n*,
> Glides gli*mm*eri*n*g o'er *m*y fleece-like floor,
>   By the *m*id*n*ight breezes strew*n*.

But sometimes *n* can be surly and mean:

> O*n*ly the mo*n*strous a*n*ger of the gu*n*s

In this case, to be sure, the short vowels contribute to
produce this effect.

The good poet is keenly sensitive to the *tone color* of words. Often deliberately he tests them for their sound and color values before he sets them down in final form in his verse. And he is as careful with his vowels as he is with his consonants. He knows, for example, that deep vowel sounds convey a correspondingly deep effect upon the human soul.

> Sweet and low, sweet and low,
> Wind of the western sea,
> Low, low, breathe and blow,
> Wind of the western sea,
> Over the rolling waters go,
> Come from the dying moon, and blow,
> Blow him again to me;
> While my little one, while my pretty one, sleeps.

The deep vowels found in *sweet, low, wind, breathe, blow,* suggest the eternal and poignant beauty of mother-love; they help to emphasize the rhythm of the wind and the rhythm of the waves. This stanza of Tennyson's *Cradle Song* is an excellent example of *onomatopoeia* comparatively free from alliteration.

RHYTHM

So far, we have seen the poet pouring out his imagination and his emotions, and by the use of figures of speech and other devices arresting our attention and communicating his mood to us. But there is one device the poet has at his command, which we have not yet considered; and it is very important, indeed fundamental. That is rhythm.

What is rhythm?

Perhaps we may understand it better if we analyze carefully some line of poetry, and with this in view let us take the opening line of Lizette Woodworth Reese's well-known sonnet, *Tears* (xli):

> When I consider Life and its few years,

Say it aloud. The voice grows loud and soft consistently, pressing heavily on one syllable, lightly on the next. That is all there is to rhythm — merely a regular grouping of accented and unaccented syllables. The accent must be present at regular intervals in the line. That is the secret.

Let us illustrate. If we use the sign ᵕ for the unaccented syllable and the sign ′ for the accented syllable, we may then write the line thus:

Whĕn Í cŏnsídĕr Lífe ănd íts fĕw yeárs,

Upon studying this line so written, can we not observe that every second syllable receives the accent? And, furthermore, that the line falls into five subdivisions, each of which has an unaccented syllable, followed by an accented one? Let us then use the mark | to denote the end of such division. We then have

Whĕn Í | cŏnsíd | ĕr Lífe | ănd íts | fĕw yeárs

Each of these divisions we call a foot. And when the two syllables within each foot are of the above nature, we designate them as an *iambic* foot. (n. *iambus, iamb*)

But there are several other kinds of feet which the pupil should know. Let us develop a second one by marking (technically, *scanning*; n. *scansion*) other lines in the same poem:

Line 10. Chíeftăins | ănd bárds | ănd keép | ĕrs óf | thĕ sheép
Line 12. Loóse mĕ | frŏm teárs | ănd máke | mĕ seé | ăríght
Line 14. Hómĕr | hĭs síght, | Dávĭd | hĭs lít | tlĕ lád

You will observe that the word *chieftains* in line 10, the phrase *loose me* in line 12, and the words *Homer* and *David* in line 14 do not make iambic feet, for in each of these cases the accented syllable *precedes* the unaccented one. Such feet we call *trochaic*. (n. *trochee*)

Now, if, returning to the poem, you will analyze the kinds

of feet in the several lines, you will discover the following
interesting facts:

1. About nine tenths of the feet are iambic.

2. About one tenth are trochaic or neither iambic nor
trochaic.

What law is deducible from the above?   Clearly this:
Poets, while following a definite rhythmic pattern of accent,
feel free to shift the accent at need.

Let us carry this discussion one step farther.   Turning to
William Rose Benét's sonnet, *Dead Letter Office*, and scanning the first two lines, we have:

Frŏm thĕ mínd | ŏf mănkínd | lĭke ráp | ĭd ĭnvís | ĭblĕ fíres
Whére dŏ | thĕ ág | ŏnĭzed práyer | ănd thĕ wíld | wĭsh gó

Here is a poem similar in form to *Tears* (a sonnet, whose
accent by definition is iambic), and yet what do we find?

1. There are only three iambic feet in the two lines.

2. Most of the feet are of three syllables.

This is strange, at first glance; but it is not unusual.   The
truth is that not only may the poet change from the iambic
to the trochaic foot and vice versa, but he may also change
from a two-syllabled to a three-syllabled foot within the
same poem.

What are the three-syllabled feet?   Obviously, there are
three possible combinations, as follows:

´ ◡ ◡ as in *urgency*   We call this *dactylic*. (n. *dactyl*)
◡ ´ ◡ " " *heroic*   This is relatively uncommon.
◡ ◡ ´ " " *from the mind* We call this *anapestic*. (n. *anapest*)

Let us summarize the present state of our knowledge:

1. The two-syllabled feet are the *iamb* and the *trochee*.

2. The two most frequently used three-syllabled feet are
the *dactyl* and the *anapest*.

3. A poet may, within the same poem, go from a two-
syllabled to a three-syllabled foot at will, and vice versa; and,
furthermore, he may shift the accent from one syllable to
another-

THE PRINCIPLE OF VARIETY

From the preceding study of rhythm we may derive the following law: the rhythmic pattern in any poem depends upon regularity and variety.

The recurrent accent at regular intervals in the line is a source of marked pleasure but, of course, if maintained beyond a certain point, grows monotonous and irksome. If every foot in a long poem were iambic, we would soon tire of reading it aloud; and, even in reading it silently, our attention would wander, for to some degree we are conscious of the spoken rhythm on the printed page. The ear demands the relief of variety in the accent.

But variety is not merely a matter of accent; it may be produced in other ways. Let us, in search of these, re-read the poem:

TEARS

1 When I consider Life and its few years —
2 A wisp of fog betwixt us and the sun;
3 A call to battle, and the battle done
4 Ere the last echo dies within our ears;
5 A rose choked in the grass; an hour of fears;
6 The gusts that past a darkening shore do beat;
7 The burst of music down an unlistening street —
8 I wonder at the idleness of tears.
9 Ye old, old dead, and ye of yesternight,
10 Chieftains, and bards, and keepers of the sheep,
11 By every cup of sorrow that you had,
12 Loose me from tears, and make me see aright
13 How each hath back what once he stayed to weep;
14 Homer his sight, David his little lad!

You will observe that you pause at the ends of the following lines: 1, 2, 4, 5, 6, 7, 8, 9, 10, 11, 13, 14. You do not pause (or you pause very slightly) at the end of lines 3 and

12.   Technically speaking, we say that all but lines 3 and 12 are *end-stopped*; these two lines, which *overflow* into the following ones, are *run-on*.   It is run-on lines in this particular poem, and indeed in any poem, which further the cause of rhythmical variety: observe how much more rigid the poem would be if every line were end-stopped.

It follows from the foregoing, therefore, that pauses may occur not only at the end of lines but also at any point in the line.   Note how in the poem such pauses come in lines 3, 5, 9, 10, 12, 14.   Above all, note how such internal pauses at different points in the line soften the severity of the fourteen-line, ten-syllable, iambic form (the sonnet); and within this framework of its regularity succeed in achieving the variety which gratifies our senses.

LENGTH OF LINE

The poet, however, does not always use the five-foot line though this happens to be the most common one in English poetry.   As the thought or mood dictates, he may vary its length from one foot to eight or more.

Let us make a table of the common English lines classified according to the number of feet:

Number of Feet	Line
1	monometer
2	dimeter
3	trimeter
4	tetrameter
5	pentameter
6	hexameter
7	heptameter
8	octameter

We are now able to describe the line of the sonnet (for example, *Tears*) in technical terms.   Since it contains five iambic feet, we call it *iambic pentameter*.   Every line in English poetry may be similarly designated by giving the prevailing kind of foot and the number of feet.

Do not suppose, however, that the kind of line used by the poet is at the mercy of mere caprice. Responsive to his mood, the poet, unconsciously or deliberately, chooses the kind of line which best suits his purpose. Where, then, is the poet's freedom? Merely in the choice of the form. Once the choice is made, he must comply, within reason, with its metrical restrictions.

This principle can be clearly observed in the study of the stanza, to which we now turn our attention.

THE STANZA

(Rhyme is indicated by the use of letters; for example, *a* for the first rhyme, *b* for the second, and so on.)

The stanza may be classified, according to the number of lines, as follows:

1. Two lines: the *couplet*

A little learning is a dangerous thing;
Drink deep or taste not the Pierian spring.

2. Three lines: the *triplet* or *tercet*:

Whoe'er she be,
That not impossible She
That shall command my heart and me.

3. Four lines: the *quatrain*

This may take several forms, of which the following may be noted:

(a) The *ballad stanza*: The first and third lines contain four iambic feet; the second and fourth, three iambic feet.

He strack the top-mast wi his hand,   (a)
The fore-mast wi his knee,   (b)
And he brake that gallant ship in twain,   (c)
And sank her in the sea.   (b)

(b) A common type:

> At daybreak on a hill they stood   (a)
> That overlook'd the moor;   (b)
> And thence they saw the bridge of wood   (a)
> A furlong from their door.   (b)

Many other rhyme-patterns within the quatrain are allowable; for example, a b b a; a a b b; a a b a.

4. Five lines: the *cinquain*.

> These be
> Three silent things:
> The falling snow ... the hour
> Before the dawn ... the mouth
> Just dead.

This five-line stanza is unrhymed. In most cases, however, some rhyme scheme is present.

5. Six lines: the *sextet* or *sestet*.

> She walks in beauty, like the night   (a)
> Of cloudless climes and starry skies,   (b)
> And all that's best of dark and bright   (a)
> Meet in her aspect and her eyes;   (b)
> Thus mellow'd to that tender light   (a)
> Which heaven to gaudy day denies.   (b)

Often the sestet takes the rhymes a b b a c c, or a b c a b c, the latter being generally found in the Italian form of the sonnet. There is, however, great latitude here because of the possible combinations which so many lines afford.

It is unnecessary to prolong this discussion by presenting stanzas of greater length; for example, the septet, the octave, and so on. Nearly always they will be found to be multiples or rearrangements of the shorter stanza forms.

RHYME

RHYME IS PLEASANT

Rhyme pleases the ear (and the eye, too, if you read poetry silently). It is like rhythm in this respect. In fact, if you think of the matter at all, you will see that it is itself a kind of rhythmic device, keeping time in an agreeable way between lines.

RULES OF RHYME

Of course, there are certain rules for writing rhyme which poets are required to follow:

1. The vowel *sounds* of the rhyming syllables should be the same. (Spelling is disregarded).

2. The consonant *sounds* preceding the vowel sounds should be different but those following must be the same.

3. In the case of accented syllables followed by unaccented syllables, the unaccented ones must be the same. These are *double* or *feminine* rhymes.

Let us apply these rules to Shelley's lines:

> Music, when soft voices die,
> Vibrates in the memory —
> Odors, when sweet violets sicken,
> Live within the sense they quicken.
> Rose leaves, when the rose is dead,
> Are heaped for the beloved's bed;
> And so thy thoughts, when Thou art gone,
> Love itself shall slumber on.

1. *Dead* (line 5) rhymes with *bed* (line 6). The consonant sounds *d* and *b* are different; the vowel sound ĕ is identical. This is a *perfect rhyme*.

2. *Die* (line 1) and *memory* (line 2) do not rhyme perfectly, the vowel sounds being different. This is an *imperfect rhyme*.

3. *Sicken* (line 4) and *quicken* (line 5) are an example of *double* or *feminine* rhyme.

BLANK VERSE

The great majority of poems are *rhymed*; but there are, nevertheless, two kinds of unrhymed verse which are quite popular. These are *blank verse* and *free verse*. We shall first consider blank verse.

Read *The Man with the Hoe* by Markham. You will observe that each of its lines is composed in iambic pentameter. This kind of unrhymed line is the one Shakespeare used in his plays, Milton in *Paradise Lost*, Tennyson in *The Idylls of the King*, Robinson in *Tristram* and Frost in *Birches*. Verse so produced is known as *heroic blank verse*.

CHARACTERISTICS OF BLANK VERSE

What are the distinguishing marks of blank verse besides its lack of rhyme? In most cases it has the uniformity of meter and the evenness of line-length that we find in rhymed poetry. But it possesses this advantage over rhymed verse which renders it particularly effective in long narrative poems or epics; freed from rhyme, it seems more natural, it yields subtler harmonies of rhythm within the line and, on the whole, appears more expressive. For these gains there are corresponding losses, too numerous here to mention. The student in quest of the secrets of blank verse will do well to study a modern master like Robinson side by side with Milton and Shakespeare.

FREE VERSE

This form, which twenty years ago all but pre-empted the poetic field, still counts its numerous admirers. These are a few of its salient traits:

1. It attempts to be as "free" and unstudied as the speech of ordinary life. Therefore, like blank verse, it dispenses with rhyme.

2. It is not as irregularly rhythmical as prose. Rhythm is present; but it is more varied and more spontaneous than that found in the usual metrical forms.

3. Its lines are of uneven length to keep pace with the normal movement of thought and emotion.

These qualities may also be discerned in a variant of free verse known as *polyphonic prose*.

POLYPHONIC PROSE

Amy Lowell, who laid down the laws for this form, explained its rather singular name as follows: "Polyphonic means many-voiced for it makes use of all the 'voices' of poetry, viz.: meter, *vers libre* (free verse), assonance, alliteration, rhyme, and balance. It employs every form of rhythm, even prose rhythm at times, but usually holds no particular one for long." Amy Lowell and John Gould Fletcher were two outstanding creators in this field.

Free verse or *vers libre* can perhaps best be understood by application to contemporary examples. The pupil is therefore advised to study such poems as *Grass* and *Jazz Fantasia* by Carl Sandburg and then to compare them with the celebrated poems in *Leaves of Grass* by Walt Whitman. The free verse form, he may conclude, is not as easy as it looks. Without the advantages of rhyme and meter, the writer braves the exposure of his talent, sometimes with cruel effect.

THE SONNET

As we have seen from previous discussion, the sonnet is one of the strictest of metrical forms. Despite this, or possibly because of this, it has attracted the greatest of poets in our literature and is today as popular as ever.

By definition, the sonnet is a lyric containing fourteen lines in rhymed iambic pentameter. There are two common forms, designated in accordance with their origin as the *Italian* or *Petrarchan*, and the *Shakespearean*.

Here is an example from Milton of the Italian sonnet:

ON HIS BLINDNESS

When I consider how my light is spent	(a)
Ere half my days, in this dark world and wide,	(b)
And that one talent which is death to hide	(b)
Lodged with me useless, though my soul more bent	(a)
To serve therewith my Maker, and present	(a)
My true account, lest He returning chide —	(b)
Doth God exact day-labor, light denied?	(b)
I fondly ask: — But Patience, to prevent	(a)
That murmur, soon replies; God doth not need	(c)
Either man's work, or His own gifts; who best	(d)
Bear His mild yoke, they serve Him best: His state	(e)
Is kingly; thousands at His bidding speed	(c)
And post o'er land and ocean without rest: —	(d)
They also serve who only stand and wait.	(e)

This sonnet divides into two sections; the octave rhyming a, b, b, a, a, b, b, a; the sestet rhyming c, d, e, c, d, e. Some variation is permitted in the sestet which occasionally may be rhymed c, d, c, d, c, d; but the octave always rhymes as in the model above.

The Italian form, furthermore, demands a peculiar rigidity in the elaboration of the theme. At its strictest — and Milton it will be noted, is somewhat rebellious in the specimen cited — it requires that the first two quatrains be end-stopped, the first presenting the theme and the second developing it; and, furthermore, that of the two tercets in the sestet, the first introduce a new direction to the theme and the second carry the theme to a satisfactory close.

No wonder that modern poets (and even the older ones) have often honored the Italian form "in the breach rather than the observance."

Let us turn now to the Shakespearean form. Analyze the following sonnet:

TRUE LOVE

Let me not to the marriage of true minds	(a)
Admit impediments. Love is not love	(b)
Which alters when it alteration finds,	(a)
Or bends with the remover to remove: —	(b)
O no! It is an ever-fixèd mark	(c)
That looks on tempests, and is never shaken;	(d)
It is the star to every wandering bark,	(c)
Whose worth's unknown, although his height be taken.	(d)
Love's not Time's Fool, though rosy lips and cheeks	(e)
Within his bending sickle's compass come;	(f)
Love alters not with his brief hours and weeks,	(e)
But bears it out ev'n to the edge of doom:	(f)
If this be error, and upon me proved,	(g)
I never writ, nor no man ever loved.	(g)

Note that it differs strikingly from the Italian sonnet, its rhyme-scheme being a, b, a, b; c, d, c, d; e, f, e, f; g, g. This form divides into four sections: three quatrains rhyming alternately, each quatrain setting up a new pair of rhymes: the whole capped with a rhyming couplet. Generally speaking, and notably in Shakespeare's practice, the quatrains are end-stopped, and the couplet is climactic in its force. (Incidentally, it should be observed that Shakespeare adds a syllable to the last words in the sixth and eighth lines — the so-called feminine ending.)

Variants of the Shakespearean form are not infrequently met. The rhyme scheme, a, b, a, b; c, d, c, d; e, f, e, g, g, f, has been used with great success, and still others may be remarked in well-known poems by Robinson, Millay, Wylie, and others. Turn to the section entitled *Remarkable Sonnets*, beginning on page 358, for illustrative examples.

WRITING POETRY

Pupils are sometimes inspired to write poetry. They feel the need for expressing themselves concerning the people and the problems they encounter. They find, for one reason or another, that prose is too sedate a vehicle for the headlong excitement of their experiences. So they turn to the rhythms and rhymes of verse.

"Poets," said Shakespeare, "are born, not made." This statement has done much to discourage aspiring verse-writers. It is, to be sure, true; but true in a way that few have understood. All human beings without exception are *born* poets, for all have thoughts and feelings, ideals, passions, longings, joys, sorrows; and all have need for expressing these states of the soul — sometimes in deed, sometimes in word.

Many a pupil will agree that this is so. He will say: "I know that I feel deeply. I can be plunged in grief like Gray in the *Elegy*; I am enraptured by beauty like Keats in his *Ode on a Grecian Urn*; I sympathize with the oppressed like Markham in *The Man with the Hoe*; I share the reverence of Whitman in *O Captain! My Captain!* There can be no doubt about it: I *feel* like a poet. But I *can't write* like a poet!"

Nevertheless, he can try to learn. He may never prove to be a master of the art but he owes himself the adventure of the effort. What should he do?

First of all, he should be intensely interested in people and the world — the people he meets daily and the immediate world he moves in. Emily Dickinson wrote immortal poetry though she never stirred from her cottage doorstep: she used her eyes to good effect, reflected deeply and jotted down her brief snatches of verse on the backs of old envelopes. It is better, however, not to be a hermit but to mingle freely with human beings, to share normal life in all its moods and thus to acquire the understanding vision based on wide experience. Keep a notebook for recording impressions. It is the homely things we have all known that make for true poetry: the sheen of the water at sunset, the troubled sleep of a dog, the straining muscles of a runner, the cry of a police siren in a silent street, the play of children in the crowded tenements. Such sights and incidents should be captured in words as soon as they present themselves. No exercise is better to train the senses and refine the heart.

Do not be daunted, at the outset, by your lack of originality. In all the arts it is necessary to serve an apprenticeship, and poetry is no different from sculpture and painting in this respect. Learn the laws of rhythm and rhyme; study the blank verse of Shakespeare and Tennyson, the sonnets of Milton and Wordsworth, the free verse of Whitman and Sandburg. Imitate them if you like. The most perfect and the most beautiful poems in the language are at your command for the purpose. You will soon discover your mistakes and profit by them. Presently, the secrets of the craft will be revealed to you.

Do not fail, finally, to master an adequate and responsive vocabulary, to understand the rôle of figures of speech, to learn the uses of assonance and alliteration, to appreciate vowel and consonantal values in the production of tone-color; in brief, to know and to be in full control of the many delicate operations involved in a sound poetic technique.

To this end, furnish yourself with a good dictionary, a synonym book such as Roget's *Thesaurus*, and a rhyming dictionary such as Walker's or Loring's. Loring's is perhaps to be preferred because its system is based not on spelling but on pronunciation.

To the Teacher

SUGGESTIONS TOWARD A GENERAL METHOD OF TEACHING THIS BOOK

As teachers, we must accept the fact that the very *form* of poetry stands in our way. The texture of poetry is often dense, its technique precious, its meaning elusive or totally withdrawn from view. And this is not all. Our pupils possess a very unequal and nearly always inadequate power of interpretation — even with prose. They have little familiarity with the raw stuff of poetry's concern; their experiences, in city or country, are confined to the steadily diminishing segment of apartment and street, or of house and field, which bounds their lives. This restricts the depth and range of their understanding; all too frequently the poet sings to ears that have been stopped.

We are not surprised, therefore, when we find amongst some of our pupils a lack of interest in the very name and nature of poetry not far removed from downright hostility. Sometimes this is because in their past reading they have developed a liking for crude sophistication. As teachers, however, we have learned the futility of condemning their reading habits; we shall conquer sooner if we meet them on their own ground. For in such souls, however primitive the taste, there is at least an interest in life; and this interest in life is all that is necessary at the start.

THE APPROACH

The teacher may find it advisable to begin his work by selecting poems which will receive an immediate welcome.

Such poems will capitalize the familiar sentiments, the normal preference for strong feeling and direct action and thus, by seizing and holding the interest, arouse a clear respect for the poetic art.   At the same time how much else there is which, all unknown to the pupil, finds lodgment somehow!

Here is such a group:

Pickett's Charge	Stephen Vincent Benét
An Incident of the French Camp	Robert Browning
The Highwayman	Alfred Noyes
Lindbergh: a Ballad	Alexander Laing
Tame Duck	Kenneth Kaufman
Mia Carlotta	Thomas Augustine Daly
The Dog	Don Marquis
O Captain, My Captain	Walt Whitman

THE UNIT METHOD

While it is true that most pupils, under the proper guidance, will enjoy the poems in this volume in whatever order they are presented, it is perhaps more in keeping with modern practice to study poems in cycles or groups which contain a common element of thought or feeling.

Let us assume that the teacher wishes to make a unit of modern American poetry.   From the elementary schools the pupil has brought some little knowledge of the works of Longfellow, Whittier, Holmes, Emerson, Bryant, and others, and this can readily be drawn upon in order to lead the class to discover the chief traits of the creative poetry written, let us say, before the death of Whitman.

The teacher may then decide to spend a period or two in reading part or all of some such group of poems as the following:

Sonnet on the Divina Comedia	Henry Wadsworth Longfellow
Thanatopsis, To a Waterfowl	William Cullen Bryant
Ichabod	William Greenleaf Whittier

The Rhodora	Ralph Waldo Emerson
The Chambered Nautilus	Oliver Wendell Holmes
The Commemoration Ode	James Russell Lowell

Such a list will suggest that there were heights as well as valleys in the older American poetry; and this is precisely what it is intended that our pupils shall understand.

Now let the teacher select several poems which were highly popular during this period. The class itself may volunteer the titles. The question may then be asked: Are these great poems? And much American poetry of the period having been dismissed as purely literary, it will be high time to clinch some first principles, not merely in poetry but in the values of life for which poetry exists. Let the pupil be encouraged to derive them from the depths of his own experience and in response to his own needs.

But let us not lose sight of our goal. We have been able to conclude, from these brief readings, that the older American poetry for all its grandeur and glory was flawed by certain weaknesses: it was derivative, bookish, static in theme and form. It was, except in the case of its chief practitioners, and then only at certain extraordinary moments, somewhat divorced from American life.

We are now ready, with the help of these older poets whose works we have studied, to show how natural it was for Whitman to lead the van of modern American poets and for Robinson, Frost, Lindsay, Sandburg, Millay, and others to follow. We should have little difficulty in proving that the modern American poet has the blood of the innovator in him, that he is not aloof from life but rather deeply immersed in it, that he knows no restrictions of subject-matter or technique except those which are self-ordained, that he considers himself free to explore every mood of the American soul, every corner of the American scene, and to speak his mind concerning them. This wide-ranging nature of the modern

American poet's art can perhaps be presented to the pupil by assigning for class reading and discussion a series of poems such as the following:

Representative Poems of Our Day

The Man with the Hoe	Edwin Markham
Mending Wall	Robert Frost
Grass	Carl Sandburg
The Congo	Vachel Lindsay
Lament	Edna St. Vincent Millay
The Drugstore	John V. A. Weaver
The Riveter	Joseph Auslander
The Negro Speaks of Rivers	Langston Hughes

With a list of this kind (which, incidentally, is arranged chronologically, according to the birth-dates of the poets), it will be possible to evolve a phrase or two, characterizing the work of the poet. The result may be, approximately, as follows:

Markham: Poet of Social Protest
Robinson: Portraitist of Human Nature
Frost: Philosopher of Nature
Sandburg: Poet of the Common Man
Lindsay: Troubadour in the Industrial Age
Hughes: Pleader for Racial Justice

Such an exercise as this leads the pupil to think critically. It helps him to understand the conditions in American life that gave rise to the poetry. Why, he may ask himself, is *The Man with the Hoe* so popular? Clearly because it registers as perhaps no other American poem does a widespread and deeply-felt attitude towards a grave social evil. And this is only one of many similar poems that may be cited. The inference is plain: such poems help to give us the picture not only of modern poetry but also of modern times.

The pupil who has learned this lesson has attained the objectives for which the unit was organized.

CORRELATING POETRY WITH OTHER SUBJECTS

Much has been said by progressive teachers in recent years concerning the correlation, wherever possible, of the various subjects in the curriculum. The teacher of poetry has every reason to assert the claim of poetry as an integrating force amongst the several school studies. It is within his power to bind together the arts and sciences, the world of life and the world of books, in this way aiding the development of a harmoniously functioning character and intelligence in the pupil before him.

Such a purpose is implicit in the following group of poems taken at random from the volume:

Miracles	Walt Whitman
The Man of Science Speaks	Harriet Monroe
The Steam Shovel	Eunice Tietjens
Poems of the Machine Age	MacKnight Black
Cargoes	John Masefield
On a Portrait of Dr. Johnson	Christopher Morley
Ulysses	Alfred Lord Tennyson
Lincoln, Man of the People	Edwin Markham
Do You Fear the Wind?	Hamlin Garland

If, however, the teacher prefers to restrict such poems to one subject at a time, there are enough in the book to make several units. For example, this list on American history:

Columbus	Joaquin Miller
Quivira	Arthur Guiterman
Paul Revere's Ride	Henry Wadsworth Longfellow
Pickett's Charge	Stephen Vincent Benét

Craven (Mobile Bay)	Sir Henry Newbolt
The Cowboy's Lament	John A. Lomax
The Dying Cowboy	John A. Lomax
The Santa Fé Trail	Vachel Lindsay
Pioneers, O Pioneers	Walt Whitman
The Eagle That is Forgotten	Vachel Lindsay

These poems should make the facts of American history more arresting. For that matter, they might well be used by teachers of history to supplement the history text. Through striking picture and breathless narrative pupils will discover the poet's superior insight as an interpreter of history by virtue of his imagination, his sympathy, and his gift of song.

THE SECTION AS A UNIT

Let us assume that it has been decided to treat a certain section as a teaching unit; that is, to lead the pupil to grasp the idea or principle which has brought the poems together. What teaching procedure here is likely to yield satisfactory results?

The section entitled *Remarkable Sonnets* will serve as an example. The aim in the selections has been to trace, within scale, the story of the sonnet by focusing attention upon the work of great artists in this form. It will be noted that the modern sonneteers — Masefield, Robinson, Millay — are among the most distinguished poets of the day. This should convince the pupil that the contemporary poet, far from being daunted by the rigid laws of the sonnet, has rejoiced in their resistance and, indeed, impressed them into the service of a masterful and myriad-purposed art.

Is this praise too high? Let the teacher put this question to the class. Here is a problem of evaluation (and a practical review assignment besides). The student may be stimulated to compile a list of his favorite sonnets, perhaps with the help of a readily accessible volume such as *The Golden Treasury*. Here is what he may like:

Sleep	Philip Sidney
A Consolation	William Shakespeare
On His Blindness	John Milton
On First Looking into Chapman's Homer	John Keats
Ozymandias	Percy Bysshe Shelley
Upon Westminster Bridge	William Wordsworth

For the sake of comparison, let us draw up a list of modern sonnets. For this purpose may be selected the following:

Puritan Sonnet	Elinor Wylie
The Dead	Rupert Brooke
On Hearing a Symphony of Beethoven	Edna St. Vincent Millay
O Little Self, Within Whose Smallness Lies	John Masefield

This project can be extended by coupling specimens of the older and the modern sonnet which possess a certain identity of substance.

On His Blindness	John Milton
Puritan Sonnet	Elinor Wylie
A Consolation	William Shakespeare
Tears	Lizette Woodworth Reese
Upon Westminster Bridge	William Wordsworth
Euclid Alone Has Looked on Beauty Bare	Edna St. Vincent Millay

By such pairing — and this comparative method can with equal success be applied to all other sections in this book — it is possible to evoke in pupils a keener responsiveness to the essentials of poetic expression.

THE INDIVIDUAL POET AS A STUDY UNIT

To vary the method outlined in the preceding pages, it may be advisable from time to time to arrange units by individual poets rather than by subjects.   Interest is easily aroused in the lives of the poets, the pupil being peculiarly susceptible to the appeal of famous living personalities. Here the radio, the newspaper, and the magazine may be utilized.   Let the pupil hear Edna St. Vincent Millay's broadcasting of her poetry; let him paste into his notebook the review of her latest book (a scrapbook of favorite poems is a consummation devoutly to be wished); let him bring to class biographical articles and photographs clipped from the magazines.   Then let him turn to this volume and read all the poems of her authorship found in its pages: *Lament, Prayer to Persephone, Elaine.*

In classroom discussion pupils will readily suggest the reasons for her present popularity.   Those reasons it will not be difficult to indicate, somewhat as follows:

1. Her deep and powerful emotional appeal as a lyric poet.
2. Her versatility, range, and perfect ease of craftsman- ship.
3. Her unforgettable diction and imagery.
4. Her keen intellect combined with a gay mockery (some- times called modern) which seeks to conceal the tender- ness of her heart.

From her it is possible to turn to a like consideration of other poets and to make comparisons among their work.

At the same time, it must be noted that while the teacher has been bent upon cultivating individual taste, he has also been traveling through the wide domain of poetry; he has, in effect, been teaching its history.   To this end he has been using one of the most fascinating methods available to him — the biographical method.

AT THE MERMAID CAFETERIA

Truth is enough for prose:
Calmly it goes
To tell just what it knows.

For verse, skill will suffice —
Delicate, nice
Casting of verbal dice.

Poetry, men attain
By subtler pain
More flagrant in the brain —

An honesty unfeigned,
A heart unchained,
A madness well restrained.

CHRISTOPHER MORLEY

Stories Brave and Strange

COLUMBUS

(August 3 — October 12, 1492)

Behind him lay the gray Azores,
  Behind the Gates of Hercules;
Before him not the ghost of shores,
  Before him only shoreless seas.
The good mate said: "Now must we pray,
  For lo! the very stars are gone.
Brave Admiral, speak, what shall I say?"
  "Why, say 'Sail on! sail on! and on!'"

"My men grow mutinous day by day;
  My men grow ghastly wan and weak."
The stout mate thought of home; a spray
  Of salt wave washed his swarthy cheek.
"What shall I say, brave Admiral, say,
  If we sight naught but seas at dawn?"
"Why, you shall say at break of day,
  'Sail on! sail on! sail on! and on!'"

They sailed and sailed, as winds might blow,
  Until at last the blanched mate said:
"Why, now not even God would know
  Should I and all my men fall dead.
These very winds forget their way,
  For God from these dread seas is gone.

Now speak, brave Admiral, speak and say ———"
   He said: "Sail on! sail on! and on!"

They sailed. They sailed. Then spake the mate:
   "This mad sea shows his teeth tonight.
He curls his lip, he lies in wait,
   With lifted teeth, as if to bite!
Brave Admiral, say but one good word:
   What shall we do when hope is gone?"
The words leapt like a leaping sword:
   "Sail on! sail on! sail on! and on!"

Then, pale and worn, he kept his deck,
   And peered through darkness. Ah, that night
Of all dark nights! And then a speck —
   A light! a light! a light! a light!
It grew, a starlit flag unfurled!
   It grew to be Time's burst of dawn.
He gained a world; he gave that world
   Its grandest lesson: "On! sail on!"

                     Joaquin Miller

QUIVIRA

Francisco Coronado rode forth with all his train,
Eight hundred savage bowmen, three hundred spears of
   Spain,
   To seek the rumored glory that pathless deserts hold —
   The city of Quivira whose walls are rich with gold.

Oh, gay they rode with plume on crest and gilded spur at
   heel,

With gonfalon of Aragon and banner of Castile!
While High Emprise and Joyous Youth, twin marshals of the
    throng,
Awoke Sonora's mountain peaks, with trumpet-note and
    song.

Beside that brilliant army, beloved of serf and lord,
There walked as brave a soldier as ever smote with sword,
Though naught of knightly harness his russet gown re-
    vealed —
The cross he bore as weapon, the missal was his shield.

But rugged oaths were changed to prayers, and angry hearts
    grew tame,
And fainting spirits waxed in faith where Fray Padilla came;
And brawny spearmen bowed their heads to kiss the helpful
    hand
Of him who spake the simple truth that brave men under-
    stand.

What pen may paint their daring — those doughty cava-
    liers!
The cities of the Zuñi were humbled by their spears.
Wild Arizona's barrens grew pallid in the glow
Of blades that won Granada and conquered Mexico.

They fared by lofty Acoma; their rally-call was blown
Where Colorado rushes down through God-hewn walls of
    stone;
Still, north and east, where deserts spread and treeless
    prairies rolled,
A fairy city lured them on with pinnacles of gold.

Through all their weary marches toward that flitting goal
They turned to Fray Padilla for aid of heart and soul.
He bound the wounds that lance thrust and flinty arrow
    made,
He cheered the sick and failing; above the dead he prayed.

Two thousand miles of hardship behind their banners lay.
And sadly fever, drought, and toil had lessened their array,
When came a message fraught with hope to all the steadfast
    band:
"Good tidings from the northward, friends! Quivira lies at
    hand!"

How joyously they spurred them! How sadly drew the
    rein!
There shone no golden palace, there blazed no jeweled fane.
Rude tents of hide of bison, dog-guarded, met their view —
A squalid Indian village; the lodges of the Sioux!

Then Coronado bowed his head. He spake unto his men:
"Our quest is vain, true hearts of Spain! Now ride we home
    again.
And would to God that I might give that phantom city's
    pride
In ransom for the gallant souls that here have sunk and
    died!"

Back, back to Compostela the wayworn handful bore;
But sturdy Fray Padilla took up the quest once more.
His soul still longed for conquest, though not by lance and
    sword;
He burned to show the Heathen the pathway to the Lord.

Again he trudged the flinty hills and dazzling desert sands,
And few were they that walked with him, and weaponless
    their hands —
But and the trusty man-at-arms, Docampo, rode him near,
Like Great Heart, guarding Christian's way through wastes
    of Doubt and Fear.

Where still in silken harvests the prairie-lilies toss,
Among the dark Quiviras, Padilla reared his cross.
Within its sacred shadow the warriors of the Kaw
In wonder heard the Gospel of Love and Peace and Law.

They gloried in their Brown-robed Priest; and oft in twi-
    light's gold
The warriors grouped, a silent ring, to hear the tale he told,
While round the gentleman-at-arms their lithe-limbed chil-
    dren played
And shot their arrows at his shield and rode his guarded
    blade.

When thrice the silver crescent had filled its curving shell,
The friar rose at dawning and spake his flock farewell:
"— And if your brothers northward be cruel, as ye say,
My Master bids me seek them; and dare I answer
    'Nay'?"

Again he strode the path of thorns; but ere the evening star
A savage cohort swept the plain in paint and plume of war.
Then Fray Padilla spake to them whose hearts were most his
    own:
"My children, bear the tidings home; let me die here
    alone."

He knelt upon the prairie, begirt by yelling Sioux. —
  "Forgive them, Oh my Father! they know not what they
    do!"
The twanging bowstrings answered.   Before his eyes, un-
  rolled
The City of Quivira whose streets are paved with gold.

Arthur Guiterman

PICKETT'S CHARGE

(The War Between the States)

The cannonade fell still.   All along the fishhook line,
The tired men stared at the smoke and waited for it to
    clear;
The men in the center waited, their rifles gripped in their
    hands,
By the trees of the riding fate, and the low stone wall, and
    the guns.

These were Hancock's men, the men of the Second Corps,
Eleven states were mixed there, where Minnesota stood
In battle order with Maine, and Rhode Island beside New
    York,
The metals of all the North, cooled into an axe of war.

The strong sticks of the North, bound into a fasces-shape,
The hard winters of snow, the wind with the cutting
    edge,
And against them came that summer that does not die with
    the year,
Magnolia and honeysuckle and the blue Virginia flag.

Tall Pickett went up to Longstreet — his handsome face was
    drawn.
George Pickett, old friend of Lincoln's in days gone by with
    the blast,
When he was a courteous youth and Lincoln the strange
    shawled man
Who would talk in a Springfield street with a boy who dreamt
    of a sword.

Dreamt of a martial sword, as swords are martial in dreams,
And the courtesy to use it, in the bright old way of the
    tales.
Those days are gone with the blast.   He has his sword in his
    hand.
And he will use it today, and remember that using long.

He came to Longstreet for orders, but Longstreet would not
    speak.
He saw Old Peter's mouth and the thought in Old Peter's
    mind.
He knew the task that was set and the men that he had to
    lead,
And a pride came into his face while Longstreet stood there
    dumb.

"I shall go forward, sir," he said and turned to his men.
The commands went down the line.   The gray ranks started
    to move.
Slowly at first, then faster, in order, stepping like deer,
The Virginians, the fifteen thousand, the seventh wave of the
    tide.

There was a death-torn mile of broken ground to cross,
And a low stone wall at the end, and behind it the Second
 Corps,
And behind that force another, fresh men who had not yet
 fought.
They started to cross that ground.   The guns began to tear
 them.

From the hill they say that it seemed more like a sea than a
 wave,
A sea continually torn by stones flung out of the sky,
And yet, as it came, still closing, closing and rolling on,
As the moving sea closes over the flaws and rips of the tide.

You could mark the path that they took by the dead that
 they left behind,
Spilled from that deadly march as a cart spills meal on a
 road,
And yet they came on unceasing, the fifteen thousand no
 more,
And the blue Virginia flag did not fall, did not fall, did not
 fall.

They halted but once to fire as they came.   Then the smoke
 closed down
And you could not see them, and then, as it cleared again for
 a breath,
They were coming still but divided, gnawed at by blue at-
 tacks,
One flank half-severed and halted, but the center still like a
 tide.

Cushing ran down the last of his guns to the battle-line.
The rest had been smashed to scrap by Lee's artillery fire.
He held his guts in his hand as the charge came up to the
    wall,
And his gun spoke out for him once before he fell to the
    ground.

Armistead leapt the wall and laid his hand on the gun,
The last of the three brigadiers who ordered Pickett's brig-
    ades,
He waved his hat on his sword and "Give 'em the steel!" he
    cried,
A few men followed him over.   The rest were beaten or dead.

A few men followed him over.   There had been fifteen thou-
    sand
When that sea began its march toward the fishhook ridge and
    the wall.
So they came on in strength, light-footed, stepping like deer,
So they died and were taken.   So the iron entered their flesh.

Lee, a mile away, in the shade of a little wood,
Stared, with his mouth shut down, and saw them go and be
    slain,
And then saw for a single moment the blue Virginia flag
Planted beyond the wall, by that other flag that he knew.

The two flags planted together, one instant, like hostile
    flowers.
Then the smoke wrapped both in a mantle — and when it
    had blown away,

Armistead lay in his blood, and the rest were dead or down,
And the valley gray with the fallen and the wreck of the
    broken wave.

Pickett gazed around him, the boy who had dreamt of a
    sword
And talked with a man named Lincoln.   The sword was still
    in his hand.
He had gone out with fifteen thousand.   He came back to his
    lines with five.
He fought well till the war was over, but a thing was cracked
    in his heart.

Stephen Vincent Benét

CRAVEN

(MOBILE BAY, AUGUST 5, 1864)

Over the turret, shut in his ironclad tower,
    Craven was conning his ship through smoke and flame;
Gun to gun he had battered the fort for an hour,
    Now was the time for a charge to end the game.

There lay the narrowing channel, smooth and grim,
    A hundred deaths beneath it, and never a sign:
There lay the enemy's ships, and sink or swim
    The flag was flying, and he was head of the line.

The fleet behind was jamming; the monitor hung
    Beating the stream; the roar for a moment hushed;
Craven spoke to the pilot; slow she swung;
    Again he spoke, and right for the foe she rushed

Into the narrowing channel, between the shore
  And the sunk torpedoes lying in treacherous rank;
She turned but a yard too short; a muffled roar,
  A mountainous wave, and she rolled, righted, and sank.

Over the manhole, up in the ironclad tower,
  Pilot and captain met as they turned to fly:
The hundredth part of a moment seemed an hour,
  For one could pass to be saved, and one must die.

They stood like men in a dream; Craven spoke,
  Spoke as he lived and fought, with a captain's pride:
"After you, Pilot!"   The pilot woke.
  Down the ladder he went, and Craven died.

All men praise the deed and the manner; but we —
  We set it apart from the pride that stoops to the proud,
The strength that is supple to serve the strong and free,
  The grave of the empty hands and promises loud;

Sidney thirsting a humbler need to slake,
  Nelson waiting his turn for the surgeon's hand,
Lucas crushed with chains for a comrade's sake,
  Outram coveting right before command,

These were paladins, these were Craven's peers,
  These with him shall be crowned in story and song,
Crowned with the glitter of steel and the glimmer of tears,
  Princes of courtesy, merciful, proud, and strong.
                              Sir Henry Newbolt

JIM BLUDSO OF THE *PRAIRIE BELLE*

Wall, no! I can't tell whar he lives,
   Becase he don't live, you see;
Leastways, he's got out of the habit
   Of livin' like you and me.
Whar have you been for the last three year
   That you haven't heard folks tell
How Jimmy Bludso passed in his checks
   The night of the *Prairie Belle?*

He weren't no saint — them engineers
   Is all pretty much alike —
One wife in Natchez-under-the-Hill
   And another one here, in Pike;
A keerless man in his talk was Jim,
   And an awkward hand in a row,
But he never flunked, and he never lied —
   I reckon he never knowed how.

And this was all the religion he had —
   To treat his engine well;
Never be passed on the river;
   To mind the pilot's bell;
And if ever the *Prairie Belle* took fire —
   A thousand times he swore
He'd hold her nozzle agin the bank
   Till the last soul got ashore.

All boats has their day on the Mississip,
   And her day come at last —
The *Movastar* was a better boat,
   But the *Belle* she *wouldn't* be passed.

And so she come tearin' along that night —
   The oldest craft on the line —
With a Negro squat on her safety-valve,
   And her furnace crammed, rosin and pine.

The fire bust out as she clared the bar,
   And burnt a hole in the night,
And quick as a flash she turned, and made
   For that willer-bank on the right.
There was runnin' and cursin', but Jim yelled out,
   Over all the infernal roar,
"I'll hold her nozzle agin the bank
   Till the last galoot's ashore."

Through the hot, black breath of the burnin' boat
   Jim Bludso's voice was heard,
And they all had trust in his cussedness,
   And knowed he would keep his word.
And, sure's you're born, they all got off
   Afore the smokestacks fell —
And Bludso's ghost went up alone
   In the smoke of the *Prairie Belle.*

He weren't no saint — but at jedgment
   I'd run my chance with Jim,
'Longside of some pious gentlemen
   That wouldn't shook hands with him.
He seen his duty, a dead-sure thing —
   And went for it thar and then;
And Christ ain't a-going to be too hard
   On a man that died for men.

                          John Hay

INCIDENT OF THE FRENCH CAMP

(APRIL 23, 1809)

You know, we French stormed Ratisbon:
  A mile or so away,
On a little mound, Napoleon
  Stood on our storming-day;
With neck outthrust, you fancy how,
  Legs wide, arms locked behind,
As if to balance the prone brow
  Oppressive with its mind.

Just as perhaps he mused, "My plans
  That soar, to earth may fall,
Let once my army-leader Lannes
  Waver at yonder wall" —
Out 'twixt the battery-smokes there flew
  A rider, bound on bound
Full-galloping; nor bridle drew
  Until he reached the mound.

Then off there flung in smiling joy,
  And held himself erect
By just his horse's mane, a boy:
  You hardly could suspect —
(So tight he kept his lips compressed,
  Scarce any blood came through),
You looked twice ere you saw his breast
  Was all but shot in two.

"Well," cried he, "Emperor, by God's grace
  We've got you Ratisbon!

The Marshal's in the market-place,
   And you'll be there anon
To see your flag-bird flap his vans
   Where I, to heart's desire,
Perched him!" The chief's eye flashed; his plans
   Soared up again like fire.

The chief's eye flashed; but presently
   Softened itself, as sheathes
A film the mother-eagle's eye
   When her bruised eaglet breathes;
"You're wounded!" "Nay," the soldier's pride
   Touched to the quick, he said:
"I'm killed, Sire!" And his chief beside,
   Smiling the boy fell dead.

                   Robert Browning

THE HIGHWAYMAN

Part I

The wind was a torrent of darkness among the gusty trees,
The moon was a ghostly galleon tossed upon cloudy seas,
The road was a ribbon of moonlight over the purple moor,
And the highwayman came riding —
      Riding — riding —
The highwayman came riding, up to the old inn-door.

He'd a French cocked-hat on his forehead, a bunch of lace
    at his chin,
A coat of the claret velvet, and breeches of brown doe-skin;
They fitted with never a wrinkle; his boots were up to the
    thigh!

And he rode with a jeweled twinkle,
> His pistol butts a-twinkle,
His rapier hilt a-twinkle, under the jeweled sky.

Over the cobbles he clattered and clashed in the dark inn-
yard,
And he tapped with his whip on the shutters, but all was
locked and barred:
He whistled a tune to the window, and who should be waiting
there
But the landlord's black-eyed daughter,
> Bess, the landlord's daughter,
Plaiting a dark red love-knot into her long black hair.

And dark in the dark old inn-yard a stable-wicket creaked
Where Tim the ostler listened; his face was white and peaked;
His eyes were hollows of madness, his hair like moldy hay,
But he loved the landlord's daughter,
> The landlord's red-lipped daughter,
Dumb as a dog he listened, and he heard the robber say —

"One kiss, my bonny sweetheart, I'm after a prize tonight,
But I shall be back with the yellow gold before the morning
light;
Yet, if they press me sharply, and harry me through the day,
Then look for me by moonlight,
> Watch for me by moonlight,
I'll come to thee by moonlight, though hell should bar the way."

He rose upright in the stirrups; he scarce could reach her
hand,
But she loosened her hair i' the casement! His face burnt
like a brand

As the black cascade of perfume came tumbling over his
     breast;
And he kissed its waves in the moonlight,
     (Oh, sweet black waves in the moonlight!)
Then he tugged at his rein in the moonlight, and galloped
     away to the West.

Part II

He did not come in the dawning; he did not come at
     noon;
And out o' the tawny sunset, before the rise o' the moon,
When the road was a gipsy's ribbon, looping the purple moor,
A red-coat troop came marching —
     Marching — marching —
King George's men came marching, up to the old inn-door.

They said no word to the landlord, they drank his ale instead,
But they gagged his daughter and bound her to the foot of
     her narrow bed;
Two of them knelt at her casement, with muskets at their
     side!
There was death at every window;
     And hell at one dark window;
For Bess could see, through her casement, the road that *he*
     would ride.

They had tied her up to attention, with many a sniggering
     jest;
They had bound a musket beside her, with the barrel beneath
     her breast!
"Now keep good watch!" and they kissed her. She heard
     the dead man say —

Look for me by moonlight;
        Watch for me by moonlight;
I'll come to thee by moonlight, though hell should bar the way!

She twisted her hands behind her; but all the knots held
        good!
She writhed her hands till her fingers were wet with sweat or
        blood!
They stretched and strained in the darkness, and the hours
        crawled by like years,
Till now, on the stroke of midnight,
        Cold, on the stroke of midnight,
The tip of one finger touched it!   The trigger at least was
        hers!

The tip of one finger touched it; she strove no more for the
        rest!
Up, she stood up to attention, with the barrel beneath her
        breast,
She would not risk their hearing: she would not strive again;
For the road lay bare in the moonlight;
        Blank and bare in the moonlight;
And the blood of her veins in the moonlight throbbed to her
        love's refrain.

Tlot-tlot; tlot-tlot!   Had they heard it?   The horse-hoofs
        ringing clear;
Tlot-tlot, tlot-tlot, in the distance?   Were they deaf that they
        did not hear?
Down the ribbon of moonlight, over the brow of the hill,
The highwayman came riding,
        Riding, riding!

The red-coats looked to their priming! She stood up, straight
    and still!

Tlot-tlot, in the frosty silence!   *Tlot-tlot*, in the echoing night!
Nearer he came and nearer!   Her face was like a light!
Her eyes grew wide for a moment; she drew one last deep
    breath,
Then her finger moved in the moonlight,
      Her musket shattered the moonlight,
Shattered her breast in the moonlight and warned him —
    with her death.

He turned; he spurred to the Westward; he did not know
    who stood
Bowed, with her head o'er the musket, drenched with her
    own red blood!
Not till the dawn he heard it, his face grew gray to hear
How Bess, the landlord's daughter,
    The landlord's black-eyed daughter,
Had watched for her love in the moonlight, and died in the
    darkness there.

Back he spurred like a madman, shrieking a curse to the sky,
With the white road smoking behind him, and his rapier
    brandished high!
Blood-red were his spurs in the golden moon; wine-red was
    his velvet coat,
When they shot him down on the highway,
    Down like a dog on the highway,
And he lay in his blood on the highway, with a bunch of lace
    at his throat.

   .   .   .   .

*And still of a winter's night, they say, when the wind is in the
        trees,*
When the moon is a ghostly galleon tossed upon cloudy seas,
When the road is a ribbon of moonlight over the purple moor,
A highwayman comes riding —
        Riding — riding —
A highwayman comes riding, up to the old inn-door.

Over the cobbles he clatters and clangs in the dark inn-yard;
*And he taps with his whip on the shutters, but all is locked and
        barred;*
*He whistles a tune to the window, and who should be waiting
        there*
But the landlord's black-eyed daughter,
        Bess, the landlord's daughter,
Plaiting a dark red love-knot into her long black hair.
                                            Alfred Noyes

THE MAN HUNT

The woods stretch wild to the mountain side,
And the brush is deep where a man may hide.

They have brought the bloodhounds up again
To the roadside rock where they found the slain.

They have brought the bloodhounds up, and they
Have taken the trail to the mountain way.

Three times they circled the trail and crossed,
And thrice they found it and thrice they lost.

Now straight through the pines and the underbrush
They follow the scent through the forest's hush.

And their deep-mouthed bay is a pulse of fear
In the heart of the wood that the man must hear.

The man who crouches among the trees
From the stern-faced men that follow these.

A huddle of rocks that the ooze has mossed —
And the trail of the hunted again is lost.

An upturned pebble; a bit of ground
A heel has trampled — the trail is found.

And the woods re-echo the bloodhounds' bay
As again they take to the mountain way.

A rock; a ribbon of road; a ledge,
With a pine-tree clutching its crumbling edge.

A pine, that the lightning long since clave,
Whose huge roots hollow a ragged cave.

A shout; a curse; and a face aghast,
And the human quarry is laired at last.

The human quarry, with clay-clogged hair
And eyes of terror, who waits them there;

That glares and crouches and rising then
Hurls clods and curses at dogs and men.

Until the blow of a gun-butt lays
Him stunned and bleeding upon his face.

A rope, a prayer, and an oak-tree near.
And a score of hands to swing him clear.

A grim black thing for the setting sun
And the moon and the stars to look upon.

Madison Cawein

GENERAL WILLIAM BOOTH ENTERS INTO HEAVEN

(TO BE SUNG TO THE TUNE OF "THE BLOOD OF THE LAMB"
WITH INDICATED INSTRUMENTS)

(Bass drum beaten loudly)

Booth led boldly with his big bass drum —
(Are you washed in the blood of the Lamb?)
The saints smiled gravely, and they said, "He's come."
    (Are you washed in the blood of the Lamb?)

Walking lepers followed, rank on rank,
Lurching bravos from the ditches dank,
Drabs from alleyways and drug-fiends pale —
Minds still passion-ridden, soul powers frail: —
Vermin-eaten saints with moldy breath,
Unwashed legions with the ways of Death —
    (Are you washed in the blood of the Lamb?)

(Banjos)

Every slum has sent its half-a-score
The round world over.   (Booth had groaned for more.)

Every banner that the wide world flies
Bloomed with glory and transcendent dyes.
Big-voiced lasses made their banjos bang,
Tranced, fanatical, they shrieked and sang: —
    "Are you washed in the blood of the Lamb?"
Hallelujah!   It was queer to see
Bull-necked convicts with that land make free.
Loons with trumpets blowed blare, blare, blare.
On, on, upward through the golden air!
    (Are you washed in the blood of the Lamb?)

(Bass drum slower and softer)

Booth died blind and still by Faith he trod,
Eyes still dazzled by the ways of God.
Booth led boldly, and he looked the chief,
Eagle countenance in sharp relief,
Beard a-flying, air of high command
Unabated in that holy land.

(Sweet flute music)

Jesus came from out the court-house door,
Stretched his hands above the passing poor.
Booth saw not, but led his queer ones there
Round and round the mighty court-house square.
Then, in an instant all that blear review
Marched on spotless, clad in raiment new,
The lame were straightened, withered limbs uncurled
And blind eyes opened on a new, sweet world.

(Bass drum louder)

Drabs and vixens in a flash made whole!
Gone was the weasel-head, the snout, the jowl!

Sages and sibyls now, and athletes clean,
Rulers of empires, and of forests green!

(Grand chorus of all instruments.   Tambourines to the foreground)

The hosts were sandaled and their wings were fire!
  (Are you washed in the blood of the Lamb?)
But their noise played havoc with the angel-choir.
  (Are you washed in the blood of the Lamb?)
Oh, shout Salvation! it was good to see
Kings and Princes by the Lamb set free.
The banjos rattled and the tambourines
Jing-jing-jingled in the hands of queens!

(Reverently sung, no instruments)

And when Booth halted by the curb for prayer
He saw his Master through the flag-filled air.
Christ came gently with a robe and crown
For Booth the soldier, while the throng knelt down.
He saw King Jesus.   They were face to face,
And he knelt a-weeping in that holy place.
   Are you washed in the blood of the Lamb?
                                    Vachel Lindsay

THE RAVEN

Once upon a midnight dreary, while I pondered, weak and
      weary,
Over many a quaint and curious volume of forgotten lore —
While I nodded, nearly napping, suddenly there came a tap-
      ping,
As of someone gently rapping, rapping at my chamber door.
"'Tis some visitor," I muttered, "tapping at my chamber
      door —
        Only this, and nothing more."

Ah, distinctly I remember it was in the bleak December,
And each separate dying ember wrought its ghost upon the
     floor.
Eagerly I wished the morrow; — vainly I had sought to bor-
     row
From my books surcease of sorrow — sorrow for the lost
     Lenore —
For the rare and radiant maiden whom the angels name
     Lenore —
          Nameless *here* for evermore.

And the silken, sad, uncertain rustling of each purple curtain
Thrilled me — filled me with fantastic terrors never felt
     before;
So that now, to still the beating of my heart, I stood repeat-
     ing,
"'Tis some visitor entreating entrance at my chamber door—
Some late visitor entreating entrance at my chamber door; —
          This it is, and nothing more."

Presently my soul grew stronger; hesitating then no longer,
"Sir," said I, "or Madam, truly your forgiveness I implore;
But the fact is I was napping, and so gently you came rap-
     ping,
And so faintly you came tapping, tapping at my chamber
     door,
That I scarce was sure I heard you" — here I opened wide
     the door; —
          Darkness there, and nothing more.

Deep into that darkness peering, long I stood there wonder-
     ing, fearing.

Doubting, dreaming dreams no mortals ever dared to dream
      before;
But the silence was unbroken, and the stillness gave no token,
And the only word there spoken was the whispered word,
      "Lenore!"
This I whispered, and an echo murmured back the word,
      "Lenore!" —
      Merely this, and nothing more.

Back into the chamber turning, all my soul within me burn-
      ing,
Soon again I heard a tapping somewhat louder than before.
"Surely," said I, "surely that is something at my window
      lattice:
Let me see, then, what thereat is, and this mystery explore —
Let my heart be still a moment and this mystery explore; —
      'Tis the wind and nothing more."

Open here I flung the shutter, when, with many a flirt and
      flutter,
In there stepped a stately raven of the saintly days of yore;
Not the least obeisance made he; not a minute stopped or
      stayed he;
But, with mien of lord or lady, perched above my chamber
      door —
Perched upon a bust of Pallas just above my chamber door —
      Perched, and sat, and nothing more.

Then this ebony bird beguiling my sad fancy into smiling,
By the grave and stern decorum of the countenance it wore.
"Though thy crest be shorn and shaven, thou," I said, "art
      sure no craven,

Ghastly grim and ancient raven wandering from the Nightly
     shore —
Tell me what thy lordly name is on the Night's Plutonian
     shore!"
        Quoth the Raven, "Nevermore."

Much I marveled this ungainly fowl to hear discourse so
     plainly,
Though its answer little meaning — little relevancy bore;
For we cannot help agreeing that no living human being
Ever yet was blessed with seeing bird above his chamber
     door —
Bird or beast upon the sculptured bust above his chamber
     door,
        With such name as "Nevermore."

But the raven, sitting lonely on the placid bust, spoke only
That one word, as if his soul in that one word he did outpour.
Nothing further then he uttered — not a feather then he
     fluttered —
Till I scarcely more than muttered, "Other friends have
     flown before —
On the morrow *he* will leave me, as my hopes have flown
     before."
        Then the bird said, "Nevermore."

Startled at the stillness broken by reply so aptly spoken,
"Doubtless," said I, "what it utters is its only stock and
     store,
Caught from some unhappy master whom unmerciful Disaster
Followed fast and followed faster till his songs one burden
     bore —

Till the dirges of his Hope that melancholy burden bore
      Of 'Never — nevermore.'"

But the Raven still beguiling all my fancy into smiling,
Straight I wheeled a cushioned seat in front of bird, and bust
      and door;
Then upon the velvet sinking, I betook myself to linking
Fancy unto fancy, thinking what this ominous bird of yore —
What this grim, ungainly, ghastly, gaunt and ominous bird
      of yore
      Meant in croaking "Nevermore."

This I sat engaged in guessing, but no syllable expressing
To the fowl whose fiery eyes now burned into my bosom's
      core;
This and more I sat divining, with my head at ease reclining
On the cushion's velvet lining that the lamplight gloated o'er,
But whose velvet violet lining with the lamplight gloating
      o'er,
      She shall press, ah, nevermore!

Then methought the air grew denser, perfumed from an
      unseen censer
Swung by seraphim whose footfalls tinkled on the tufted
      floor.
"Wretch," I cried, "thy God hath lent thee — by these angels
      he hath sent thee
Respite — respite and nepenthe, from thy memories of
      Lenore!
Quaff, oh quaff this kind nepenthe and forget this lost
      Lenore!"
      Quoth the Raven, "Nevermore."

"Prophet!" said I, "thing of evil! — prophet still, if bird or
    devil! —
Whether Tempter sent, or whether tempest tossed thee here
    ashore,
Desolate yet all undaunted, on this desert land enchanted —
On this home by horror haunted — tell me truly, I implore —
Is there — *is* there balm in Gilead? — tell me — tell me, I
    implore!"
        Quoth the Raven, "Nevermore."

"Prophet!" said I, "thing of evil — prophet still, if bird or
    devil!
By that Heaven that bends above us — by that God we both
    adore —
Tell this soul with sorrow laden if, within the distant Aidenn,
It shall clasp a sainted maiden whom the angels name
    Lenore —
Clasp a rare and radiant maiden whom the angels name
    Lenore."
        Quoth the Raven, "Nevermore."

"Be that word our sign of parting, bird or fiend!" I shrieked,
    upstarting —
"Get thee back into the tempest and the Night's Plutonian
    shore!
Leave no black plume as a token of that lie thy soul hath
    spoken!
Leave my loneliness unbroken! — quit the bust above my
    door!
Take thy beak from out my heart, and take thy form from
    off my door!"
        Quoth the Raven, "Nevermore."

And the Raven, never flitting, still is sitting, *still* is sitting
On the pallid bust of Pallas just above my chamber door;
And his eyes have all the seeming of a demon's that is dream-
     ing,
And the lamplight o'er him streaming throws his shadow on
     the floor;
And my soul from out that shadow that lies floating on the
     floor
          Shall be lifted — nevermore!

Edgar Allan Poe

THE MOUNTAIN WHIPPOORWILL

OR, HOW HILL-BILLY JIM WON THE GREAT FIDDLERS' PRIZE

(A GEORGIA ROMANCE)

Up in the mountains, it's lonesome all the time,
(Sof' win' slewin' thu' the sweet-potato vine).

Up in the mountains, it's lonesome for a child,
(Whippoorwills a-callin' when the sap runs wild).

Up in the mountains, mountains in the fog,
Everythin's as lazy as an old houn' dog.

Born in the mountains, never raised a pet,
Don't want nuthin' an' never got it yet.

Born in the mountains, lonesome-born,
Raised runnin' ragged thu' the cockleburrs and corn.

Never knew my pappy, mebbe never should.
Think he was a fiddle made of mountain laurel-wood.

Never had a mammy to teach me pretty-please.
Think she was a whippoorwill, a-skitin' thu' the trees.

Never had a brother ner a whole pair of pants,
But when I start to fiddle, why, yuh got to start to dance!

Listen to my fiddle — Kingdom Come — Kingdom Come!
Hear the frogs a-chunkin' "Jug o' rum, Jug o' rum!"
Hear that mountain-whippoorwill be lonesome in the air,
An' I'll tell yuh how I traveled to the Essex County Fair.

Essex County has a mighty pretty fair,
All the smarty fiddlers from the South come there.

Elbows flyin' as they rosin up the bow
For the First Prize Contest in the Georgia Fiddlers' Show.

Old Dan Wheeling, with his whiskers in his ears,
King-pin fiddler for nearly twenty years.

Big Tom Sargent, with his blue wall-eye,
An' Little Jimmy Weezer that can make a fiddle cry.

All sittin' roun', spittin' high an' struttin' proud,
(Listen, little whippoorwill, yuh better bug yore eyes!)
Tun-a-tun-a-tunin' while the jedges told the crowd
Them that got the mostest claps 'd win the bestest prize.

Everybody waitin' for the first tweedle-dee,
When in comes a-stumblin' — hill-billy me!

Bowed right pretty to the jedges an' the rest,
Took a silver dollar from a hole inside my vest,

Plunked it on the table an' said, "There's my callin' card!
An' anyone that licks me — well, he's got to fiddle hard!"

Old Dan Wheeling, he was laughin' fit to holler,
Little Jimmy Weezer said, "There's one dead dollar!"

Big Tom Sargent had a yaller-toothy grin,
But I tucked my little whippoorwill spang underneath my
    chin,
An' petted it an' tuned it till the jedges said, "Begin!"

Big Tom Sargent was the first in line;
He could fiddle all the bugs off a sweet-potato vine.
He could fiddle down a possum from a mile-high tree.
He could fiddle up a whale from the bottom of the sea.

Yuh could hear hands spankin' till they spanked each other
    raw,
When he finished variations on "Turkey in the Straw."

Little Jimmy Weezer was the next to play;
He could fiddle all night, he could fiddle all day.

He could fiddle chills, he could fiddle fever,
He could make a fiddle rustle like a lowland river.

He could make a fiddle croon like a lovin' woman.
An' they clapped like thunder when he'd finished strummin'.

Then came the ruck of the bob-tailed fiddlers,
The let's go-easies, the fair-to-middlers.

They got their claps an' they lost their bicker,
An' settled back for some more corn-licker.

An' the crowd was tired of their no-count squealing,
When out in the center steps Old Dan Wheeling.

He fiddled high and he fiddled low,
(Listen, little whippoorwill; yuh got to spread yore wings!)
He fiddled with a cherrywood bow.
(Old Dan Wheeling's got bee-honey in his strings.)

He fiddled the wind by the lonesome moon,
He fiddled a most almighty tune.

He started fiddling like a ghost,
He ended fiddling like a host.

He fiddled north an' he fiddled south,
He fiddled the heart right out of yore mouth.

He fiddled here an' he fiddled there.
He fiddled salvation everywhere.

When he was finished, the crowd cut loose,
(Whippoorwill, they's rain on yore breast.)
An' I sat there wonderin', "What's the use?"
(Whippoorwill, fly home to yore nest.)

But I stood up pert an' I took my bow,
An' my fiddle went to my shoulder, so.

An' — they wasn't no crowd to get me fazed —
But I was alone where I was raised.

Up in the mountains, so still it makes yuh skeered.
Where God lies sleepin' in his big white beard.

An' I heard the sound of the squirrel in the pine,
An' I heard the earth a-breathin' thu' the long night-time.

They've fiddled the rose an' they've fiddled the thorn,
But they haven't fiddled the mountain-corn.

They've fiddled sinful an' fiddled moral,
But they haven't fiddled the breshwood-laurel.

They've fiddled loud, an' they've fiddled still,
But they haven't fiddled the whippoorwill.

I started off with a *dump-diddle-dump*,
(*Oh, Hell's broke loose in Georgia!*)
Skunk-cabbage growin' by the bee-gum stump,
(*Whippoorwill, yo're singin' now!*)

Oh, Georgia booze is mighty fine booze,
The best yuh ever poured yuh,
But it eats the soles right offen yore shoes,
For Hell's broke loose in Georgia.

My mother was a whippoorwill pert,
My father, he was lazy,
But I'm Hell broke loose in a new store shirt
To fiddle all Georgia crazy.

Swing yore partners — up an' down the middle!
Sashay now — oh, listen to that fiddle!
Flapjacks flippin' on a red-hot griddle,

An' Hell broke loose,
Hell broke loose,
Fire on the mountains — snakes in the grass.
Satin's here a-bilin' — oh, Lordy, let him pass!
Go down Moses, set my people free,
Pop goes the weasel thu' the old Red Sea!
Jonah sittin' on a hickory-bough,
Up jumps a whale — an' where's yore prophet now?
Rabbit in the pea-patch, possum in the pot,
Try an' stop my fiddle, now my fiddle's gettin' hot!
Whippoorwill, singin' thu' the mountain hush,
Whippoorwill, shoutin' from the burnin' bush,
Whippoorwill, cryin' in the stable-door,
Sing tonight as yuh never sang before!
Hell's broke loose like a stompin' mountain-shoat,
Sing till yuh bust the gold in yore throat!
Hell's broke loose for forty miles aroun'
Bound to stop yore music if yuh don't sing it down.
Sing on the mountains, little whippoorwill,
Sing to the valleys, an' slap 'em with a hill,
For I'm struttin' high as an eagle's quill,
An' Hell's broke loose,
Hell's broke loose,
Hell's broke loose in Georgia!

They wasn't a sound when I stopped bowin',
(*Whippoorwill, yuh can sing no more.*)
But, somewhere or other, the dawn was growin',
(*Oh, mountain whippoorwill!*)

An' I thought, "I've fiddled all night an' lost.
Yo're a good hill-billy, but yuh've been bossed."

So I went to congratulate old man Dan,
— But he put his fiddle into my han' —
An' then the noise of the crowd began.

Stephen Vincent Benét

THE CONGO

A STUDY OF THE NEGRO RACE

(Being a memorial to Ray Eldred, a Disciple missionary of the
Congo River)

I. THEIR BASIC SAVAGERY

(A deep rolling bass)

Fat black bucks in a wine-barrel room,
Barrel-house kings, with feet unstable,
Sagged and reeled and pounded on the table,
Pounded on the table,
Beat an empty barrel with the handle of a broom,
Hard as they were able,
Boom, boom, Boom,
With a silk umbrella and the handle of a broom,
Boomlay, boomlay, boomlay, Boom.
THEN I had religion, THEN I had a vision.
I could not turn from their revel in derision.

(More deliberate.   Solemnly chanted)

THEN I SAW THE CONGO, CREEPING THROUGH THE BLACK,
CUTTING THROUGH THE FOREST WITH A GOLDEN TRACK.
Then along that riverbank
A thousand miles
Tattooed cannibals danced in files;
Then I heard the boom of the blood-lust song
And a thigh-bone beating on a tin-pan gong.

(A rapidly piling climax of speed and racket)

And "BLOOD" screamed the whistles and the fifes of the
      warriors,
"BLOOD" screamed the skull-faced, lean witch-doctors,
"Whirl ye the deadly voo-doo rattle,
Harry the uplands,
Steal all the cattle,
Rattle-rattle, rattle-rattle,
Bing.

(With a philosophic pause)

Boomlay, boomlay, boomlay, BOOM,"
A roaring, epic, rag-time tune
From the mouth of the Congo
To the Mountains of the Moon.

Death is an Elephant,
Torch-eyed and horrible,
Foam-flanked and terrible.

(Shrilly and with a heavily accented meter)

BOOM, steal the pygmies,
BOOM, kill the Arabs,
BOOM, kill the white men,
Hoo, Hoo, Hoo.

(Like the wind in the chimney)

Listen to the yell of Leopold's ghost
Burning in Hell for his hand-maimed host.
Hear how the demons chuckle and yell
Cutting his hands off, down in Hell.
Listen to the creepy proclamation,

Blown through the lairs of the forest-nation,
Blown past the white-ants' hill of clay,
Blown past the marsh where the butterflies play: —

*(All the " o " sounds very golden.   Heavy accents very heavy.   Light
accents very light.   Last line whispered)*

"Be careful what you do,
Or Mumbo-Jumbo, God of the Congo,
And all of the other
Gods of the Congo,
Mumbo-Jumbo will hoo-doo you,
Mumbo-Jumbo will hoo-doo you,
Mumbo-Jumbo will hoo-doo you."

II. THEIR IRREPRESSIBLE HIGH SPIRITS

(Rather shrill and high)

Wild crap-shooters with a whoop and a call
Danced the juba in their gambling hall
And laughed fit to kill, and shook the town,
And guyed the policemen and laughed them down
With a boomlay, boomlay, boomlay, Boom.

(Read exactly as in first section)

THEN I SAW THE CONGO, CREEPING THROUGH THE BLACK,
CUTTING THROUGH THE FOREST WITH A GOLDEN TRACK.

(Lay emphasis on the delicate ideas.   Keep as lightfooted as possible)

A Negro fairyland swung into view,
A minstrel river
Where dreams come true.
The ebony palace soared on high

Through the blossoming trees to the evening sky.
The inlaid porches and casements shone
With gold and ivory and elephant-bone.
And the black crowd laughed till their sides were sore
At the baboon butler in the agate door,
And the well-known tunes of the parrot band
That trilled on the bushes of that magic land.

(With pomposity)

A troop of skull-faced witch-men came
Through the agate doorway in suits of flame —
Yea, long-tailed coats with a gold-leaf crust
And hats that were covered with diamond-dust.
And the crowd in the court gave a whoop and a call
And danced the juba from wall to wall.

(With a great deliberation and ghostliness)

But the witch-men suddenly stilled the throng
With a stern cold glare, and a stern old song:
"Mumbo-Jumbo will hoo-doo you." . . .

(With overwhelming assurance, good cheer, and pomp)

Just then from the doorway, as fat as shotes
Came the cake-walk princes in their long red coats,
Canes with a brilliant lacquer shine,
And tall silk hats that were red as wine.

(With growing speed and sharply marked dance-rhythm)

And they pranced with their butterfly partners there,
Coal-black maidens with pearls in their hair,
Knee-skirts trimmed with the jessamine sweet,
And bells on their ankles and little black feet.

And the couples railed at the chant and the frown
Of the witch-men lean, and laughed them down.
(Oh, rare was the revel, and well worth while
That made those glowering witch-men smile.)

The cake-walk royalty then began
To walk for a cake that was tall as a man
To the tune of "Boomlay, boomlay, Boom,"
While the witch-men laughed, with a sinister air,
And sang with the scalawags prancing there:

(With a touch of Negro dialect, and as rapidly as possible toward the end)

"Walk with care, walk with care,
Or Mumbo-Jumbo, god of the Congo,
And all of the other Gods of the Congo,
Mumbo-Jumbo will hoo-doo you.
Beware, beware, walk with care,
Boomlay, boomlay, boomlay, boom,
Boomlay, boomlay, boomlay, boom,
Boomlay, boomlay, boomlay, boom,
Boomlay, boomlay, boomlay,
Boom."

(Slow, philosophic calm)

(Oh, rare was the revel, and well worth while
That made those glowering witch-men smile.)

III. THE HOPE OF THEIR RELIGION

(Heavy bass. With a literal imitation of camp-meeting racket and trance)

A good old Negro in the slums of the town
Preached at a sister for her velvet gown.

Howled at a brother for his low-down ways,
His prowling, guzzling, sneak-thief days.
Beat on the Bible till he wore it out
Starting the jubilee revival shout.
And some had visions, as they stood on chairs,
And sang of Jacob, and the golden stairs,
And they all repented, a thousand strong
From their stupor and savagery and sin and wrong
And slammed with their hymn books till they shook the room
With "Glory, glory, glory,"
And "Boom, boom, Boom."

(Exactly as in the first section.   Begin with terror and power, end with joy)
THEN I SAW THE CONGO, CREEPING THROUGH THE BLACK,
CUTTING THROUGH THE JUNGLE WITH A GOLDEN TRACK.
And the gray sky opened like a new-rent veil
And showed the Apostles with their coats of mail.
In bright white steel they were seated round
And their fire eyes watched where the Congo wound.
And the twelve Apostles, from their thrones on high
Thrilled all the forest with their heavenly cry:

(Sung to the tune of " Hark, ten thousand harps and voices")
"Mumbo-Jumbo will die in the jungle;
Never again will he hoo-doo you,
Never again will he hoo-doo you."

(With growing deliberation and joy)
Then along that river, a thousand miles
The vine-snared trees fell down in files.
Pioneer angels cleared the way
For a Congo paradise, for babes at play,

For sacred capitals, for temples clean.
Gone were the skull-faced witch-men lean.

(In a rather high key — as delicately as possible)
There, where the wild ghost-gods had wailed
A million boats of the angels sailed
With oars of silver, and prows of blue
And silken pennants that the sun shone through.
'Twas a land transfigured, 'twas a new creation.
Oh, a singing wind swept the negro nation
And on through the backwoods clearing flew:

(To the tune of "Hark, ten thousand harps and voices")
"Mumbo-Jumbo is dead in the jungle.
Never again will he hoo-doo you.
Never again will he hoo-doo you."

Redeemed were the forests, the beasts and the men,
And only the vulture dared again
By the far, lone mountains of the moon

(Dying down into a penetrating, terrified whisper)
To cry, in the silence, the Congo tune:
"Mumbo-Jumbo will hoo-doo you,
Mumbo-Jumbo will hoo-doo you.
Mumbo ... Jumbo ... will ... hoo-doo ... you."
                                        Vachel Lindsay

THE SACK OF OLD PANAMA

They sat in a tavern in wicked Port Royal,
Grim Morgan and Brodley and one or two others,

A flagon of rum on the table between them
And villainy binding them closer than brothers.

And Morgan dropped hint of Old Panama's riches;
Said little, but said it with evil suggestion,
Till Brodley swayed up, with his glass in his fingers,
And swore that a Don was an aid to digestion!

But Morgan said, idly, "'Twould be a long journey" —
Cried Brodley: "What odds, when the end of it's yellow?
I mind me the pockets of dead men I lightened
That year of our Lord when we sacked Porto Bello!"

Then Morgan stood straight, with his face of dark smiling:
"I'll rake them once more — then I'll stop all such capers;
Come home and be Governor!   Aye, but I will, though,
And hang every master that can't show his papers.

"I'll have me a house that will front the blue water,
And devil a pirate shall sit at my table;
But now, and once more, I've a will to go courting,
To dance with a Don while I'm hearty and able."

He laughed and drew breath; and they tipped up the flagon,
And fashioned his words in a stormy sea ditty.
Then swiftly fell silent, with dream-darkened faces,
And thought of their hands at the throat of a city....

                *   *   *

The sea was as blue as the breast of the morning
When Morgan went down to his last buccaneering;
His sails were like low-fallen clouds in the distance,
Blown onward, and fading, and slow disappearing.

And so he put out — and was part of the distance,
A blur of slow wings on the blue ring of heaven,
With two thousand devils adream below hatches,
And steel, and dry powder, and ships thirty-seven.

And all down the decks there was talk of the venture —
How Morgan had wind of unthinkable treasure;
How Panama's streets were the sweetness of silver,
Where men in gold gutters threw pearls for their pleasure!

And Brodley went forward and took San Lorenzo,
With patience and passion, as men take a woman,
And Morgan came up, with his face of dark smiling,
And saw the sword's kiss on the heart of the foeman.

*   *   *

The dawn saw them marching — twelve hundred brown
    devils,
With steel and dry powder and gay crimson sashes;
And so they put on ... and were dead in the jungle
Of great shaking fevers and little barbs' gashes.

*   *   *

The tenth day was sleeping in tents of red splendor
When Morgan crept up to the walls of the city —
Behind him his madmen came shouting and sobbing,
And mouthing the words of an old pirate ditty.

Their souls were in tatters!   And still they came singing,
Till all the hushed foreland was waked from its dreaming,
And high in their towers the sweet bells of vesper
Were drowned and made dim by the mad, measured scream-
    ing.

A gun roared, and deep in the heart of the city
Wild pulses began.... A young mother ran crying,
"*The English are on us!*" Swords silvered the twilight,
And priests turned their books to the prayers for the dying.

Then out from his gates came the desperate Spaniard;
The swords were like flame, and the towers were ringing!
But Morgan's men waited; lay down with choked muzzles,
And dealt out their death to the pulse of their singing.

Their volleys belched forth like a chorus of thunder,
A great whining Song that went on without pity,
Till night drew her veil ... then they rose from their
        bellies,
And spat at the dead — and went into the city.

                    *   *   *

The Governor sat in his window at evening,
His window that looked on the star-furrowed water;
A ship had come into the clasp of the harbor,
Clear-lined from the darkness the bright moon had wrought
        her.

                    *   *   *

He clapped his fat hands; and a black lad stood bowing.
"Bring candles — and rum," said the Governor, grinning.
And then he sat down with his boots on the table,
And dozed until Morgan should come from his sinning....

He came, with an oath, in his great greasy sea-boots,
A sash at his waist, and a pistol stuck in it,
His beard to his throat, and his little eyes leering —
"Your voice," said Sir Thomas, "is sweet as a linnet!"

"My pockets are sweeter," said Morgan; and, winking,
He drew from his sash a creased bag of black leather,
Unloosed it and spilled on the bare wooden table
Red jewels that kindled like swords struck together!

*   *   *

The jewels lay warm in the dusk of the candles,
Like soulless red eyes that no tears might set blinking . . .
And Thomas Sir Modyford crooked his hot fingers,
And chose the King's profit, whilst Morgan sat drinking.

"Sweet baubles! Sweet pretties! They've blinded my
        candles.
They're flame, Pirate, flame! See my hand, how they've
        burned it."
He laughed, and drew forth from his pocket a parchment —
"It's yours, by our bargain; and damme, you've earned it."

They spread out the parchment between them. Said Mor-
        gan:
"God's name! I'm respectable!" "Aye," said Sir Thomas,
"Ye're Leftenant-Governor, lately appointed
By will of the Crown — in accord with our promise!"

*   *   *

Day broke . . . and the throat of the harbor was clouded
With sail. 'Twas the fleet of the pirates returning —
But down their grim ports no black muzzles peered frowning,
Nor naked steel leaped for the dawn to set burning.

They came as calm merchantmen, shriven with morning
(For in the King's harbors the law is hard-fisted!)
And so they stole in, like whipped hounds to a kennel,
Their loosed anchors lolling like tongues when they listed.

The candles were dead in the Governor's chamber;
And in at the window the young light came creeping —
Asprawl at the table sat Morgan the Pirate,
And under his boot-heels Sir Thomas lay sleeping.

The anchors splashed down in the ruffled blue water,
The great wings were furled with a rattle of gearing;
But Morgan sat clutching a folded gray parchment,
A glass at his lips, and his little eyes leering.

Dana Burnet

GO DOWN, DEATH

(A FUNERAL SERMON)

Weep not, weep not,
She is not dead;
She's resting in the bosom of Jesus.
Heart-broken husband — weep no more;
Grief-stricken son — weep no more,
Left-lonesome daughter — weep no more;
She's only just gone home.

Day before yesterday morning,
God was looking down from his great, high heaven,
Looking down on all his children,
And his eye fell on Sister Caroline,
Tossing on her bed of pain.
And God's big heart was touched with pity,
With the everlasting pity.

And God sat back on his throne,
And he commanded that tall, bright angel standing
      at his right hand:

Call me Death!
And that tall, bright angel cried in a voice
That broke like a clap of thunder:
Call Death! — Call Death!
And the echo sounded down the streets of heaven
Till it reached away back to that shadowy place,
Where Death waits with his pale, white horses.

And Death heard the summons,
And he leaped on his fastest horse,
Pale as a sheet in the moonlight.
Up the golden street Death galloped,
And the hoofs of his horse struck fire from the gold,
But they didn't make no sound.
Up Death rode to the Great White Throne,
And waited for God's command.

And God said: Go down, Death, go down,
Go down to Savannah, Georgia,
Down in Yamacraw,
And find Sister Caroline.
She's borne the burden and heat of the day,
She's labored long in my vineyard,
And she's tired —
She's weary —
Go down, Death, and bring her to me.

And Death didn't say a word,
But he loosed the reins on his pale, white horse,
And he clamped the spurs to his bloodless sides,
And out and down he rode,
Through heaven's pearly gates,

Past suns and moons and stars;
On Death rode,
And the foam from his horse was like a comet in the sky;
On Death rode,
Leaving the lightning's flash behind;
Straight on down he came.

While we were watching round her bed,
She turned her eyes and looked away,
She saw what we couldn't see;
She saw Old Death.   She saw Old Death,
Coming like a falling star.
But Death didn't frighten Sister Caroline;
He looked to her like a welcome friend.
And she whispered to us: I'm going home,
And she smiled and closed her eyes.

And Death took her up like a baby,
And she lay in his icy arms,
But she didn't feel no chill.
And Death began to ride again —
Up beyond the evening star,
Out beyond the morning star,
Into the glittering light of glory,
On to the Great White Throne.
And there he laid Sister Caroline
On the loving breast of Jesus.

And Jesus took his own hand and wiped away her tears,
And he smoothed the furrows from her face,
And the angels sang a little song,
And Jesus rocked her in his arms,

And kept a-saying: Take your rest,
Take your rest, take your rest.

Weep not — weep not,
She is not dead;
She's resting in the bosom of Jesus.

James Weldon Johnson

JESSE JAMES

(AMERICAN MYTH)

DESIGN IN RED AND YELLOW FOR A NICKEL LIBRARY [1]

Jesse James was a two-gun man,
        (*Roll on, Missouri!*)
Strong-arm chief of an outlaw clan.
        (*From Kansas to Illinois!*)
He twirled an old Colt forty-five,
        (*Roll on, Missouri!*)
They never took Jesse James alive.
        (*Roll, Missouri, roll!*)

Jesse James was King of the Wes';
        (*Cataracks in the Missouri!*)
He'd a di'mon' heart in his lef' breas';
        (*Brown Missouri rolls!*)
He'd a fire in his heart no hurt could stifle;
        (*Thunder, Missouri!*)
Lion eyes an' a Winchester rifle.
        (*Missouri, roll down!*)

[1] In the refrain the proper native pronunciation of "Missouri" is, of course, "Mizzoura."

Jesse James rode a pinto hawse;
Come at night to a water-cawse;
Tetched with the rowel that pinto's flank;
She sprang the torrent from bank to bank.

Jesse rode through a sleepin' town;
Looked the moonlit street both up an' down;
Crack-crack-crack, the street ran flames
An' a great voice cried, "I'm Jesse James!"

Hawse an' afoot they're after Jess!
   (*Roll on, Missouri!*)
Spurrin' an' spurrin' — but he's gone Wes'.
   (*Brown Missouri rolls!*)
He was ten foot tall when he stood in his boots;
   (*Lightnin' light the Missouri!*)
More'n a match fer sich galoots.
   (*Roll, Missouri, roll!*)

Jesse James rode outa the sage;
Roun' the rocks come the swayin' stage;
Straddlin' the road a giant stan's
An' a great voice bellers, "Throw up yer han's!"

Jesse raked in the di'mon' rings,
The big gold watches an' the yuther things;
Jesse divvied 'em then an' thar
With a cryin' child had lost her mar.

The U.S. troopers is after Jess;
   (*Roll on, Missouri!*)
Their hawses sweat foam, but he's gone Wes';
   (*Hear Missouri roar!*)

He was broad as a b'ar, he'd a ches' like a drum,
(Wind an' rain through Missouri!)
An' his red hair flamed like Kingdom Come.
(Missouri down to the sea!)

Jesse James all alone in the rain
Stopped an' stuck up the Eas'-boun' train;
Swayed through the coaches with horns an' a tail,
Lit out with the bullion an' the registered mail.

Jess made 'em all turn green with fright,
Quakin' in the aisles in the pitch-black night;
An' he give all the bullion to a pore ole tramp
Campin' nigh the cuttin' in the dirt an' damp.

The whole U.S. is after Jess;
(Roll on, Missouri!)
The son-of-a-gun, if he ain't gone Wes';
(Missouri to the Sea!)
He could chaw cold iron an' spit blue flame;
(Cataracks down the Missouri!)
He rode on a catamount he'd larned to tame.
(Hear that Missouri roll!)

Jesse James rode into a bank;
Give his pinto a tetch on the flank;
Jumped the teller's window with an awful crash;
Heaved up the safe an' twirled his mustache;

He said, "So long, boys!" He yelped, "So long!
Feelin' porely today — I ain't feelin' strong!"
Rode right through the wall agoin' crack-crack-crack, —
Took the safe home to mother in a gunny-sack.

They're creepin', they're crawlin', they're stalkin' Jess;
   (Roll on, Missouri!)
They's a rumor he's gone much further Wes';
   (Roll, Missouri, roll!)
They's word of a cayuse hitched to the bars
   (Ruddy clouds on Missouri!)
Of a golden sunset that busts into stars.
   (Missouri, roll down!)

Jesse James rode hell fer leather;
He was a hawse an' a man together;
In a cave in a mountain high up in air
He lived with a rattlesnake, a wolf, an' a bear.

Jesse's heart was as sof' as a woman;
Fer guts an' stren'th he was sooper-human;
He could put six shots through a woodpecker's eye
And take in one swaller a gallon o' rye.

They sought him here an' they sought him there,
   (Roll on, Missouri!)
But he strides by night through the ways of the air,
   (Brown Missouri rolls!)
They say he was took an' they say he is dead;
   (Thunder, Missouri!)
But he ain't — he's a sunset overhead!
   (Missouri down to the sea!)

Jesse James was a Hercules.
When he went through the woods he tore up the trees.
When he went on the plains he smoked the groun'
An' the hull lan' shuddered fer miles aroun'.

Jesse James wore a red bandanner
That waved on the breeze like the Star Spangled Banner;
In seven states he cut up dadoes.
He's gone with the buffler an' the desperadoes.

Yes, Jesse James was a two-gun man
        (*Roll on, Missouri!*)
The same as when this song began;
        (*From Kansas to Illinois!*)
An' when you see a sunset bust into flames
        (*Lightnin' light the Missouri!*)
Or a thunderstorm blaze — that's Jesse James!
        (*Hear that Missouri roll!*)

                                        William Rose Benét

THE GLORY TRAIL

'Way high up the Mogollons,
    Among the mountain tops,
A lion cleaned a yearlin's bones
    And licked his thankful chops,
When on the picture who should ride,
    A-trippin' down a slope,
But High-Chin Bob, with sinful pride
    And mav'rick-hungry rope.

    "Oh, glory be to me," says he,
        "And fame's unfadin' flowers!
    All meddlin' hands are far away;
    I ride my good top-hawse today
    And I'm top-rope of the Lazy J—
        Hi! kitty cut, you're ours!"

That lion licked his paw so brown
   And dreamed soft dreams of veal —
And then the circlin' loop sung down
   And roped him 'round his meal.
He yowled quick fury to the world
   Till all the hills yelled back;
The top-hawse gave a snort and whirled
   And Bob caught up the slack.

> *"Oh, glory be to me," laughs he.*
> *"We've hit the glory trail.*
> *No human man as I have read*
> *Darst loop a ragin' lion's head,*
> *Nor ever hawse could drag one dead*
> *Until we told the tale."*

'Way high up the Mogollons
   That top-hawse done his best,
Through whippin' brush and rattlin' stones,
   From canyon-floor to crest.
But ever when Bob turned and hoped
   A limp remains to find,
A red-eyed lion, belly roped
   But healthy, loped behind.

> *"Oh, glory be to me," grunts he.*
> *"This glory trail is rough,*
> *Yet even till the Judgment Morn*
> *I'll keep this dally 'round the horn,*
> *For never any hero born*
> *Could stoop to holler: 'Nuff!'"*

Three suns had rode their circle home
    Beyond the desert's rim,
And turned their star-herds loose to roam
    The ranges high and dim;
Yet up and down and 'round and 'cross
    Bob pounded, weak and wan,
For pride still glued him to his hawse
    And glory drove him on.

    "Oh, glory be to me," sighs he.
      "He kaint be drug to death,
    But now I know beyond a doubt
    Them heroes I have read about
    Was only fools that stuck it out
      To end of mortal breath."

'Way high up the Mogollons
    A prospect man did swear
That moon dreams melted down his bones
    And hoisted up his hair:
A ribby cow-hawse thundered by,
    A lion trailed along,
A rider, ga'nt but chin on high,
    Yelled out a crazy song.

    "Oh, glory be to me!" cries he,
      "And to my noble noose!
    Oh, stranger, tell my pards below
    I took a rampin' dream in tow,
    And if I never lay him low,
      I'll never turn him loose!"

                        Badger Clark

THE COWBOY'S LAMENT [1]

As I walked out in the streets of Laredo,
As I walked out in Laredo one day,
I spied a poor cowboy wrapped up in white linen,
Wrapped up in white linen as cold as the clay.

"Oh, beat the drum slowly and play the fife lowly,
Play the Dead March as you carry me along;
Take me to the green valley, there lay the sod o'er me,
For I'm a young cowboy and I know I've done wrong.

"I see by your outfit that you are a cowboy,"
These words he did say as I boldly stepped by.
"Come sit down beside me and hear my sad story;
I was shot in the breast and I know I must die.

"Let sixteen gamblers come handle my coffin,
Let sixteen cowboys come sing me a song,
Take me to the graveyard and lay the sod o'er me,
For I'm a poor cowboy and I know I've done wrong.

.   .   .   .

It was once in the saddle I used to go dashing,
It was once in the saddle I used to go gay;
First to the dram-house, then to the card-house,
Got shot in the breast, I am dying today.

"Get six jolly cowboys to carry my coffin;
Get six pretty maidens to bear up my pall.
Put bunches of roses all over my coffin,
Put roses to deaden the clods as they fall.

[1] This ballad has been abbreviated from Mr. Lomax's version.

"Then swing your rope slowly and rattle your spurs lowly,
And give a wild whoop as you carry me along;
And in the grave throw me and roll the sod o'er me,
For I'm a young cowboy and I know I've done wrong.

"Go bring me a cup, a cup of cold water,
To cool my parched lips," the cowboy said;
Before I turned, the spirit had left him
And gone to its Giver — the cowboy was dead.

We beat the drum slowly and played the fife lowly,
And bitterly wept as we bore him along;
For we all loved our comrade, so brave, young, and hand-
        some,
We all loved our comrade although he'd done wrong.

                                            John A. Lomax

THE DYING COWBOY [1]

"O bury me not on the lone prairie."
These words came low and mournfully
From the pallid lips of a youth who lay
On his dying bed at the close of day.

He had wailed in pain till o'er his brow
Death's shadows fast were gathering now;
He thought of his home and his loved ones nigh
As the cowboys gathered to see him die.

"O bury me not on the lone prairie
Where the wild coyotes will howl o'er me,

[1] This ballad has been abbreviated from Mr. Lomax's version.

In a narrow grave just six by three,
O bury me not on the lone prairie.

"In fancy I listen to the well-known words
Of the free, wild winds and the song of the birds;
I think of home and the cottage in the bower
And the scenes I loved in my childhood's hour.

"It matters not, I've oft been told,
Where the body lies when the heart grows cold;
Yet grant, Oh grant this wish to me,
O bury me not on the lone prairie.

 · · · · · · · · ·

"O bury me not on the lone prairie
Where the wild coyotes will howl o'er me,
Where the rattlesnakes hiss and the crow flies free
O bury me not on the lone prairie."

O we buried him there on the lone prairie
Where the wild rose blooms and the wind blows free,
O his pale young face nevermore to see —
For we buried him there on the lone prairie.

Yes, we buried him there in the lone prairie
Where the owl all night hoots mournfully,
And the blizzard beats and the winds blow free
O'er his lowly grave on the lone prairie.

And the cowboys now as they roam the plain —
For they marked the spot where his bones were lain —
Fling a handful of roses o'er his grave,
With a prayer to Him who his soul will save.

"O bury me not on the lone prairie
Where the wolves can howl and growl o'er me;
Fling a handful of roses o'er my grave
With a prayer to Him who my soul will save."

John A. Lomax

EVE

Eve, with her basket, was
Deep in the bells and grass,
Wading in bells and grass
Up to her knees.
Picking a dish of sweet
Berries and plums to eat,
Down in the bells and grass
Under the trees.

Mute as a mouse in a
Corner the cobra lay,
Curled round a bough of the
Cinnamon tall. . . .
Now to get even and
Humble proud heaven and
Now was the moment or
Never at all.

"Eva!"   Each syllable
Light as a flower fell,
"Eva!" he whispered the
Wondering maid,
Soft as a bubble sung
Out of a linnet's lung,

Soft and most silverly
"Eva!" he said.

Picture that orchard sprite;
Eve, with her body white,
Supple and smooth to her
Slim fingertips;
Wondering, listening,
Listening, wondering,
Eve with a berry
Halfway to her lips.

Oh, had our simple Eve
Seen through the make-believe!
Had she but known the
Pretender he was!
Out of the boughs he came,
Whispering still her name,
Tumbling in twenty rings
Into the grass.

Here was the strangest pair
In the world anywhere,
Eve in the bells and grass
Kneeling, and he
Telling his story low....
Singing birds saw them go
Down the dark path to
The Blasphemous Tree.

Oh, what a clatter when
Titmouse and Jenny Wren

Saw him successful and
Taking his leave!
How the birds rated him,
How they all hated him!
How they all pitied
Poor motherless Eve!

Picture her crying
Outside in the lane,
Eve, with no dish of sweet
Berries and plums to eat,
Haunting the gate of the
Orchard in vain....
Picture the lewd delight
Under the hill tonight —
"Eva!" the toast goes round,
"Eva!" again.

Ralph Hodgson

THE HAUNTED PALACE

In the greenest of our valleys
  By good angels tenanted,
Once a fair and stately palace —
  Radiant palace — reared its head.
In the monarch Thought's dominion —
  It stood there!
Never seraph spread a pinion
  Over fabric half so fair!

Banners yellow, glorious, golden,
  On its roof did float and flow,

(This — all this — was in the olden
 Time long ago),
And every gentle air that dallied,
 In that sweet day,
Along the ramparts plumed and pallid,
 A wingèd odor went away.

Wanderers in that happy valley,
 Through two luminous windows, saw
Spirits moving musically,
 To a lute's well-tunèd law,
Round about a throne where, sitting,
 Porphyrogene,
In state his glory well befitting,
 The ruler of the realm was seen.

And all with pearl and ruby glowing
 Was the fair palace door,
Through which came flowing, flowing, flowing
 And sparkling evermore,
A troop of Echoes, whose sweet duty
 Was but to sing,
In voices of surpassing beauty,
 The wit and wisdom of their king.

But evil things, in robes of sorrow,
 Assailed the monarch's high estate.
(Ah, let us mourn! — for never morrow
 Shall dawn upon him, desolate!)
And round about his home the glory
 That blushed and bloomed,
Is but a dim-remembered story
 Of the old-time entombed.

And travelers, now, within that valley,
   Through the red-litten windows see
Vast forms, that move fantastically
   To a discordant melody,
While, like a ghastly rapid river,
   Through the pale door
A hideous throng rush out forever
   And laugh — but smile no more.

Edgar Allan Poe

KUBLA KHAN

In Xanadu did Kubla Khan
   A stately pleasure-dome decree:
Where Alph, the sacred river, ran
Through caverns measureless to man
   Down to a sunless sea.
So twice five miles of fertile ground
With walls and towers were girdled round:
And there were gardens bright with sinuous rills,
Where blossomed many an incense-bearing tree;
And here were forests ancient as the hills,
Enfolding sunny spots of greenery.

But O! that deep romantic chasm which slanted
Down the green hill athwart a cedarn cover!
A savage place! as holy and enchanted
As e'er beneath a waning moon was haunted
By woman wailing for her demon-lover!
And from this chasm, with ceaseless turmoil seething,
As if this Earth in fast thick pants were breathing,
A mighty fountain momently was forced,

Amid whose swift half-intermitted burst
Huge fragments vaulted like rebounding hail,
Or chaffy grain beneath the thresher's flail:
And 'mid these dancing rocks at once and ever
It flung up momently the sacred river.
Five miles meandering with a mazy motion
Through wood and dale the sacred river ran,
Then reached the caverns measureless to man,
And sank in tumult to the lifeless ocean:
And 'mid this tumult Kubla heard from far
Ancestral voices prophesying war!

    The shadow of the dome of pleasure
    Floated midway on the waves;
    Where was heard the mingled measure
    From the fountain and the caves.
It was a miracle of rare device,
A sunny pleasure-dome with caves of ice!

    A damsel with a dulcimer
    In a vision once I saw:
    It was an Abyssinian maid,
    And on her dulcimer she played,
    Singing of Mount Abora.
    Could I revive within me
    Her symphony and song,
    To such a deep delight 'twould win me
That with music loud and long,
I would build that dome in air,
That sunny dome! those caves of ice!
And all who heard should see them there,
And all should cry, Beware! Beware!

His flashing eyes, his floating hair!
Weave a circle round him thrice,
And close your eyes with holy dread,
For he on honey-dew hath fed,
And drunk the milk of Paradise.

Samuel Taylor Coleridge

THE LISTENERS

"Is there anybody there?" said the Traveler,
   Knocking on the moonlit door;
And his horse in the silence champed the grasses
   Of the forest's ferny floor;
And a bird flew up out of the turret,
   Above the Traveler's head;
And he smote upon the door again a second time;
   "Is there anybody there?" he said.
But no one descended to the Traveler;
   No head from the leaf-fringed sill
Leaned over and looked into his gray eyes,
   Where he stood perplexed and still.
But only a host of phantom listeners
   That dwelt in the lone house then
Stood listening in the quiet of the moonlight
   To that voice from the world of men:
Stood thronging the faint moonbeams on the dark stair,
   That goes down to the empty hall,
Hearkening in an air stirred and shaken
   By the lonely Traveler's call.
And he felt in his heart their strangeness,
   Their stillness answering his cry,
While his horse moved, cropping the dark turf,

'Neath the starred and leafy sky;
For he suddenly smote on the door, even
  Louder, and lifted his head: —
"Tell them I came, and no one answered,
  That I kept my word," he said.
Never the least stir made the listeners,
  Though every word he spake
Fell echoing through the shadowiness of the still house
  From the one man left awake:
Ay, they heard his foot upon the stirrup,
  And the sound of iron on stone,
And how the silence surged softly backward,
  When the plunging hoofs were gone.

Walter de la Mare

Modern Marvels

MACHINES

I hear them grinding, grinding through the night,
The gaunt machines with arteries of fire,
Muscled with iron, boweled with smouldering light;
I watch them pulsing, swinging, climbing higher,
Derrick on derrick, wheel on rhythmic wheel,
Swift band on whirring band, lever on lever,
Shouting their songs in raucous notes of steel,
Blinding a village with their light, damming a river,
I hear them grinding, grinding hour on hour,
Cleaving the night in twain, shattering the dark
With all the rasping torrents of their power,
Groaning and belching spark on crimson spark.
I cannot hear my voice above their cry
Shaking the earth and thundering to the sky.

Slowly the dawn comes up. No motors stir
The brightening hilltops as the sunrise flows
In yellow tides where daybreak's lavender
Clings to a waiting valley. No derrick throws
The sun into the heavens and no pulley
Unfolds the wildflowers thirsting for the day;
No wheel unravels ferns deep in a gulley;
No engine starts the brook upon its way.
The butterflies drift idly, wing to wing,
Knowing no measured rhythm they must follow;
No turbine drives the white clouds as they swing

Across the cool blue meadows of the swallow.
With all the feathered silence of a swan
They whir and beat — the engines of the dawn.
Daniel Whitehead Hickey

AND YET FOOLS SAY

He captured light and caged it in a glass,
Then harnessed it forever to a wire;
He gave men robots with no backs to tire
In bearing burdens for the toiling mass.

He freed the tongue in wood and wax and brass,
Imbued dull images with motions' fire,
Transmuted metal into human choir —
These man-made miracles he brought to pass.

Bulbs banish night along the Great White Way,
Thin threads of copper throb with might unseen;
On silver curtains shadow-actors play
That walk and talk from magic-mouthed machine,

While continents converse through skies o'erhead
And yet fools say that Edison is dead!
George S. Holmes

THE AUTOMOBILE

Fluid the world flowed under us: the hills
    Billow on billow of umbrageous green
    Heaved us, aghast, to fresh horizons, seen
One rapturous instant, blind with flash of rills

And silver-rising storms and dewy stills
    Of dripping boulders, till the dim ravine
    Drowned us again in leafage, whose serene
Coverts grew loud with our tumultuous wills.

Then all of Nature's old amazement seemed
    Sudden to ask us: "Is this also Man?
    This plunging, volant, land-amphibian
What Plato mused and Paracelsus dreamed?
    Reply!" And piercing us with ancient scan,
The shrill, primeval hawk gazed down — and screamed.
                        Percy MacKaye

THE SANTA FÉ TRAIL — A HUMORESQUE

I

In Which a Racing Auto Comes from the East

(To be sung delicately to an improvised tune)

This is the order of the music of the morning: —
First, from the far East comes but a crooning;
The crooning turns to a sunrise singing.
Hark to the *calm*-horn, *balm*-horn, *psalm*-horn;
Hark to the *faint*-horn, *quaint*-horn, *saint*-horn . . .

(To be sung or read with great speed)

Hark to the *pace*-horn, *chase*-horn, *race*-horn!
And the holy veil of the dawn has gone,
Swiftly the brazen car comes on.
It burns in the East as the sunrise burns.
I see great flashes where the far trail turns.
Its eyes are lamps like the eyes of dragons.
It drinks gasoline from big red flagons.

Butting through the delicate mists of the morning,
It comes like lightning, goes past roaring.
It will hail all the windmills, taunting, ringing,
Dodge the cyclones,
Count the milestones,
On through the ranges the prairie-dog tills —
Scooting past the cattle on the thousand hills . . .

(To be read or sung in a rolling bass with some deliberation)

Ho for the tear-horn, scare-horn, dare-horn,
Ho for the gay-horn, bark-horn, bay-horn.
Ho for Kansas, land that restores us
When houses choke us, and great books bore us!
Sunrise Kansas, harvester's Kansas,
A million men have found you before us.

II

In Which Many Autos Pass Westward

(In an even, deliberate, narrative manner)

I want live things in their pride to remain.
I will not kill one grasshopper vain
Though he eats a hole in my shirt like a door.
I let him out, give him one chance more.
Perhaps, while he gnaws my hat in his whim,
Grasshopper lyrics occur to him.

I am a tramp by the long trail's border,
Given to squalor, rags, and disorder.
I nap and amble and yawn and look,
Write fool-thoughts in my grubby book,
Recite to the children, explore at my ease,

Work when I work, beg when I please,
Give crank-drawings, that make folks stare,
To the half-grown boys in the sunset-glare;
And get me a place to sleep in the hay
At the end of a live-and-let-live day.

I find in the stubble of the new-cut weeds
A whisper and a feasting, all one needs:
The whisper of the strawberries, white and red,
Here where the new-cut weeds lie dead.

But I would not walk all alone till I die
Without some life-drunk horns going by.
Up round this apple-earth they come,
Blasting the whispers of the morning dumb: —
Cars in a plain realistic row.
And fair dreams fade
When the raw horns blow.

On each snapping pennant
A big black name —
The careering city
Whence each car came.

(*Like a train-caller in Union Depot*)

They tour from Memphis, Atlanta, Savannah,
Tallahassee and Texarkana.
They tour from St. Louis, Columbus, Manistee,
They tour from Peoria, Davenport, Kankakee.
Cars from Concord, Niagara, Boston,
Cars from Topeka, Emporia and Austin.
Cars from Chicago, Hannibal, Cairo,

Cars from Alton, Oswego, Toledo.
Cars from Buffalo, Kokomo, Delphi,
Cars from Lodi, Carmi, Loami.
Ho for Kansas, land that restores us
When houses choke us, and great books bore us!
While I watch the highroad
And look at the sky,
While I watch the clouds in amazing grandeur
Roll their legions without rain
Over the blistering Kansas plain —
While I sit by the milestone
And watch the sky,
The United States
Goes by!

(To be given very harshly with a snapping explosiveness)
Listen to the iron horns, ripping, racking.
Listen to the quack horns, slack and clacking!
Way down the road, trilling like a toad,
Here comes the *dice*-horn, here comes the *vice*-horn,
Here comes the *snarl*-horn, *brawl*-horn, *lewd*-horn,
Followed by the *prude*-horn, bleak and squeaking: —
(Some of them from Kansas, some of them from Kansas.)
Here comes the *hod*-horn, *plod*-horn, *sod*-horn,
Nevermore-to-*roam*-horn, *loam*-horn, *home*-horn,
(Some of them from Kansas, some of them from Kansas.)

(To be read or sung well-nigh in a whisper)
> *Far away the Rachel-Jane*
> *Not defeated by the horns*
> *Sings amid a hedge of thorns: —*
> *"Love and life,*

Eternal youth —
Sweet, sweet, sweet, sweet!
Dew and glory,
Love and truth,
Sweet, sweet, sweet, sweet!"

(Louder and louder, faster and faster)

While smoke-black freights on the double-tracked rail-
   road
Driven as though by the foul-fiend's ox-goad,
Screaming to the west coast, screaming to the east,
Carry off a harvest, bring back a feast,
And harvesting machinery and harness for the beast.
The hand-cars whiz, and rattle on the rails;
The sunlight flashes on the tin dinner-pails.

(In a rolling bass with increasing deliberation)

And then, in an instant, ye modern men,
Behold the procession once again,
The United States goes by.

(With a snapping explosiveness)

Listen to the iron-horns, ripping, racking!
Listen to the *wise*-horn, desperate-to-*advise* horn,
Listen to the *fast*-horn, *kill*-horn, *blast*-horn ...

(To be sung or read well-nigh in a whisper)

Far away the Rachel-Jane,
Not defeated by the horns,
Sings amid a hedge of thorns: —
"Love and life,
Eternal youth,

Sweet, sweet, sweet, sweet!
Dew and glory,
Love and truth,
Sweet, sweet, sweet, sweet!"

(*To be brawled in the beginning with a snapping explosiveness*
ending in languorous chant)

The mufflers open on a score of cars
With wonderful thunder,
CRACK, CRACK, CRACK,
CRACK–CRACK, CRACK–CRACK,
CRACK–CRACK–CRACK, . . .
Listen to the gold-horn . . .
Old-horn . . .
Cold-horn . . .
And all of the tunes, till the night comes down
On hay-stack, and ant-hill, and wind-bitten town.

(*To be sung to exactly the same whispered tune as the first five lines*)

Then far in the west, as in the beginning,
Dim in the distance, sweet in retreating,
Hark to the faint-horn, quaint-horn, saint-horn,
Hark to the calm-horn, balm-horn, psalm-horn . . .

(*This section beginning sonorously ending in a languorous whisper*)

They are hunting the goals that they understand: —
San Francisco and the brown sea-sand.
My goal is the mystery the beggars win.
I am caught in the web the night-winds spin.
The edge of the wheat-ridge speaks to me;
I talk with the leaves of the mulberry tree.
And now I hear, as I sit all alone
In the dusk, by another big Santa-Fé stone,

The souls of the tall corn gathering round,
And the gay little souls of the grass in the ground.
Listen to the tale the cottonwood tells.
Listen to the windmills, singing o'er the wells.
Listen to the whistling flutes without price
Of myriad prophets out of paradise.

(*To the same whispered tune as the Rachel-Jane song — but very
    slowly*)

Hearken to the wonder
That the night-air carries. . . .
Listen . . . to . . . . the . . . . whisper . . .
Of . . . . the . . . . prairie . . . . fairies
Singing o'er the fairy plain: —
"Sweet, sweet, sweet, sweet!
Love and glory,
Stars and rain,
Sweet, sweet, sweet, sweet!"

Vachel Lindsay

BROOKLYN BRIDGE AT DAWN

Out of the cleansing night of stars and tides,
Building itself anew in the slow dawn,
The long sea-city rises: night is gone,
Day is not yet; still merciful, she hides
Her summoning brow, and still the night-car glides
Empty of faces; the night-watchmen yawn
One to the other, and shiver and pass on,
Nor yet a soul over the great bridge rides.

Frail as a gossamer, a thing of air,
A bow of shadow o'er the river flung,

Its sleepy masts and lonely lapping flood;
Who, seeing thus the bridge a-slumber there,
Would dream such softness, like a picture hung,
Is wrought of human thunder, iron and blood?

Richard Le Gallienne

RADIO

"I caught a fella last night in the South Pacific—
He was on a freighter way beyond New Zealand.
And what do you think he said to me, that guy?"
The young radio man was talking.

"'How did the Cubs come out today?' he said—
'How did the Cubs come out?'   Nothing he wanted
But that fool game!   'They got it in the neck,'
I answered him—ten thousand miles across—
'The Pirates chewed 'em up.'   'The hell they did!'
'Say, where's the sun out your way?'   I ticked off—
'Here it went down an hour or two ago.'
'It'll be coming up in half an hour,' he answered,
'It's Sunday here.'   'Oh, get a move on you!—
Sunday's most over—you're in yesterday.'
'Well, it's the same old sun coming or going—
Yesterdays and tomorrows get all mixed up;
We'll cross the line pretty soon.   Where are you, buddy?'
'Oh, near Chicago.   So long—see you again.'
So I clicked off and went to bed—and he
To breakfast probably."

               "Do you often talk
So far?"   I asked him, wondering.

"Oh, that's nothing!
I talked with Byrd's Antarctic Expedition
The other night.   Say, but it's cold down there!"

Harriet Monroe

RADIO

We have picked the pocket of silence.   By this feat
Is set another pace for light to beat.
With coil of silk-covered wire to snare a song
Between whose breaths a thousand miles belong!
We brand our sounds and loose them pigeon-free
And practice on them some new falconry.

Therese Lindsey

THE SONG OF THE PRESS

When old Gutenburg, inventor of the printing press, and
     mentor
Of the clumsy-fingered typos in a sleepy German town
Used to spread the sheets of vellum on the form and plainly
     tell 'em
That the art was then perfected, as he pressed the platen
     down —
He had not the faintest notion of the rhythmical commotion,
Of the brabble and the clamor and the unremitting roar
Of the mighty triple-decker, while the steel rods flicker
And the papers ready folded fall in thousands to the floor.

" They can beat me like the nation when the job's for recreation —
Say a fancy Christmas cover full of foolish filigree —

But I tell you what, my honey, if you want to make some money
On a run of half a million, then just pass it up to me.
You can watch the sheets a-snowing through my folder when I'm
*   going,*
And I print them by the thousand while the happy moments flit,
I can cut a pretty caper with a half a mile of paper
While the little poky fogies are a-hauling off to hit!"

As the publication hour draweth nigh, a subtle power
Seems to thrill through every sinew, and he hungers for the
        fight.
And he hears the forms descending and with strident voices
        blending
As the smell of molten metal rises hotly through the night.
Now the last form is ready; and his giant frame is steady
And for one decisive moment he awaits the signal-word.
"All in!"   Faster, faster, faster, with a tumult that grows
        vaster
Moves the press. Upon the sidewalk soon the newsboy's cry
        is heard.

Like the deafening surge of ocean swells the rhythmical
        commotion
And the brabble and the clamor and the unremitting roar
Of the mighty triple-decker, while the steel rods flicker,
And the papers, ready folded, fall in thousands to the floor.

                                        William Hurd Hillyer

SKY–SIGNS

        This is the hour when the city
        puts off its glittering scales of sunlight
        on a thousand panes,

and lays aside the rumbling shackles of its preoccupations,
and draws about itself
veils and the quiet shimmer of mists.

The sinking sun
spreads upward through the darkening air
a fan of silver radiance.
And as the rumble and hum dies down
into the pearly row of lamps along the quay
and the gleam, here and there, of lighted windows,
sky-signs of silver gilt,
like pale fireworks threaded on a mesh of wire,
begin to ripple and fling,
over and over and over again,
kittens that play with skeins of stars
and eagles flapping flaming wings
across the soft subsiding plumes of steam
in the chimney pots.

I watch the sun sink,
and the sky-signs turn their silver gilt to gold;
while higher than they,
higher than the teeth of the skyscrapers even,
a fleet of swollen clouds blown out of the sea
steers into the West.

Like a file of sails laid trim for a secret harbor,
like a fleet of misty far-voyaging sails,
the billowy, darkly distended clouds
slide, filling and sagging
over the white and gold pulsation of the sky-signs.

                                        Frederick Mortimer Clapp

I LIKE TO SEE IT LAP THE MILES

I like to see it lap the miles,
And lick the valleys up,
And stop to feed itself at tanks;
And then, prodigious, step

Around a pile of mountains,
And, supercilious, peer
In shanties by the sides of roads;
And then a quarry pare

To fit its sides, and crawl between,
Complaining all the while
In horrid, hooting stanza;
Then chase itself down hill

And neigh like Boanerges;
Then, punctual as a star,
Stop — docile and omnipotent —
At its own stable door.

Emily Dickinson

TO ENGINEERS

(To John Livingston Lowes)

I taste of tunnel benefits
And ride in darkened trains
Among the mountains' canceled roots
To reach the nether plains.

I know the surety of a bridge
Flung over a sharp height:
Ravines have been erased, that I
May cross them in the night.

But so have words made ways for me
Where no way was before;
Cut landings in the rock, and dried
The swamps to a firm floor.

In trepidation with the hills
Suddenly I have known
From crazy cliff to precipice
Suspension bridges thrown —

Then over sentences I passed
Safe into promised land.
I bless their ingenuity
Who make me understand;

Who rule across the wastes of thought
A narrow, certain lane,
And open their blue clearings
In the jungle of the brain.

Roberta Teale Swartz

UNDER A TELEPHONE POLE

I am a copper wire slung in the air,
Slim against the sun I make not even a clear line of shadow.
Night and day I keep singing — humming and thrumming:

It is love and war and money; it is the fighting and the tears,
    the work and want,
*D*eath and laughter of men and women passing through me,
    carrier of your speech,
In the rain and the wet dripping, in the dawn and the shine
    drying,
        A copper wire.

Carl Sandburg

THE LINEMAN

Thin, scattered ranks of snow
    Stampede along the street;
And sagging wires betray the slow
    Chill mischief of the sleet.

In homely garb of toil,
    With tools of quaint device,
The lineman comes, his shouldered coil
    Gray with a rime of ice.

Upraised adventurer,
    He climbs enchanted towers,
And mends the magic threads that stir
    The world's remotest powers.

From heights wind-desolate
    His torch flames cheerless blue.
(Red, red the hearth where loved ones wait
    The winter twilight through.)

Lineman, what hindereth
    That message I would hear?

Can'st mend the web 'twixt Life and Death?
   Can'st gain responses clear?

I call, but still behold
   No spark of answering fire.
O for some lineman true and bold
   To mend that broken wire!

William Hurd Hillyer

THE FLYERS

We are the children of Science that mated with Vision,
Sons of a song that was wedded to furnace and wheel;
We are the riders of vapor and vastness Elysian —
Oceans impalpable dying in light at our keel:
We are the stranglers of storms and the wild playfellows
Of dusk that obscures and empurples, of dawn that yellows
The path of Icarus over an earth engirdled
With rail of iron and rope of copper and steel!

We are the bearers of thunder to sector and city,
We are the sowers of death from the heights of the world,
Flinging our missiles of flame on the thousands we pity,
Watching the harvest that leaps to the seed we have hurled;
We are the stalkers of prey for the hard-lipped slayers,
We are the makers of sorrow for mourners and prayers,
Makers of hate for the fury and glory of battle
Till slaying is slain and the flags of the slayers are furled.

We are the merchants of morrow whose caravels marry
Lima with London, and Boston with Omsk or Bombay,
Carrying cargoes or men as the cables that carry

Thought on a flutter of sound in a flutter of day;
We are the sellers of speed and the strong-souled buyers
Of time that the millions mourn and a world desires —
The gem men lust for, the thief that ruins and plunders,
The beast we hunt through the heavens and find and slay.

We are the bearers of freedom to millions besotted,
Men that have moiled in the mill of the office or trade,
Losing their souls in the grind of the labor allotted,
Slaves by surrender to habit, the starved and dismayed;
We are the masters that bind to a new indenture,
Waking the soul with imperial call of adventure
In cloud and cold and infinite isolation —
The lure, the challenge, the quest, and the high crusade!

Ye that are cheated of life by the toil that sustains you,
Ye that have wasted your days for the want of a goal,
Ye that have need of a sword for the sin that profanes you,
Ye that are avid of life to the least of its whole —
Come to the gates of the sky and the great-sailed galleys,
Seek ye the wine of speed in the cloud-walled alleys,
Riding the road of gods till the paths ye follow
Shall wake the god that sleeps in the dust of your soul!
                                        Frank Ernest Hill

CLOUDS

Earth dies to haze below, the cables sing,
The motor drones like some gigantic fly,
A monstrous mound of vapor bathes my wing
And backward with the wind goes sweeping by;
Above the voids white crags go sharp and dim,

Oaks wave, the discs of rootless islands swim,
And arches climb and crumble in the sun
Over gray dinosaur and mastodon.

Earth, dim and fluid, seals the ragged spaces
Where misty islands meet and part below;
Cities that mask eternal hungering faces,
Black wood and water mingle in its flow.
Down, down ten mountain heights beneath this floor
Of marble-smooth and marble-solid air,
The shout and pride and color are no more
Than moon-faint mottlings.   Distance does not spare.
They are the clouds now.   Icy-lipped I ride
A window-floor immeasurably wide,
Firmer than rooted stone.   And through its glass
I watch their formless, sunken shadows pass.

Frank Ernest Hill

LONDON TO PARIS, BY AIR

I

The droning roar is quickened, and we lift
On steady wing, like upward sweep of air,
Into the fleece-strewn heaven.   The great plane
Draws to herself the leagues: onward we bear
In one resistless eddy toward the south
Over the English fields, trim-hedged and square,
And countless, winding lanes, a vast expanse
Of flattened green: huge shapes of shadow float
Inconsequent as bubbles: haunts of men
Stripped of their cherished privacy we note

And crawling multitudes within a town —
On all we rangers of the wind look down.

The coast-line swings to us: beneath our feet
The gray-green carpet of the sliding sea
Stretches afar, on it small, busy ships
Whose comet-tails in foamy whiteness flee:
We lift, and snowy cloudlets roam below,
Frail, wistful spirits of pure charity
Blessing the waters: like green marble veined,
The waves roll in upon the yellowing sand,
Then break to myriad, filmy curves of lace
Where they eternally caress the land:
Now low lies France — the kingdom of the breeze
Parts not the nations like the severing seas.

III

Down the wide river, jauntily outspread,
A fishing fleet comes seaward, to our eyes
Mere walnut shells with autumn leaves for sails:
And now a fellow pilgrim of the skies,
Like a big insect droning past our flank,
Cruises to England home: before us lies
The rolling plain with its great, hedgeless strips
Of close-tilled fields, red roofs, and pointed trees,
The feathered arrows of the long French roads,
And all the stretch of quiet harmonies:
Then haven shows, and downward to earth's breast,
Like homing bird, we wheel and sink to rest.

Lord Gorell

LINDBERGH: A BALLAD

The lamp of valor flickered low;
The Viking banners all were furled
And put away where shadows go
When nightfall wanders in the world.

With wary eyes and voices hushed
We rendered our unlovely parts.
A god of yellow metal crushed
The hero-hunger in our hearts.

We wrote a tale of wasted days,
Successes that were not success.
What we had won in little ways
We spent for little, or for less...

And then the silver monoplane,
Humming an iron monotone,
Leaped; and a glory filled the brain:
"*Lindbergh, the eagle, flies alone.*"

A hush of wonder stilled the air.
Cold men forgot their scorn, and prayed
Some half-remembered wisp of prayer.
We feared for him, the unafraid.

No news, until, on every hand
The word rang like a sudden bell:
Between the crags of Newfoundland
He waved a hemisphere farewell.

Fog laid its icy film of death
Along the silver, cambered wings.
The shifting ocean snarled beneath
In promise of the end of things.

The ocean lost, as onward hurled
The Spirit, lonely and elate.
Dawn swept across the bending world
To meet them off the Irish gate.

Ireland, the Continent, and night
Once more; and then a distant spark
Glimmered and grew.   The signal light
That marks Le Bourget split the dark.

"I am Charles Lindbergh."   Thus he taught
Humility and fearlessness,
And spoke a name that could be bought
For science, but for nothing less.

A little while he talked with kings;
He walked with crowds a little while
Before he buckled on his wings,
Lifting the world's heart with a smile.

Will we remember, as we settle
Back to our littleness again:
We, who are strangers to his mettle
That grows too seldom among men?

Whatever memory may do,
One proud truth has been written plain

For men in every age to view:
That valor never is in vain.

Though we forget, before we die,
The steady courage of his face,
His leap across the curving sky
Has changed the story of the race.

In valor's trophied corridors
Immutable the glory stands
With banners of forgotten wars
That flamed through unremembered lands.

Alexander Laing

GOETHALS, THE PROPHET-ENGINEER

A man went down to Panama
Where many a man had died
To slit the sliding mountains
And lift the Eternal tide:
A man stood up in Panama,
And the mountains stood aside.

.   .   .   .

For a poet wrought in Panama
With a continent for his theme,
And he wrote with flood and fire
To forge a planet's dream,
And the derricks rang in dithyrambs
And his stanzas roared in steam.

.   .   .   .

Where old Balboa bent his gaze
He leads the liners through,

And the Horn that tossed Magellan
Bellows a far halloo.
For where the navies never sailed
Steamed Goethals and his crew.

So nevermore the tropic routes
Need poleward warp and veer,
But on through the Gates of Goethals
The steady keels shall steer,
Where the tribes of man are led toward peace
By the prophet-engineer.

Percy MacKaye

PITTSBURGH

Over his face his gray hair drifting hides his Labor-glory in
    smoke,
Strange through his breath the soot is sifting, his feet are
    buried in coal and coke.
By night hands twisted and lurid in fires, by day hands
    blackened with grime and oil,
He toils at the foundries and never tires, and ever and ever
    his lot is toil.

He speeds his soul till his body wrestles with terrible tonnage
    and terrible time,
Out through the yards and over the trestles the flat cars clank
    and the engines chime,
His mills through windows seem eaten with fire, his high
    cranes travel, his ingots roll,
And billet and wheel and whistle and wire shriek with the
    speeding up of his soul.

Lanterns with reds and greens a-glisten wave the way and
    the headlight glares,
The back-bent laborers glance and listen and out through the
    night the tail-light flares —
Deep in the mills like a tipping cradle the huge converter
    turns on its wheel
And sizzling spills in the ten-ton ladle a golden water of
    molten steel.

Yet screwed with toil his low face searches shadow-edged
    fires and whited pits,
Gripping his levers his body lurches, grappling his irons he
    prods and hits,
And deaf with the roll and clangor and rattle with its sharp
    escaping staccato of steam,
And blind with flame and worn with battle, into his tonnage
    he turns his dream.

The world he has builded rises around us, our wonder-cities
    and weaving rails,
Over his wires a marvel has found us, a glory rides in our
    wheeled mails,
For the Earth grows small with strong Steel woven, and they
    come together who plotted apart —
But he who has wrought this thing in his oven knows only toil
    and the tired heart.

James Oppenheim

LINES WRITTEN AFTER THE DISCOVERY BY THE AUTHOR OF THE GERM OF YELLOW FEVER

This day relenting God
  Hath placed within my hand
A wondrous thing; and God
  Be praised.   At His command,

Seeking His secret deeds
  With tears and toiling breath,
I find thy cunning seeds,
  O million-murdering Death.

I know this little thing
  A myriad men will save.
O Death, where is thy sting?
  Thy victory, O Grave?

                    Ronald Ross

THE MAN OF SCIENCE SPEAKS

Throw your little dreams away,
  Scrap philosophies and creeds.
Can your vision of truth climb higher
  Than our calculation leads?

While you speculate in vain,
  Making little gods, forsooth,
We fathom infinities —
  Mathematics *is* the truth.

You put limits of your own
   On the illimitable power —
We explore immensities
   Beyond our little place and hour.

With small beliefs or coward doubts
   You lean upon the rotted past.
We neither believe nor doubt — we know;
   Our rock of faith is anchored fast.

Yesterday's failure is today
   The take-off for tomorrow's goal.
We watch you trembling while we win
   New spaces for the searching soul.

You dream the same old idle dreams,
   You move not in the drift of years.
We count the paces of the stars,
   We hear the singing of the spheres.

                Harriet Monroe

POEMS OF THE MACHINE AGE

POWER HOUSE

Here, as where the measured sun
Hammers the cold earth with Springs unending,
A piston beats immobile steel
To flight as fertile as awakened lands.
This covered place is splendid as a sky,
This pounded wheel blooms like the earth;
Whoever stands here must be moved

Deep in his blood, as when he stands
And stares across live April fields
Beneath the steady lightning of the sun.

CORLISS ENGINE AT REST

This is the world's end, and the world's beginning.
This is the stillness, the motionless perfection,
That awaited the burning of the first star,
That will take back to its peace the charred sun.
This is the quietness our blood remembers, and flows toward
    again;
This is the moment after strength,
Before fullness; and Time, the white tree
Whose roots have buckled the fields of space,
Is a seed now, and lies cool in the sky, unflowering.

RECIPROCATING ENGINES

How softly, as the great wings of eagles flow through a sky
These tons of shaped steel
Ply through motionless air, how strongly they mesh
The stillness with a peace of their own.
The birth of a star is like this, the birth of a star
Is a blooming from quietness; wheel-flight and star-flight
Are one peace of clear motion.
The bodies of men, and of women, of lovers,
Stirring with atoms, perfect in breast and limb,
Are like steel-flight; they are softly in being,
As blossoms are white on a pear tree in April;
Springing from stillness, they have their peace.

MacKnight Black

From SMOKE AND STEEL

A bar of steel — it is only
Smoke at the heart of it, smoke and the blood of a man.
A runner of fire ran in it, ran out, ran somewhere else,
And left — smoke and the blood of a man
And the finished steel, chilled and blue.

So fire runs in, runs out, runs somewhere else again,
And the bar of steel is a gun, a wheel, a nail, a shovel,
A rudder under the sea, a steering-gear in the sky;
And always dark in the heart and through it,
    Smoke and the blood of a man.
Pittsburgh, Youngstown, Gary — they make their steel with
    men.

In the blood of men and the ink of chimneys
The smoke nights write their oaths:
Smoke into steel and blood into steel;
Homestead, Braddock, Birmingham, they make their steel
    with men.
Smoke and blood is the mix of steel.

    The birdmen drone
    in the blue; it is steel
    a motor sings and zooms.

o   •   •   •   •   •   •   •   •   •

Carl Sandburg

The Workaday World and Its People

ALL LIFE MOVING TO ONE MEASURE

All life moving to one measure —
Daily bread, daily bread —
Bread of life and bread of labor,
Bread of bitterness and sorrow,
Hand-to-mouth and no tomorrow,
Dearth for housemate, death for neighbor ...

"Yet when all the babes are fed,
Love, are there not crumbs to treasure?"
Wilfrid Wilson Gibson

I HEAR AMERICA SINGING

I hear America singing, the varied carols I hear,
Those of mechanics, each one singing his as it should be blithe
and strong,
The carpenter singing his as he measures his plank or
beam,
The mason singing his as he makes ready for work, or leaves
off work,
The boatman singing what belongs to him in his boat, the
deckhand singing on the steamboat deck,
The shoemaker singing as he sits on his bench, the hatter
singing as he stands,

The wood-cutter's song, the ploughboy's on his way in the
    morning, or at noon intermission or at sundown,
The delicious singing of the mother, or of the young wife at
    work, or of the girl sewing or washing,
Each singing what belongs to him or her and to none else,
The day what belongs to the day — at night the party of
    young fellows, robust, friendly,
Singing with open mouths their strong melodious songs.

Walt Whitman

AMERICA

You are the buffalo-ghost, the broncho-ghost
With dollar-silver in your saddle-horn,
The cowboys riding in from Painted Post,
The Indian arrow in the Indian corn,

And you are the clipped velvet of the lawns
Where Shropshire grows from Massachusetts sods,
The gray Maine rocks — and the war-painted dawns
That break above the Garden of the Gods.

The prairie-schooners crawling toward the ore
And the cheap car, parked by the station-door.

Where the skyscrapers lift their foggy plumes
Of stranded smoke out of a stony mouth
You are that high stone and its arrogant fumes,
And you are ruined gardens in the South,

And bleak New England farms, so winter-white
Even their roofs look lonely, and the deep

The middle grainland where the wind of night
Is like all blind earth sighing in her sleep.

A friend, an enemy, a sacred hag
With two tied oceans in her medicine-bag.

They tried to fit you with an English song
And clip your speech into the English tale.
But, even from the first, the words went wrong,
The catbird pecked away the nightingale.

The homesick men begot high-cheekboned things
Whose wit was whittled with a different sound
And Thames and all the rivers of the kings
Ran into Mississippi and were drowned.

They planted England with a stubborn trust.
But the cleft dust was never English dust.

Stepchild of every exile from content
And all the disavouched, hard bitten pack
Shipped overseas to steal a continent
With neither shirts nor honor to their back.

Pimping grandee and rump-faced regicide,
Apple-cheeked younkers from a windmill-square,
Puritans stubborn as the nails of Pride,
Rakes from Versailles and thieves from County Clare,
The black-robed priests who broke their hearts in vain
To make you God and France or God and Spain.

These were your lovers in your buckskin-youth.
And each one married with a dream so proud

He never knew it could not be the truth
And that he coupled with a girl of cloud.

And now to see you is more difficult yet
Except as an immensity of wheel
Made up of wheels, oiled with inhuman sweat
And glittering with the heat of ladled steel.

All these you are, and each is partly you,
And none is false, and none is wholly true.

Stephen Vincent Benét

I AM AN AMERICAN

I am an American.
My father belongs to the Sons of the Revolution;
My mother, to the Colonial Dames.
One of my ancestors pitched tea overboard in Boston
    Harbor;
Another stood his ground with Warren;
Another hungered with Washington at Valley Forge.
My forefathers were America in the making:
They spoke in her council halls;
They died on her battle-fields;
They commanded her ships;
They cleared her forests.
Dawns reddened and paled.
Stanch hearts of mine beat fast at each new star
In the nation's flag.
Keen eyes of mine foresaw her greater glory:
The sweep of her seas,
The plenty of her plains,

The man-hives in her billion-wired cities.
Every drop of blood in me holds a heritage of patriotism.
I am proud of my past.
I AM AN AMERICAN.

I am an American.
My father was an atom of dust,
My mother a straw in the wind,
To His Serene Majesty.
One of my ancestors died in the mines of Siberia;
Another was crippled for life by twenty blows of the knout.
Another was killed defending his home during the massacres.
The history of my ancestors is a trail of blood
To the palace-gate of the Great White Czar.
But then the dream came —
The dream of America.
In the light of the Liberty torch
The atom of dust became a man
And the straw in the wind became a woman
For the first time.
"See," said my father, pointing to the flag that fluttered
        near,
"That flag of stars and stripes is yours;
It is the emblem of the promised land.
It means, my son, the hope of humanity.
Live for it — die for it!"
Under the open sky of my new country I swore to do so;
And every drop of blood in me will keep that vow.
I am proud of my future.
I AM AN AMERICAN.

Elias Lieberman

THE RIVETER

The steam-shovels had sunk their teeth
  Through earth and rock until a hole
Yawned like a black hell underneath,
  Like a coal-crater with all the coal
Torn out of her: the shovels bit
The stinking stony broth — and spit.

The Wops went up and down; they spilled
  Cement like a groggy soup in chutes;
They mixed the mortar and they filled
  The gash with it. . . . Short swarthy brutes
They were, who reeked of rock and wet
Lime and accumulated sweat.

At first the work was tame enough:
  Only another foundation like
Hundreds before and just as tough
  To stand under a ten-ton spike.
But it was different when a whir
Of steel announced the riveter.

One long lad of them took the crowd
  As he straddled the girders and hooked the nuts
Livid-white hot: and we allowed
  He was the lunatic for guts;
The sidewalk bleachers yelled as he
Speared a sizzler dizzily.

They got to call him the "Rivet Ruth" —
  That crisp corn shock of gusty hair,

That blue hawk-eye and devil of youth
    Juggling with death on a treacherous stair,
Tipping his heart on a beam of steel
That made his pavement audience reel.

The riveting hammers stuttered and kicked;
    The ten-ton trestles whined in the winch;
And still this golden Icarus picked
    The hissing rivets by half an inch,
Twirled and nailed them on the spin
Out of the air and rocked them in.

And one fine sun-splashed noon he lunged
    Over the stark deadline — and missed!
Swung for an instant and then plunged
    While the lone insane rivet hissed
Him all the way down from truss to truss
And dropped beside its Icarus!

The old straphanger thumbed his paper;
    Feet shuffled sidewalks; traffic roared. . . .
Icarus had performed his caper —
    Little New York minced by bored:
Leave the lads with the broken backs,
Soiled feathers, and some melted wax!

                                    Joseph Auslander

THE STEAM SHOVEL

Beneath my window in a city street
A monster lairs, a creature huge and grim
And only half believed: the strength of him —

Steel-strung and fit to meet
The strength of earth —
Is mighty as men's dreams that conquer force.
Steam belches from him.   He is the new birth
Of old Behemoth, late-sprung from the source
Whence Grendel sprang, and all the monster clan
Dead for an age, now born again of man.

The iron head,
Set on a monstrous jointed neck,
Glides here and there, lifts, settles on the red
Moist floor, with nose dropped in the dirt, at beck
Of some incredible control.
He snorts, and pauses couchant for a space;
Then slowly lifts, and tears the gaping hole
Yet deeper in earth's flank.   A sudden race
Of loosened earth and pebbles trickles there
Like blood-drops in a wound.
But he, the monster, swings his load around —
Weightless it seems as air.
His mammoth jaw
Drops widely open with a rasping sound,
And all the red earth vomits from his maw.

O thwarted monster, born at man's decree,
A lapdog dragon, eating from his hand
And doomed to fetch and carry at command,
Have you no longing ever to be free?
In warm electric days to run amuck,
Ranging like some mad dinosaur,
Your fiery heart at war
With this strange world, the city's restless ruck,

Where all drab things that toil, save you alone,
Have life;
And you the semblance only, and the strife?

Do you not yearn to rip the roots of stone
Of these great piles men build,
And hurl them down with shriek of shattered steel,
Scorning your own sure doom, so you may feel,
You too, the lust with which your fathers killed?
Or is your soul in very deed so tame,
The blood of Grendel watered to a gruel,
That you are well content
With heart of flame
Thus placidly to chew your cud of fuel
And toil in peace for man's aggrandizement?

Poor helpless creature of a half-grown god,
Blind of yourself and impotent!
At night,
When your forerunners, sprung from quicker sod,
Would range through primal woods, hot on the scent,
Or wake the stars with amorous delight,
You stand, a soiled unwieldy mass of steel,
Black in the arc light, modern as your name,
Dead and unsouled and trite;
Till I must feel
A quick creator's pity for your shame:
That man, who made you and who gave so much,
Yet cannot give the last transforming touch;
That with the work he cannot give the wage —
For day, no joy of night,
For toil, no ecstasy of primal rage.

Eunice Tietjens

CALIBAN IN THE COAL MINES

God, we don't like to complain —
   We know that the mine is no lark —
But — there's the pools from the rain;
   But — there's the cold and the dark.

God, You don't know what it is —
   You, in Your well-lighted sky,
Watching the meteors whizz;
   Warm, with the sun always by.

God, if You had but the moon
   Stuck in Your cap for a lamp,
Even You'd tire of it soon,
   Down in the dark and the damp.

Nothing but blackness above,
   And nothing that moves but the cars —
God, if You wish for our love,
   Fling us a handful of stars!

Louis Untermeyer

MAN CARRYING BALE

The tough hand closes gently on the load;
   Out of the mind, a voice
Calls "Lift!" and the arms, remembering well their work,
   Lengthen and pause for help.
Then a slow ripple flows along the body,
While all the muscles call to one another:
   "Lift!" and the bulging bale
   Floats like a butterfly in June.

So moved the earliest carrier of bales,
    And the same watchful sun
Glowed through his body feeding it with light.
    So will the last one move,
And halt, and dip his head, and lay his load
Down, and the muscles will relax and tremble....
    Earth, you designed your man
Beautiful both in labor, and repose.

Harold Monro

IN THE SUBWAY

Chaos is tamed and ordered as we ride;
The rock is rent, the darkness torn aside,
And all the nightmares of the deep defied.

A coil of wire, a throb, a hissing spark,
And on a thundering meteor we embark
That flies, on schedule, through the breathless dark.

The centuries disclose their secret graves;
Riding in splendor through a world of waves
The very elements become our slaves.

And here, entombed in steel and glass, I see
The row of (are they dead) men facing me,
Reading their morning murder gratefully.

Louis Untermeyer

IN A RESTAURANT

He wears a red rose in his buttonhole,
A city-clerk on Sunday dining out:
And as the music surges over the din

The heady quavering of the violin
Sings through his blood, and puts old cares to rout,
And tingles, quickening, through his shrunken soul,

Till he forgets his ledgers, and the prim
Black, crabbed figures, and the qualmy smell
Of ink and musty leather and leadglaze
As, in eternities of Summer days,
He dives through shivering waves, or rides the swell
On rose-red seas of melody aswim.

Wilfrid Wilson Gibson

"A PITCHER OF MIGNONETTE"

A pitcher of mignonette
  In a tenement's highest casement, —
Queer sort of flower-pot — yet
That pitcher of mignonette
Is a garden in heaven set,
  To the little sick child in the basement —
    The pitcher of mignonette
  In the tenement's highest casement.

H. C. Bunner

FOG

The fog comes
on little cat feet.

It sits looking
over harbor and city
on silent haunches
and then moves on.

Carl Sandburg

THE BARREL ORGAN

There's a barrel-organ caroling across a golden street
  In the City as the sun sinks low;
And the music's not immortal; but the world has made it
    sweet
  And fulfilled it with the sunset glow;
And it pulses through the pleasures of the City and the pain
  That surround the singing organ like a large eternal
    light;
And they've given it a glory and a part to play again
  In the Symphony that rules the day and night.

And now it's marching onward through the realms of old
    romance,
  And trolling out a fond familiar tune,
And now it's roaring cannon down to fight the King of
    France,
  And now it's prattling softly to the moon,
And all around the organ there's a sea without a shore
  Of human joys and wonders and regrets;
To remember and to recompense the music evermore
  For what the cold machinery forgets....

      Yes; as the music changes,
        Like a prismatic glass,
     It takes the light and ranges
       Through all the moods that pass;
    Dissects the common carnival
      Of passions and regrets,
    And gives the world a glimpse of all
      The colors it forgets.

And there *La Traviata* sighs
  Another sadder song;
And there *Il Trovatore* cries
  A tale of deeper wrong;
And bolder knights to battle go
  With sword and shield and lance,
Than ever here on earth below
  Have whirled into — *a dance!* —

Go down to Kew in lilac-time, in lilac-time, in lilac-time;
  Go down to Kew in lilac-time (it isn't far from London!)
And you shall wander hand in hand with love in summer's
    wonderland;
  Go down to Kew in lilac-time (it isn't far from London!)

The cherry-trees are seas of bloom and soft perfume and
    sweet perfume,
  The cherry-trees are seas of bloom (and oh, so near to
    London!)
And there they say, when dawn is high and all the world's
    a blaze of sky
  The cuckoo, though he's very shy, will sing a song for
    London.

The Dorian nightingale is rare and yet they say you'll hear
    him there
  At Kew, at Kew in lilac-time (and oh, so near to London!)
The linnet and the throstle, too, and after dark the long
    halloo
  And the golden-eyed *tu-whit, tu-whoo* of owls that ogle
    London.

For Noah hardly knew a bird of any kind that isn't heard
   At Kew, at Kew in lilac-time (and oh, so near to London.)
And when the rose begins to pout and all the chestnut spires
   are out
   You'll hear the rest without a doubt, all chorusing for
     London: —

Come down to Kew in lilac-time, in lilac-time, in lilac-time;
   Come down to Kew in lilac-time (it isn't far from Lon-
    don!)
And you shall wander hand in hand with love in summer's
   wonderland,
   Come down to Kew in lilac-time (it isn't far from London!)

And then the troubadour begins to thrill the golden street,
   In the City as the sun sinks low;
And in all the gaudy busses there are scores of weary feet
Marking time, sweet time, with a dull mechanic beat,
And a thousand hearts are plunging to a love they'll never
    meet,
Through the meadows of the sunset, through the poppies
   and the wheat,
   In the land where the dead dreams go.

Verdi, Verdi, when you wrote *Il Trovatore* did you dream
   Of the City when the sun sinks low,
Of the organ and the monkey and the many-colored stream
On the Piccadilly pavement, of the myriad eyes that seem
To be litten for a moment with a wild Italian gleam
As *A che la morte* parodies the world's eternal theme
   And pulses with the sunset-glow.

There's a thief, perhaps, that listens with a face of frozen
    stone
    In the City as the sun sinks low;
There's a portly man of business with a balance of his own,
There's a clerk and there's a butcher of soft reposeful
    tone.
And they're all of them returning to the heavens they have
    known:
They are crammed and jammed in busses and — they're
    each of them alone
    In the land where the dead dreams go.

There's a very modish woman and her smile is very bland
    In the City as the sun sinks low;
And her hansom jingles onward, but her little jeweled hand
Is clenched a little tighter and she cannot understand
What she wants or why she wanders to that undiscovered
    land,
For the parties there are not at all the sort of thing she
    planned,
    In the land where the dead dreams go.

There's a rowing man that listens and his heart is crying out
    In the City as the sun sinks low;
For the barge, the eight, the Isis, and the coach's whoop and
    shout,
For the minute-gun, the counting and the long disheveled
    rout,
For the howl along the towpath and a fate that's still in
    doubt,
For a roughened oar to handle and a race to think about
    In the land where the dead dreams go.

There's a laborer that listens to the voices of the dead
   In the City as the sun sinks low;
And his hand begins to tremble and his face to smoulder red
As he sees a loafer watching him and — there he turns his
     head
And stares into the sunset where his April love is fled,
For he hears her softly singing and his lonely soul is led
   Through the land where the dead dreams go.

There's an old and haggard demi-rep, it's ringing in her ears,
   In the City as the sun sinks low;
With the wild and empty sorrow of the love that blights and
     sears,
Oh, and if she hurries onward, then be sure, be sure she hears,
Hears and bears the bitter burden of the unforgotten years,
And her laugh's a little harsher and her eyes are brimmed
     with tears
   For the land where the dead dreams go.

There's a barrel-organ caroling across a golden street
   In the City as the sun sinks low;
Though the music's only Verdi there's a world to make it
     sweet
Just as yonder yellow sunset where the earth and heaven
     meet
Mellows all the sooty City! Hark, a hundred thousand feet
Are marching on to glory through the poppies and the wheat
   In the land where the dead dreams go.

       So it's Jeremiah, Jeremiah,
         What have you to say
       When you meet the garland girls
         Tripping on their way?

All around my gala hat
   I wear a wreath of roses
(A long and lonely year it is
   I've waited for the May!)
If any one should ask you,
   The reason why I wear it is —
My own love, my true love
   Is coming home today.

And it's buy a bunch of violets for the lady
   (*It's lilac-time in London; it's lilac-time in London!*)
Buy a bunch of violets for the lady
   While the sky burns blue above:

On the other side the street you'll find it shady
   (*It's lilac-time in London; it's lilac-time in London!*)
But buy a bunch of violets for the lady
   And tell her she's your own true love.

There's a barrel-organ caroling across a golden street
   In the City as the sun sinks glittering and slow;
And the music's not immortal; but the world has made it
   sweet
And enriched it with the harmonies that make a song com-
   plete
In the deeper heavens of music where the night and morning
   meet,
   As it dies into the sunset-glow;
And it pulses through the pleasures of the City and the pain
   That surround the singing organ like a large eternal light,
And they've given it a glory and a part to play again
   In the Symphony that rules the day and night.

And there, as the music changes,
　The song runs round again.
Once more it turns and ranges
　Through all its joy and pain,
Dissects the common carnival
　Of passions and regrets;
And the wheeling world remembers all
　The wheeling song forgets.

Once more *La Traviata* sighs
　Another sadder song:
Once more *Il Trovatore* cries
　A tale of deeper wrong;
Once more the knights to battle go
　With sword and shield and lance
Till once, once more, the shattered foe
　Has whirled into — a dance!

Come down to Kew in lilac-time, in lilac-time, in lilac-time;
　Come down to Kew in lilac-time (it isn't far from London!)
And you shall wander hand in hand with love in summer's
　　wonderland;
　Come down to Kew in lilac-time (it isn't far from London!)
　　　　　　　　　　　　　　　　　Alfred Noyes

TAME DUCK

There are three tame ducks in our back yard,
Dabbling in mud and trying hard
To get their share and maybe more
Of the overflowing barnyard store,
Satisfied with the task they're at

Of eating and sleeping and getting fat.
But whenever the free wild ducks go by
In a long line streaming down the sky,
They cock a quizzical, puzzled eye,
And flap their wings and try to fly.

I think my soul is a tame old duck,
Dabbling around in barnyard muck,
Fat and lazy, with useless wings;
But sometimes when the north wind sings
And the wild ones hurtle over head,
It remembers something lost and dead
And cocks a wary, bewildered eye
And makes a feeble attempt to fly.
It's fairly content with the state it's in,
But it isn't the duck it might have been.

Kenneth Kaufman

From "THE TROUBADOUR OF EZE"

High on this point of rock, this mighty needle
Sewing the multitudinous cloths of wind,
Where the living and the Roman eagles soared,
I will not think of all the history
That loosed its rainfall here, but I will grasp
The living present, seek the now, not in
The ruined walls of Eze, but in my town.
For there, in a land new to man's destruction,
Is a far greater building to be done
Than piling stone and laying out a room —
There, with the blue steel chisel of the mind
Shaped by the hammer of a new world's dream,

And tempered in the clear flame of the heart,
There can be carved, from the quarried stone of time,
A proud and shining symbol of new life,
Not a fixed figure like the signs of Europe,
But a moving body that will run the plains,
Swim the Mississippi, climb the Rockies,
Hurl the plunging piston in its cycle,
Twist the steel-town smoke into a rope
And stride on it across a continent
With a chimney stack balanced in each hand,
Take living steam for breath, and for its blood
Electric current with wild sunlight mingled.

Here to my town has the world's great power come over
The torn, dream-furrowed ocean, and now waits
A stronger form than the new world alone
Can give to its old and proud nobility.
But if my town, like Eze, should fail, and leave
No nobler symbol than a fallen stone,
The world fails with it, and it will be best
To swing the huge gnarled war club that is doom
And crush again the patient walls of Eze,
Hurl into its centuries-quiet mouth
The half-remembered chant of misery,
Forget that new world image, and beat back
The towers of all our towns into the earth.

Paul Engle

EVERYDAY ALCHEMY

Men go to women mutely for their peace;
And they, who lack it most, create it when

They make — because they must, loving their men —
A solace for sad bosom-bended heads.   There
Is all the meagre peace men get — no otherwhere;
No mountain space, no tree with placid leaves,
Or heavy gloom beneath a young girl's hair,
No sound of valley bell on autumn air,
Or room made home with doves along the eaves,
Ever holds peace like this, poured by poor women
Out of their heart's poverty, for worn men.

Genevieve Taggard

DRUGSTORE

Pardon me, lady, but I wanta ast you,
For God's sake, stop that tappin'!   I'll go nuts,
Plain bug-house if I hear that tap-tap-tap
Much longer!
                    Now I went and used such language,
I got to tell you why ... Well, in the first place,
My business is all shot.   Now drugs theirselves
Don't pay much, and the extra stuff, like candy,
Cigars and stationery and et cetery,
Don't make their keep.   And that damn soda-fountain —
Excuse me, lady, but I just can't help it! ...

Some day I'm gointa catch the guy I bought it off —
I'm losin' money every day it's here.
And soda-jerkers — now I can't get none
For love or money, so myself I got to
Mess with them malted milks, banana splits,
And slop like that.   And just as doggone sure
As I start workin' on some fine prescription,

The kind I love to mix — got to be careful
The weights is hittin' on that perfect balance —
Why, then some fool wants a marshmallow sundae,
And tap-tap-tap he starts in on the show-case,
And taps and taps till I come runnin' out,
Leavin' the drugs half-done.

      And that ain't all;
Here's the big trouble — I can't talk good grammar.
People don't think a man that mixes drugs
Can do it right and talk the way I do.
It makes me sick — why have I got to sound
Like a school-teacher? Why, I know my stuff.
"Registered Pharmacist" — see? I taught myself,
Workin' at night whiles I was four years clerkin';
And then I took three months down at the U,
And passed a fine exam. But here's the thing:
I quit the public school in seventh grade,
And I never paid no attention to my talk.
So it's the way I tell you — they're suspicious
Because I use such slang. I try to stop,
But it's too late now. I found out too late....

I got a dream of what I'll do some day:
I want to quit this drug stuff altogether,
Have a nice office, with a big oak desk,
And sell just real estate. I'd like to bet
I'd make a clean-up at it. It'd be swell,
That office ...

     But this life is killin' me.
It's the fool questions they keep askin' me!
You see that clock there? Well, just on a guess
Three times an hour some silly fish comes in here

And calls me out, and asts me, "Is that right? —
Is your clock right?"   Honest to heaven, lady,
One day I got so sore I took a hammer
And smashed the face in.   And it cost twelve dollars
To fix it.   But I had peace for a week.
Oh, gosh, my nerves!... But that's the way it is.
I'm sorry I spoke so rough about that tappin',
But when I get to sellin' real estate,
They'll be no place where folks can take a coin
And tap, and tap, till I come runnin' out.
That's a man's business!...
If I ever get it ...
John V. A. Weaver

TO A POST–OFFICE INKWELL

How many humble hearts have dipped
In you, and scrawled their manuscript!
Have shared their secrets, told their cares,
Their curious and quaint affairs!

Your pool of ink, your scratchy pen,
Have moved the lives of unborn men,
And watched young people, breathing hard,
Put heaven on a postal card.
Christopher Morley

THE FACTORIES

I have shut my little sister in from life and light
  (For a rose, for a ribbon, for a wreath across my hair),
I have made her restless feet still until the night,
  Locked from sweets of summer and from wild spring air;

I who ranged the meadowlands, free from sun to sun,
　Free to sing and pull the buds and watch the far wings fly,
I have bound my little sister till her playing time was done —
　Oh, my little sister, was it I?　Was it I?

I have robbed my sister of her day of maidenhood
　(For a robe, for a feather, for a trinket's restless spark),
Shut from Love till dusk shall fall, how shall she know good,
　How shall she go scatheless through the sin-lit dark?
I who could be innocent, I who could be gay,
　I who could have love and mirth before the light went by,
I have put my sister in her mating time away —
　Sister, my young sister, was it I?　Was it I?

I have robbed my sister of the lips against her breast,
　(For a coin, for the weaving of my children's lace and
　　lawn),
Feet that pace beside the loom, hands that cannot rest —
　How can she know motherhood, whose strength is gone?
I who took no heed of her, starved and labor-worn,
　I, against whose placid heart my sleepy gold-heads lie,
Round my path they cry to me, little souls unborn —
　God of Life!　Creator!　It was I!　It was I!
                                        Margaret Widdemer

THE GOLF LINKS

The golf links lie so near the mill
　That almost every day
The laboring children can look out
　And see the men at play.
                        Sarah N. Cleghorn

CHICAGO

Hog Butcher for the World,
Tool Maker, Stacker of Wheat,
Player with Railroads and the Nation's Freight
      Handler;
Stormy, husky, brawling,
City of the Big Shoulders:

They tell me you are wicked and I believe them, for I have
    seen your painted women under the gas lamps luring
    the farm boys.
And they tell me you are crooked and I answer: Yes, it is true
    I have seen the gunman kill and go free to kill again.
And they tell me you are brutal and my reply is: On the faces
    of women and children I have seen the marks of
    wanton hunger.
And having answered so I turn once more to those who sneer
    at this my city, and I give them back the sneer and
    say to them:
Come and show me another city with lifted head singing so
    proud to be alive and coarse and strong and cunning.
Flinging magnetic curses amid the toil of piling job on job,
    here is a tall bold slugger set vivid against the little
    soft cities;
Fierce as a dog with tongue lapping for action, cunning as a
    savage pitted against the wilderness,
        Bareheaded,
        Shoveling,
        Wrecking,
        Planning,
        Building, breaking, rebuilding.

Under the smoke, dust all over his mouth, laughing with
    white teeth,
Under the terrible burden of destiny laughing as a young
    man laughs,
Laughing even as an ignorant fighter laughs who has never
    lost a battle,
Bragging and laughing that under his wrist is the pulse, and
    under his ribs the heart of the people,
                    Laughing!
Laughing the stormy, husky, brawling laughter of Youth,
    half-naked, sweating, proud to be Hog Butcher, Tool
    Maker, Stacker of Wheat, Player with Railroads and
    Freight Handler to the Nation.

Carl Sandburg

PIONEERS, O PIONEERS

  Come, my tan-faced children,
Follow well in order, get your weapons ready;
Have you your pistols? have you your sharp-edged axes?
        Pioneers! O pioneers!

  For we cannot tarry here,
We must march, my darlings, we must bear the brunt of
    danger,
We, the youthful sinewy races, all the rest on us depend,
        Pioneers! O pioneers!

  O you youths, Western youths,
So impatient, full of action, full of manly pride and friend-
    ship,
Plain I see you, Western youths, see you tramping with the
    foremost,
        Pioneers! O pioneers!

Have the elder races halted?
Do they droop and end their lesson, wearied, over there
beyond the seas?
We take up the task eternal, and the burden, and the lesson,
Pioneers! O pioneers!

All the past we leave behind;
We debouch upon a newer mightier world, varied world;
Fresh and strong the world we seize, world of labor and the
march,
Pioneers! O pioneers!

We detachments steady throwing,
Down the edges, through the passes, up the mountains
steep,
Conquering, holding, daring, venturing as we go the un-
known ways.
Pioneers! O pioneers!

We primeval forests felling,
We the rivers stemming, vexing we, and piercing deep the
mines within;
We the surface broad surveying, we the virgin soil upheaving,
Pioneers! O pioneers!

Colorado men are we,
From peaks gigantic, from the great sierras and the high
plateaus,
From the mine and from the gully, from the hunting trail we
come,
Pioneers! O pioneers!

From Nebraska, from Arkansas,
Central inland race are we, from Missouri, with the conti-
nental blood intervein'd;
All the hands of comrades clasping, all the Southern, all the
Northern.
                        Pioneers! O pioneers!

O resistless restless race!
O beloved race in all! O my heart aches with tender love for
all!
O I mourn and yet exult — I am rapt with love for all,
                        Pioneers! O pioneers!

Raise the mighty mother mistress,
Waving high the delicate mistress, over all the starry
mistress (bend your heads all),
Raise the fang'd and warlike mistress, stern, impassive,
weaponed mistress,
                        Pioneers! O pioneers!

See, my children, resolute children,
By those swarms upon our rear we must never yield or
falter,
Ages back in ghostly millions frowning there behind us urging,
                        Pioneers! O pioneers!

On and on the compact ranks,
With accessions ever waiting, with the places of the dead
quickly fill'd,
Through the battle, through defeat, moving yet and never
stopping,
                        Pioneers! O pioneers!

O to die advancing on!
Are there some of us to droop and die? has the hour come?
Then upon the march we fittest die, soon and sure the gap is
      fill'd
                Pioneers! O pioneers!

All the pulses of the world,
Falling in they beat for us, with the western movement beat,
Holding single or together, steady moving to the front, all of
      us,
                Pioneers! O pioneers!

Life's involv'd and varied pageants,
All the forms and shows, all the workmen at their work,
All the seamen and the landsmen, all the masters with their
      slaves,
                Pioneers! O pioneers!

All the hopeless silent lovers,
All the prisoners in the prisons, all the righteous and the
      wicked,
All the joyous, all the sorrowing, all the loving, all the dying,
                Pioneers! O pioneers!

I too with my soul and body,
We, a curious trio, picking, wandering on our way,
Through these shores amid the shadows, with the apparitions
      pressing,
                Pioneers! O pioneers!

Lo, the darting, bowling orb!
Lo, the brother orbs around, all the clustering suns and
      planets,

All the dazzling days, all the mystic nights with dreams,
          Pioneers! O pioneers!

  These are of us, they are with us,
All for primal needed work, while the followers there in the
     embryo wait behind,
We today's procession heading, we the route for travel
     clearing,
          Pioneers! O pioneers!

  O you daughters of the West!
O you young and elder daughters! O you mothers and you
     wives!
Never must you be divided, in our ranks you move united,
          Pioneers! O pioneers!

  Minstrels latent on the prairies!
(Shrouded bards of other lands, you may rest, you have done
     your work),
Soon I hear you coming warbling, soon you rise and tramp
     amid us,
          Pioneers! O pioneers!

  Not for delectations sweet,
Not the cushion and the slipper, not the peaceful or the
     studious,
Not the riches safe and palling, not for us the tame enjoyment,
          Pioneers! O pioneers!

  Do the feasters gluttonous feast?
Do the corpulent sleepers sleep? Have they lock'd and
     bolted doors?

Still be ours the diet hard, and the blanket on the ground,
   Pioneers! O pioneers!

Has the night descended?
Was the road of late so toilsome? did we stop discouraged
  nodding on our way?
Yet a passing hour I yield you in your tracks to pause
  oblivious,
   Pioneers! O pioneers!

Till the sound of trumpet,
Far, far off the daybreak call — hark! how loud and clear I
  hear it wind;
Swift! to the head of the army! — swift! spring to your places,
   Pioneers! O pioneers!

        Walt Whitman

THE BELLS

  Hear the sledges with the bells —
    Silver bells!
What a world of merriment their melody foretells!
  How they tinkle, tinkle, tinkle,
   In the icy air of night!
  While the stars that oversprinkle
  All the Heavens seem to twinkle
   With a crystalline delight;
  Keeping time, time, time,
  In a sort of Runic rhyme,
To the tintinnabulation that so musically wells
  From the bells, bells, bells, bells,
    Bells, bells, bells —
  From the jingling and the tinkling of the bells.

Hear the mellow wedding bells,
   Golden bells!
What a world of happiness their harmony foretells!
 Through the balmy air of night
 How they ring out their delight!
  From the molten-golden notes,
    And all in tune,
  What a liquid ditty floats
To the turtle-dove that listens, while she gloats
    On the moon!
 Oh, from out the sounding cells,
What a gush of euphony voluminously wells!
    How it swells!
    How it dwells
  On the future; how it tells
  Of the rapture that impels
 To the swinging and the ringing
  Of the bells, bells, bells,
  Of the bells, bells, bells, bells,
    Bells, bells, bells —
To the rhyming and the chiming of the bells!

 Hear the loud alarum bells —
    Brazen bells!
What a tale of terror, now, their turbulency tells!
 In the startled ear of night
 How they scream out their affright!
  Too much horrified to speak,
  They can only shriek, shriek,
    Out of tune,
In a clamorous appealing to the mercy of the fire,
In a mad expostulation with the deaf and frantic fire.

Leaping higher, higher, higher,
With a desperate desire,
And a resolute endeavor
Now, now to sit, or never,
By the side of the pale-faced moon.
Oh, the bells, bells, bells!
What a tale their terror tells
Of despair!
How they clang, and clash, and roar!
What a horror they outpour
On the bosom of the palpitating air!
Yet the ear it fully knows,
By the twanging,
And the clanging,
How the danger ebbs and flows;
Yes, the ear distinctly tells,
In the jangling,
And the wrangling,
How the danger sinks and swells,
By the sinking or the swelling in the anger of the bells —
Of the bells —
Of the bells, bells, bells, bells,
Bells, bells, bells —
In the clamor and the clangor of the bells!

Hear the tolling of the bells —
Iron bells!
What a world of solemn thought their monody compels!
In the silence of the night,
How we shiver with affright
At the melancholy menace of their tone!
For every sound that floats

From the rust within their throats,
      Is a groan.
And the people — ah, the people —
They that dwell up in the steeple,
      All alone,
And who tolling, tolling, tolling,
  In that muffled monotone,
Feel a glory in so rolling
  On the human heart a stone —
They are neither man nor woman —
They are neither brute nor human —
  They are ghouls:
And their king it is who tolls: —
And he rolls, rolls, rolls,
      Rolls
  A paean from the bells!
And his merry bosom swells
With the paean of the bells!
And he dances and he yells;
Keeping time, time, time,
In a sort of Runic rhyme,
To the paean of the bells;
  Of the bells: —
Keeping time, time, time,
In a sort of Runic rhyme
  To the throbbing of the bells; —
Of the bells, bells, bells —
  To the sobbing of the bells; —
Keeping time, time, time,
  As he knells, knells, knells,
In a happy Runic rhyme,
  To the rolling of the bells —

Of the bells, bells, bells: —
To the tolling of the bells —
Of the bells, bells, bells, bells,
Bells, bells, bells —
To the moaning and the groaning of the bells.
Edgar Allan Poe

THE MAN WITH THE HOE

WRITTEN AFTER SEEING MILLET'S WORLD-FAMOUS PAINTING
OF A BRUTALIZED TOILER

God created man in his own image, in the image of God created he
him. — Genesis

Bowed by the weight of centuries he leans
Upon his hoe and gazes on the ground,
The emptiness of ages in his face,
And on his back the burden of the world.
Who made him dead to rapture and despair,
A thing that grieves not and that never hopes,
Stolid and stunned, a brother to the ox?
Who loosened and let down this brutal jaw?
Whose was the hand that slanted back this brow?
Whose breath blew out the light within this brain?

Is this the Thing the Lord God made and gave
To have dominion over sea and land;
To trace the stars and search the heavens for power;
To feel the passion of Eternity?
Is this the dream He dreamed who shaped the suns
And marked their ways upon the ancient deep? —
Down all the caverns of Hell to their last gulf

There is no shape more terrible than this —
More tongued with censure of the world's blind greed —
More filled with signs and portents for the soul —
More packt with danger to the universe.

What gulfs between him and the seraphim!
Slave of the wheel of labor, what to him
Are Plato and the swing of Pleiades?
What the long reaches of the peaks of song,
The rift of dawn, the reddening of the rose?
Through this dread shape the suffering ages look;
Time's tragedy is in that aching stoop;
Through this dread shape humanity betrayed,
Plundered, profaned and disinherited,
Cries protest to the powers that made the world,
A protest that is also prophecy.

O masters, lords and rulers in all lands,
Is this the handiwork you give to God,
This monstrous thing distorted and soul-quencht?
How will you ever straighten up this shape;
Touch it again with immortality;
Give back the upward looking and the light;
Rebuild in it the music and the dream;
Make right the immemorial infamies,
Perfidious wrongs, immedicable woes?

O masters, lords and rulers in all lands,
How will the future reckon with this Man?
How answer his brute question in that hour
When whirlwinds of rebellion shake all shores?
How will it be with kingdoms and with kings —

With those who shaped him to the thing he is —
When this dumb Terror shall rise to judge the world,
After the silence of the centuries?

Edwin Markham

LONDON SNOW

When men were all asleep the snow came flying,
In large white flakes falling on the city brown,
Stealthily and perpetually settling and loosely lying,
   Hushing the latest traffic of the drowsy town;
Deadening, muffling, stifling its murmurs failing;
Lazily and incessantly floating down and down:
   Silently sifting and veiling road, roof, and railing;
Hiding difference, making unevenness even,
Into angles and crevices softly drifting and sailing.
   All night it fell, and when full inches seven
It lay in the depth of its uncompacted lightness,
The clouds blew off from a high and frosty heaven;
   And all woke earlier for the unaccustomed brightness
Of the winter dawning, the strange unheavenly glare:
The eye marveled — marveled at the dazzling whiteness;
   The ear harkened to the stillness of the solemn air;
No sound of wheel rumbling nor of foot falling,
And the busy morning cries came thin and spare.
   Then boys I heard, as they went to school, calling,
They gathered up the crystal manna to freeze
Their tongues with tasting, their hands with snow-balling;
   Or rioted in a drift, plunging up to their knees;
Or peering up from under the white-mossed wonder,
"O look at the trees!" they cried, "O look at the trees!"
   With lessened load a few carts creak and blunder,

Following along the white deserted way,
A country company long dispersed asunder:
  When now already the sun, in pale display
Standing by Paul's high dome, spread forth below
His sparkling beams, and awoke the stir of the day.
  For now doors open, and war is waged with the snow:
And trains of somber men, past tale of number,
Tread along brown paths, as toward their toil they go:
  But even for them awhile no cares encumber
Their minds diverted; the daily word is unspoken,
The daily thoughts of labor and sorrow slumber
At the sight of the beauty that greets them, for the charm
    they have broken.

Robert Bridges

"THROUGH STREETS WHERE CROOKED WICKLOW FLOWS"

Through streets where crooked Wicklow flows
I saw a man with broken nose:
His venomous eyes turned full on me
And cursed the ancient poverty
That scarred his limbs and mired his clothes.

O cursed wind-driven poverty
That breaks the man and mires his clothes!

Beyond the street, beyond the town,
Rose hill and tree and sea and down:
O drear and shadowy green ash-tree,
O hills that neither sleep nor rest
But are like waves in that dark sea
That rides the wind, nor-east, nor-west,

O cursed, wind-driven poverty!

Below the hill, below the town,
Deep, whispering voices everywhere
Break quiet in the morning air
And mount the skies to pierce the sun.

I saw the naked, cowering man
Shrink in the midnight of his eye,
There, to eat bitterness within,
And close the door and hide the sin
That made his withering heart run dry.
O venomous, dark, unceasing eye
That turned on street and town and me,
Between the waves of hill and sea
Until his eyelid closed the sky.

The rain-rilled, shaken, green ash-tree
Spread roots to gather him and me
In downward pull of earth that drains
The blood that empties through men's veins
Under the churchyard, under stone
Until the body lies alone
And will not wake: nor wind, nor sky
Bring sunlight into morning air
And breathe disquiet everywhere
Into the heart of hill and town.

O heart whose heart is like my own
And not to rest or sleep but climb
Wearily out of earth again
To feed again that venomous eye

That is the manhood of my time,
Whether at home or Wicklow town.

This is my street to walk again,
O cursed, wind-driven poverty,
I hear the coming of the rain.
Horace Gregory

THE GREAT LOVER

I have been so great a lover: filled my days
So proudly with the splendor of Love's praise,
The pain, the calm, and the astonishment,
Desire illimitable, and still content,
And all dear names men use, to cheat despair,
For the perplexed and viewless streams that bear
Our hearts at random down the dark of life.
Now, ere the unthinking silence on that strife
Steals down, I would cheat drowsy Death so far,
My night shall be remembered for a star
That outshone all the suns of all men's days.
Shall I not crown them with immortal praise
Whom I have loved, who have given me, dared with me,
High secrets, and in darkness knelt to see
The inenarrable godhead of delight?
Love is a flame; — we have beaconed the world's night.
A city: — and we have built it, these and I.
An emperor: — we have taught the world to die.
So, for their sakes I loved, ere I go hence,
And the high cause of Love's magnificence,
And to keep loyalties young, I'll write those names
Golden for ever, eagles, crying flames,

And set them as a banner, that men may know,
To dare the generations, burn, and blow
Out on the wind of Time, shining and streaming. . . .

These I have loved:
                    White plates and cups, clean-gleaming,
Ringed with blue lines; and feathery, faery dust;
Wet roofs, beneath the lamp-light; the strong crust
Of friendly bread; and many-tasting food;
Rainbows; and the blue bitter smoke of wood;
And radiant raindrops couching in cool flowers;
And flowers themselves, that sway through sunny hours,
Dreaming of moths that drink them under the moon:
Then, the cool kindliness of sheets, that soon
Smooth away trouble; and the rough male kiss
Of blankets; grainy wood; live hair that is
Shining and free; blue-massing clouds; the keen
Unpassioned beauty of a great machine;
The benison of hot water; furs to touch;
The good smell of old clothes; and other such —
The comfortable smell of friendly fingers,
Hair's fragrance, and the musty reek that lingers
About dead leaves and last year's ferns. . . .
                                        Dear names,
And thousand other throng to me! Royal flames;
Sweet water's dimpling laugh from tap or spring;
Holes in the ground; and voices that do sing;
Voices in laughter, too; and body's pain,
Soon turned to peace; and the deep-panting train;
Firm sands; the little dulling edge of foam
That browns and dwindles as the wave goes home;
And washen stones, gay for an hour; the cold

Graveness of iron; moist black earthen mould;
Sleep; and high places; footprints in the dew;
And oaks; and brown horse-chestnuts, glossy-new;
And new-peeled sticks; and shining pools on grass; —
All these have been my loves. And these shall pass,
Whatever passes not, in the great hour,
Nor all my passion, all my prayers, have power
To hold them with me through the gate of Death.
They'll play deserter, turn with the traitor breath,
Break the high bond we made, and sell Love's trust
And sacramented covenant to the dust.
— Oh, never a doubt but, somewhere, I shall wake,
And give what's left of love again, and make
New friends, now strangers....
                              But the best I've known,
Stays here, and changes, breaks, grow old, is blown
About the winds of the world, and fades from brains
Of living men, and dies.
                    Nothing remains.
O dear my loves, O faithless, once again
This one last gift I give: that after men
Shall know, and later lovers, far-removed,
Praise you, "All these were lovely"; say, "He loved."

Rupert Brooke

THE SLEEPERS

As I walked down the waterside
    This silent morning, wet and dark;
Before the cocks in farmyards crowed,
    Before the dogs began to bark;
Before the hour of five was struck
By old Westminster's mighty clock:

As I walked down the waterside
  This morning, in the cold damp air,
I saw a hundred women and men
  Huddled in rags and sleeping there:
These people have no work, thought I,
And long before their time they die.

That moment, on the waterside,
  A lighted car came at a bound;
I looked inside and saw a score
  Of pale and weary men that frowned;
Each man sat in a huddled heap,
Carried to work while fast asleep.

Ten cars rushed down the waterside,
  Like lighted coffins in the dark;
With twenty dead men in each car,
  That must be brought alive by work:
These people work too hard, thought I,
And long before their time they die.

                              William H. Davies

THE SHELL

And then I pressed the shell
Close to my ear
And listened well,
And straightway like a bell
Came low and clear
The slow, sad murmur of far distant seas,
Whipped by an icy breeze
Upon a shore
Wind-swept and desolate.

It was a sunless strand that never bore
The footprint of a man,
Nor felt the weight
Since time began
Of any human quality or stir
Save what the dreary winds and waves incur.
And in the hush of waters was the sound
Of pebbles rolling round,
For ever rolling with a hollow sound.
And bubbling sea-weeds as the waters go,
Swish to and fro
Their long, cold tentacles of shiny gray.
There was no day,
Nor ever came a night
Setting the stars alight
To wonder at the moon:
Was twilight only and the frightened croon,
Smitten to whimpers, of the dreary wind
And waves that journeyed blind —
And then I loosed my ear — O, it was sweet
To hear a cart go jolting down the street.

James Stephens

MARTIN

When I am tired of earnest men,
    Intense and keen and sharp and clever,
Pursuing fame with brush or pen,
    Or counting metal disks forever,
Then from the halls of Shadowland,
    Beyond the trackless purple sea,
Old Martin's ghost comes back to stand
    Beside my desk and talk to me.

Still on his delicate pale face
  A quizzical thin smile is showing,
His cheeks are wrinkled like fine lace,
  His kind blue eyes are gay and glowing.
He wears a brilliant-hued cravat,
  A suit to match his soft gray hair,
A rakish stick, a knowing hat,
  A manner blithe and debonair.

How good that he who always knew
  That being lovely was a duty,
Should have gold halls to wander through
  And should himself inhabit beauty.
How like his old unselfish way
  To leave those halls of splendid mirth
And comfort those condemned to stay
  Upon the dull and somber earth.

Some people ask: "What cruel chance
  Made Martin's life so sad a story?"
Martin? Why, he exhaled romance,
  And wore an overcoat of glory.
A fleck of sunlight in the street,
  A horse, a book, a girl who smiled,
Such visions made each moment sweet
  For this receptive ancient child.

Because it was old Martin's lot
  To be, not make, a decoration,
Shall we then scorn him, having not
  His genius of appreciation?

Rich joy and love he got and gave;
    His heart was merry as his dress;
Pile laurel wreaths upon his grave
    Who did not gain, but was, success!

Joyce Kilmer

OLD SUSAN

When Susan's work was done, she'd sit,
With one fat guttering candle lit,
And window opened wide to win
The sweet night air to enter in;
There, with a thumb to keep her place,
She'd read, with stern and wrinkled face,
Her mild eyes gliding very slow,
Across the letters to and fro,
While wagged the guttering candle flame
In the wind that through the window came.
And sometimes in the silence she
Would mumble a sentence audibly,
Or shake her head as if to say,
"You silly souls, to act this way!"
And never a sound from night I'd hear,
Unless some far-off cock crowed clear;
Or her old shuffling thumb should turn
Another page; and rapt and stern,
Through her great glasses bent on me,
She'd glance into reality;
And shake her round old silvery head,
With — "You! — I thought you was in bed." —
Only to tilt her book again,
And rooted in Romance remain.

Walter de la Mare

THE NEGRO SPEAKS OF RIVERS

(To W. E. B. DuBois)

I've known rivers:
I've known rivers ancient as the world and older than the
    flow of human blood in human veins.

My soul has grown deep like the rivers.

I bathed in the Euphrates when dawns were young.
I built my hut near the Congo and it lulled me to sleep.
I looked upon the Nile and raised the pyramids above it.
I heard the singing of the Mississippi when Abe Lincoln
    went down to New Orleans, and I've seen its muddy
    bosom turn all golden in the sunset.

I've known rivers:
Ancient, dusky rivers.

My soul has grown deep like the rivers.

Langston Hughes

A LADY

You are beautiful and faded,
Like an old opera tune
Played upon a harpsichord;
Or like the sun-flooded silks
Of an eighteenth-century boudoir.
In your eyes
Smoulder the fallen roses of outlived minutes,

And the perfume of your soul
Is vague and suffusing,
With the pungence of sealed spice jars.
Your half-tones delight me,
And I grow mad with gazing
At your blent colors.

My vigor is a new-minted penny,
Which I cast at your feet.
Gather it up from the dust,
That its sparkle may amuse you.

Amy Lowell

THE SON

SOUTHERN OHIO MARKET TOWN

I heard an old farm-wife,
    Selling some barley,
Mingle her life with life
    And the name "Charley."

Saying: "The crop's all in,
    We're about through now;
Long nights will soon begin,
    We're just us two now.

"Twelve bushel at sixty cents,
    It's all I carried —
He sickened making fence;
    He was to be married.

"It feels like frost was near —
His hair was curly.
The spring was late that year,
But the harvest early."

Ridgely Torrence

UNCLE ANANIAS

His words were magic and his heart was true,
  And everywhere he wandered he was blessed
Out of all ancient men my childhood knew
  I choose him and I mark him for the best.
Of all authoritative liars, too,
  I crown him loveliest.

How fondly I remember the delight
  That always glorified him in the spring;
The joyous courage and the benedight
  Profusion of his faith in everything!
He was a good old man, and it was right
  That he should have his fling.

And often, underneath the apple-trees,
  When we surprised him in the summer-time,
With what superb magnificence and ease
  He sinned enough to make the day sublime!
And if he liked us there about his knees,
  Truly it was no crime.

All summer long we loved him for the same
  Perennial inspiration of his lies;
And when the russet wealth of autumn came,

There flew but fairer visions to our eyes —
Multiple, tropical, winged with a feathery flame,
  Like birds of paradise.

So to the sheltered end of many a year
  He charmed the seasons out with pageantry
Wearing upon his forehead, with no fear,
  The laurel of approved iniquity.
And every child who knew him, far or near,
  Did love him faithfully.

Edwin Arlington Robinson

LAMENT

Listen, children:
Your father is dead.
From his old coats
I'll make you little jackets;
I'll make you little trousers
From his old pants.
There'll be in his pockets
Things he used to put there,
Keys and pennies,
Covered with tobacco;
Dan shall have the pennies
To save in his bank;
Anne shall have the keys
To make a pretty noise with.
Life must go on,
And the dead be forgotten;
Life must go on,
Though good men die.

Anne, eat your breakfast;
Dan, take your medicine.
Life must go on;
I forget just why.

Edna St. Vincent Millay

TO A PHOTOGRAPHER

I have known love and hate and work and fight;
  I have lived largely, I have dreamed and planned,
  And Time, the Sculptor, with a master hand
Has graven on my face for all men's sight
Deep lines of joy and sorrow, growth and blight
  Of labor and of service and command
  — And now you show me this, this waxen, bland
And placid face, unlined, unwrinkled, white.

This is not I — this fatuous thing you show,
  Retouched and smoothed and prettified to please,
Put back the wrinkles and the lines I know;
  I have spent blood and tears achieving these,
Out of the pain, the struggle and the wrack
These are my scars of battle — put them back!

Berton Braley

SYMPHONY PATHÉTIQUE

That woman with the somber eyes
Had come to write and criticize,
But see her now with ardent face
Transfigured for a little space,
Leaning far forward in her seat,
Wrapt in the rhythm and the beat —

The volume and the surge of it,
The lovely lilt and swell of it;
The vigor and the urge of it;
The rapture ... and the knell of it;
The rose and gold, the warmth and glow,
The mauve and gray, the ice and snow.
   Trembling, swaying,
   Pleading, praying,
   Spurning, lashing,
   Climbing, crashing —
     Titanic rage ... and tenderness. ...
     To hurt, to heal; to curse, to bless ...
And now the year's at June again,
And now the day's at noon again!
  She settles back, and with a sigh
  She puts her stubby pencil by.
  She will not try to shape and frame,
  To pack sensations in a name, —
  To harness up the cyclone's march;
  To reinforce the rainbow's arch;
  Stab Pegasus with iron spur:
  Use symbols for a tool
  To chisel to a granite word
  The subtleties she felt and heard,
  Nor wind a web of gossamer
  Upon a wooden spool.

Ruth Comfort Mitchell

OF A CHILD THAT HAD FEVER

I bid you, mock not Eros
Lest Eros mock with you —

His is a hot distemper
    That hath no feverfew.

Love, like a child in sickness,
    Brilliant, languid, still,
In fiery weakness lying,
    Accepts, and hath no will.

See, in that warm dispassion
    Less grievance than surprise:
And pitiable brightness
    In his poor wondering eyes.

O delicate heat and madness,
    O lust unnerved and faint:
Sparkling in veins and fibers
    Division and attaint!

I bid you, mock not Eros:
    He knows not doubt nor shame,
And unaware of proverbs
    The burnt child craves the flame.

Christopher Morley

SMELLS

Why is it that the poets tell
So little of the sense of smell?
These are the odors I love well:

The smell of coffee freshly ground;
Or rich plum pudding, holly-crowned;
Or onions fried and deeply browned.

The fragrance of a fumy pipe;
The smell of apples, newly ripe;
And printer's ink on leaden type.

Woods by moonlight in September
Breathe most sweet; and I remember
Many a smoky campfire ember.

Camphor, turpentine, and tea,
The balsam of a Christmas tree,
These are whiffs of gramaryc...
A ship smells best of all to me!
Christopher Morley

THE LEADEN-EYED

Let not young souls be smothered out before
They do quaint deeds and fully flaunt their pride.
It is the world's one crime its babes grow dull,
Its poor are ox-like, limp, and leaden-eyed.
Not that they starve, but starve so dreamlessly,
Not that they sow, but that they seldom reap,
Not that they serve, but have no gods to serve;
Not that they die, but that they die like sheep.
Vachel Lindsay

FACTORY WINDOWS ARE ALWAYS BROKEN

Factory windows are always broken.
Somebody's always throwing bricks,
Somebody's always heaving cinders,
Playing ugly Yahoo tricks.

Factory windows are always broken.
Other windows are let alone.
No one throws through the chapel window
The bitter, snarling, derisive stone.

Factory windows are always broken.
Something or other is going wrong.
Something is rotten — I think, in Denmark.
End of the factory-window song.

Vachel Lindsay

WIND RISING IN THE ALLEYS

Wind, rising in the alleys,
My spirit lifts in you like a banner
    streaming free of hot walls.
You are full of unshaped dreams. . . .
You are laden with beginnings. . . .
There is hope in you . . . not sweet . . .
    acrid as blood in the mouth.
Come into my tossing dust
Scattering the peace of old deaths,
Wind rising out of the alleys,
Carrying stuff of flame.

Lola Ridge

THE BRUTE

Through his might men work their wills.
They have boweled out the hills
For food to keep him toiling in the cages they have wrought;
And they fling him, hour by hour,

Limbs of men to give him power;
Brains of men to give him cunning; and for dainties to de-
　　vour
Children's souls, the little worth; hearts of women, cheaply
　　bought:
He takes them and he breaks them, but he gives them scanty
　　thought.

For about the noisy land,
Roaring, quivering 'neath his hand,
His thoughts brood fierce and sullen or laugh in lust of pride
O'er the stubborn things that he
Breaks to dust and brings to be.
Some he mightily establishes, some flings down utterly.
There is thunder in his stride, nothing ancient can abide,
When he hales the hills together and bridles up the tide.

Quietude and loveliness,
Holy sights that heal and bless,
They are scattered and abolished where his iron hoof is set;
When he splashes through the brae
Silver streams are choked with clay,
When he snorts the bright cliffs crumble and the woods go
　　down like hay;
He lairs in pleasant cities, and the haggard people fret
Squalid 'mid their new-got riches, soot-begrimed and deso-
　　late.

They who caught and bound him tight
Laughed exultant at his might,
Saying, "Now behold, the good time comes for the weariest
　　and the least!

We will use this lusty knave:
No more need for men to slave;
We may rise and look about us and have knowledge ere the
    grave."
But the Brute said in his breast, "Till the mills I grind have
    ceased,
The riches shall be dust of dust, dry ashes be the feast!

"On the strong and cunning few
Cynic favors I will strew;
I will stuff their maw with overplus until their spirit dies;
From the patient and the low
I will take the joys they know;
They shall hunger after vanities and still an-hungered go.
Madness shall be on the people, ghastly jealousies arise;
Brother's blood shall cry on brother up the dead and empty
    skies.

"I will burn and dig and hack
Till the heavens suffer lack;
God shall feel a pleasure fail Him, crying to his cherubim,
'Who hath flung yon mud-ball there
Where my world went green and fair?'
I shall laugh and hug me, hearing how his sentinels declare,
"'Tis the Brute they chained to labor!   He has made the
    bright earth dim.
Stores of wares and pelf a plenty, but they got no good of
    him.'"

So he plotted in his rage:
So he deals it, age by age.
But even as he roared his curse a still small Voice befell;

Lo, a still and pleasant voice bade them none the less rejoice,
For the Brute must bring the good time on; he has no other
    choice.
He may struggle, sweat, and yell, but he knows exceeding well
He must work them out salvation ere they send him back to
    hell.

All the desert that he made
He must treble bless with shade,
In primal wastes set precious seed of rapture and of pain;
All the strongholds that he built
For the powers of greed and guilt —
He must strew their bastions down the sea and choke their
    towers with silt;
He must make the temples clean for the gods to come again,
And lift the lordly cities under skies without a stain.

In a very cunning tether
He must lead the tyrant weather;
He must loose the curse of Adam from the worn neck of the
    race;
He must cast out hate and fear,
Dry away each fruitless tear,
And make the fruitful tears to gush from the deep heart and
    clear.
He must give each man his portion, each his pride and
    worthy place;
He must batter down the arrogant and lift the weary face,
On each vile mouth set purity, on each low forehead grace.

Then, perhaps, at the last day,
They will whistle him away,

Lay a hand upon his muzzle in the face of God, and say,
"Honor, Lord, the Thing we tamed!
Let him not be scourged or blamed,
Even through his wrath and fierceness was thy fierce wroth
    world reclaimed!
Honor Thou thy servants' servant; let thy justice now be
    shown."
Then the Lord will heed their saying, and the Brute come to
    his own,
'Twixt the Lion and the Eagle, by the armpost of the Throne.

William Vaughn Moody

The Funny Side

THE BALLAD OF THE OYSTERMAN

It was a tall young oysterman lived by the river-side,
His shop was just upon the bank, his boat was on the tide;
The daughter of a fisherman, that was so straight and slim,
Lived over on the other bank, right opposite to him.

It was the pensive oysterman that saw a lovely maid,
Upon a moonlight evening, a-sitting in the shade;
He saw her wave a handkerchief, as much as if to say,
"I'm wide awake, young oysterman, and all the folks away."

Then up arose the oysterman, and to himself said he,
"I guess I'll leave the skiff at home, for fear that folks should
        see;
I read it in the story-book, that, for to kiss his dear,
Leander swam the Hellespont — and I will swim this here."

And he has leaped into the waves, and crossed the shining
        stream,
And he has clambered up the bank, all in the moonlight
        gleam;
Oh, there are kisses sweet as dew, and words as soft as rain —
But they have heard her father's step, and in he leaps again!

Out spoke the ancient fisherman: "Oh, what was that, my
        daughter?"
"'Twas nothing but a pebble, sir, I threw into the water."

"And what is that, pray tell me, love, that paddles off so
          fast?"
"It's nothing but a porpoise, sir, that's been a-swimming
          past."

Out spoke the ancient fisherman: "Now bring me my har-
          poon!
I'll get into my fishing-boat, and fix the fellow soon."
Down fell that pretty innocent, as falls a snow-white lamb;
Her hair drooped around her pallid cheeks, like seaweed on
          a clam.

Alas for those two loving ones! she waked not from her
          swound,
And he was taken with the cramp, and in the waves was
          drowned;
But Fate has metamorphosed them, in pity of their woe,
And now they keep an oyster-shop for mermaids down below.
                                        Oliver Wendell Holmes

YOU ARE OLD, FATHER WILLIAM

"You are old, father William," the young man said,
    "And your hair has become very white;
And yet you incessantly stand on your head —
    Do you think, at your age, it is right?"

"In my youth," father William replied to his son,
    "I feared it might injure the brain;
But now that I'm perfectly sure I have none,
    Why, I do it again and again."

"You are old," said the youth, "as I mentioned before,
   And have grown most uncommonly fat;
Yet you turned a back somersault in at the door —
   Pray, what is the reason of that?"

"In my youth," said the sage, as he shook his gray locks,
   "I kept all my limbs very supple
By the use of this ointment — one shilling the box —
   Allow me to sell you a couple."

"You are old," said the youth, "and your jaws are too weak
   For anything tougher than suet;
Yet you finished the goose, with the bones and the beak —
   Pray, how did you manage to do it?"

"In my youth," said his father, "I took to the law,
   And argued each case with my wife;
And the muscular strength which it gave to my jaw,
   Has lasted the rest of my life."

"You are old," said the youth, "one would hardly suppose
   That your eye was as steady as ever;
Yet you balanced an eel on the end of your nose —
   What made you so awfully clever?"

"I have answered three questions, and that is enough,"
   Said his father; "don't give yourself airs!
Do you think I can listen all day to such stuff?
   Be off, or I'll kick you downstairs!"

                              Charles Lutwidge Dodgson
                                 ("*Lewis Carroll*")

THE YARN OF THE *NANCY BELL*

'Twas on the shores that round our coast
    From Deal to Ramsgate span,
That I found alone on a piece of stone
    An elderly naval man.

His hair was weedy, his beard was long,
    And weedy and long was he,
And I heard this wight on the shore recite,
    In a singular minor key:

"Oh, I am a cook, and a captain bold,
    And the mate of the *Nancy* brig
And a bo'sun tight, and a midshipmite,
    And the crew of the captain's gig."

And he shook his fists and he tore his hair,
    Till I really felt afraid,
For I couldn't help thinking the man had been drinking,
    And so I simply said:

"Oh, elderly man, it's little I know
    Of the duties of men of the sea,
But I'll eat my hand if I understand
    How you can possibly be

"At once a cook, and a captain bold,
    And the mate of the *Nancy* brig,
And a bo'sun tight, and a midshipmite,
    And the crew of the captain's gig."

Then he gave a hitch to his trousers, which
  Is a trick all seamen larn,
And having got rid of a thumping quid,
  He spun this painful yarn:

"'Twas in the good ship *Nancy Bell*
  That we sailed to the Indian sea,
And there on a reef we came to grief,
  Which has often occurred to me.

"And pretty nigh all o' the crew was drowned
  (There was seventy-seven o' soul),
And only ten of the *Nancy's* men
  Said 'Here!' to the muster-roll.

"There was me and the cook and the captain bold,
  And the mate of the *Nancy* brig,
And the bo'sun tight, and a midshipmite,
  And the crew of the captain's gig.

"For a month we'd neither wittles nor drink,
  Till a-hungry we did feel,
So we drawed a lot, and accordin' shot
  The captain for our meal.

"The next lot fell to the *Nancy's* mate,
  And delicate dish he made;
Then our appetite with the midshipmite
  We seven survivors stayed.

"And then we murdered the bo'sun tight,
  And he much resembled pig;

Then we wittled free, did the cook and me,
　　On the crew of the captain's gig.

"Then only the cook and me was left,
　　And the delicate question 'Which
Of us two goes to the kettle?' arose
　　And we argued it out as sich.

"For I loved that cook as a brother, I did,
　　And the cook he worshipped me;
But we'd both be blowed if we'd either be stowed
　　In the other chap's hold, you see.

"'I'll be eat if you dines of me,' says Tom,
　　'Yes, that,' says I, 'you'll be' —
'I'm boiled if I die, my friend,' quoth I,
　　And 'Exactly so,' quoth he.

"Says he, 'Dear James, to murder me
　　Were a foolish thing to do,
For don't you see that you can't cook *me*,
　　While I can — and will — cook *you*!'

"So he boils the water, and takes the salt
　　And the pepper in proportions true
(Which he never forgot), and some chopped shalot,
　　And some sage and parsley too.

"'Come here,' says he, with a proper pride,
　　Which his smiling features tell,
"Twill soothing be if I let you see,
　　How extremely nice you'll smell.'

"And he stirred it round and round and round
  And he sniffed at the foaming froth;
When I ups with his heels, and smothers his squeals
  In the scum of the boiling broth.

"And I eat that cook in a week or less,
  And — as I eating be
The last of his chops, why, I almost drops,
  For a vessel in sight I see!

    .   .   .   .   .

"And I never grieve, and I never smile,
  And I never larf nor play,
But I sit and croak, and a single joke
  I have — which is to say:

"Oh, I am a cook and captain bold,
  And the mate of the *Nancy* brig,
And a bo'sun tight, and a midshipmite,
  And the crew of the captain's gig!"
                Sir William Schwenck Gilbert

ONE WEEK

The year had gloomily begun
For Willie Weeks, a poor man's
              SUN.

He was beset with bill and dun,
And he had very little
              MON.

"This cash," said he, "won't pay my dues,
I've nothing here but ones and
                        TUES.

A bright thought struck him, and he said:
"The rich Miss Goldrocks I will
                        WED.

But when he paid his court to her,
She lisped, but firmly said, "No
                        THUR.

"Alas," said he, "then I must die!
Although hereafter I may
                        FRI.

They found his gloves, and coat, and hat,
The coroner upon them
                        SAT.
                              Carolyn Wells

THE HEIGHT OF THE RIDICULOUS

I wrote some lines, once on a time,
  In wondrous merry mood,
And thought, as usual, men would say
  They were exceedingly good.

They were so queer, so very queer,
  I laughed as I would die;
Albeit, in a general way,
  A sober man am I.

I called my servant, and he came;
   How kind it was of him,
To mind a slender man like me,
   He of the mighty limb!

"These to the printer," I exclaimed,
   And, in my humorous way,
I added (as a trifling jest),
   "There'll be the devil to pay."

He took the paper, and I watched,
   And saw him peep within;
At the first line he read, his face
   Was all upon the grin.

He read the next; the grin grew broad,
   And shot from ear to ear;
He read the third; a chuckling noise
   I now began to hear.

The fourth; he broke into a roar;
   The fifth; his waistband split;
The sixth; he burst the buttons off,
   And tumbled in a fit.

Ten days and nights, with sleepless eye,
   I watched that wretched man,
And since, I never dare to write
   As funny as I can.

Oliver Wendell Holmes

PLAIN LANGUAGE FROM TRUTHFUL JAMES

Which I wish to remark,
   And my language is plain,
That for ways that are dark,
   And for tricks that are vain,
The heathen Chinee is peculiar,
   Which the same I would rise to explain.

Ah Sin was his name,
   And I shall not deny,
In regard to the same,
   What that name might imply;
But his smile it was pensive and childlike,
   As I frequent remarked to Bill Nye.

It was August the third;
   And quite soft were the skies:
Which it might be inferred
   That Ah Sin was likewise;
Yet he played it that day upon William
   And me in a way I despise.

Which we had a small game,
   And Ah Sin took a hand:
It was euchre.   The same
   He did not understand;
But he smiled as he sat by the table,
   With the smile that was childlike and bland.

Yet the cards that were stocked
   In a way that I grieve,

And my feelings were shocked
    At the state of Nye's sleeve,
Which was stuffed full of aces and bowers,
    And the same with intent to deceive.

But the hands that were played
    By that heathen Chinee,
And the points that he made,
    Were quite frightful to see —
Till at last he put down a right bower,
    Which the same Nye had dealt unto me.

Then I looked up at Nye,
    And he gazed upon me;
And he rose with a sigh,
    And said, "Can this be?
We are ruined by Chinese cheap labor!" —
    And he went for that heathen Chinee.

In the scene that ensued
    I did not take a hand,
But the floor it was strewed,
    Like the leaves on the strand,
With the cards that Ah Sin had been hiding,
    In the game "he did not understand."

In his sleeves, which were long,
    He had twenty-four packs,
Which was coming it strong,
    Yet I state but the facts,
And we found on his nails, which were taper,
    What is frequent in tapers — that's wax.

Which is why I remark,
  And my language is plain,
That for ways that are dark,
  And for tricks that are vain,
The Heathen Chinee is peculiar,
    Which the same I am free to maintain.
                              Francis Bret Harte

THE TWINS

In form and feature, face and limb,
  I grew so like my brother,
That folks got taking me for him,
  And each for one another.
It puzzled all our kith and kin,
  It reached a fearful pitch;
For one of us was born a twin,
  Yet not a soul knew which.

One day, to make the matter worse,
  Before our names were fixed,
As we were being washed by nurse,
  We got completely mixed;
And thus, you see, by fate's decree,
  Or rather nurse's whim,
My brother John got christened me,
  And I got christened him.

This fatal likeness even dogged
  My footsteps when at school,
And I was always getting flogged,
  For John turned out a fool.

I put this question, fruitlessly,
    To everyone I knew,
"What *would* you do, if you were me,
    To prove that you were *you*?"

Our close resemblance turned the tide
    Of my domestic life,
For somehow, my intended bride
    Became my brother's wife.
In fact, year after year the same
    Absurd mistakes went on,
And when I died, the neighbors came
    And buried brother John.

                    Henry Sambrooke Leigh

THE JESTER CONDEMNED TO DEATH

One of the Kings of Scanderoon
        A royal jester
Had in his train, a gross buffoon,
        Who used to pester
The court with tricks inopportune,
Venting on the highest folks his
Scurvy pleasantries and hoaxes.

It needs some sense to play the fool;
        Which wholesome rule
Occurr'd not to our jackanapes,
        Who consequently found his freaks
Led to innumerable scrapes,
        And quite as many kicks and tweaks,
Which only seemed to make him faster
Try the patience of his master.

Some sin at last, beyond all measure,
Incurred the desperate displeasure
    Of his serene and raging Highness:
Whether the wag had twitch'd his beard,
Which he felt bound to have revered,
    Or had intruded on the shyness
Of the seraglio, or let fly
An epigram at royalty,
None knows — his sin was an occult one;
But records tell us that the sultan,
Meaning to terrify the knave,
    Exclaim'd — "'Tis time to stop that breath;
Thy doom is seal'd; — presumptuous slave!
    Thou stand'st condemned to certain death
Silence, base rebel! — no replying! —
    But such is my indulgence still,
    That, of my own free grace and will,
I leave to thee the mode of dying."

"Thy royal will be done — 'tis just,"
Replied the wretch, and kissed the dust;
    "Since my last moments to assuage,
Your Majesty's humane decree
Has deign'd to leave the choice to me,
    I'll die, so please you, of old age!"

                                    Horace Smith

AN ELEGY ON THE DEATH OF A MAD DOG

Good people all, of every sort,
    Give ear unto my song;
And if you find it wondrous short,
    It cannot hold you long.

In Islington there was a man
   Of whom the world might say,
That still a godly race he ran,
   Whene'er he went to pray.

A kind and gentle heart he had,
   To comfort friends and foes:
The naked every day he clad,
   When he put on his clothes.

And in that town a dog was found,
   As many dogs there be,
Both mongrel, puppy, whelp, and hound,
   And curs of low degree.

This dog and man at first were friends;
   But when a pique began,
The dog, to gain some private ends,
   Went mad, and bit the man.

Around from all the neighboring streets
   The wondering neighbors ran,
And swore the dog had lost his wits,
   To bite so good a man.

The wound it seemed both sore and sad
   To every Christian eye:
And while they swore the dog was mad,
   They swore the man would die.

But soon a wonder came to light
   That showed the rogues they lied:
The man recovered of the bite,
   The dog it was that died.

Oliver Goldsmith

RAVIN'S OF PIUTE POET POE

Once upon a midnight dreary, eerie, scary,
I was wary, I was weary, full of worry, thinking of my lost
    Lenore,
Of my cheery, airy, faery, fiery Dearie — (Nothing more).
I was napping, when a tapping on the overlapping coping,
    woke me gapping, yapping, groping... toward the
    rapping. I went hopping, leaping... hoping that the
    rapping on the coping
Was my little lost Lenore.
That on opening the shutter to admit the latter critter,
    in she'd flutter from the gutter with her bitter eyes
    aglitter;
So I opened wide the door, what was there? The dark weir
    and drear moor, — or I'm a liar — the dark mire,
    the drear moor, the mere door, and nothing more!

Then in stepped a stately Raven, shaven like the bard of
    Avon; yes, a rovin' grievin' Raven, seeking haven at
    my door.
Yes, that shaven, rovin' Raven had been movin' (Get me,
    Stephen) for the warm and lovin' haven of my stove
    and oven door —
    Oven door, and nothing more.

Ah, distinctly I remember, every ember that December
    turned from amber to burnt umber;
I was burning limber lumber in my chamber that December,
    and it left an amber ember.
With a silken, sad uncertain flirtin' of a certain curtain,
That old Raven, cold and callous, perched upon the bust of
    Pallas,

Just above my chamber door;
(A lusty, trusty bust, thrust just
    Above my chamber door.)
Had that callous cuss shown malice?   Or sought solace, there
        on Pallas?
    (You may tell us, Alice Wallace).
Tell this soul with sorrow laden, hidden in the shade, an'
        broodin' —
If a maiden out of Eden sent this sudden bird invadin'
My poor chamber; and protrudin' half an inch above my
        door.
Tell this broodin' soul (he's breedin' bats by too much sodden
        readin' — readin'
    Snowden's ode to Odin)
Tell this soul by nightmares ridden, if (no kiddin') on a sudden
He shall clasp a radiant maiden born in Aiden or in Leyden
        or indeed in
    Baden Baden —
Will he grab this buddin' maiden, gaddin' in forbidden
        Eden,
    Whom the angels named Lenore?
Then that bird said: "Nevermore."

"Prophet," said I, "thing of evil, navel, novel, or boll weevil,
You shall travel, on the level!   Scratch the gravel, now, and
        travel!
Leave my hovel, I implore."
And that Raven never flitting, never knitting, never tatting,
        never spouting "Nevermore."
Still is sitting (out this ballad) on the solid bust (and pallid)
        — on the solid, valid, pallid bust above my chamber
        door:

And my soul is in his shadow, which lies floating on the floor,
Fleeting, floating, yachting, boating on the fluting of the
     matting —
Matting on my chamber floor.

Charles L. Edson

THE JACKDAW OF RHEIMS

The Jackdaw sat on the Cardinal's chair!
Bishop and abbot and prior were there;
    Many a monk, and many a friar,
    Many a knight, and many a squire,
With a great many more of lesser degree, —
In sooth a goodly company;
And they served the Lord Primate on bended knee.
    Never, I ween,
    Was a prouder seen,
Read of in books, or dreamt of in dreams,
Than the Cardinal Lord Archbishop of Rheims.

    In and out
    Through the motley rout,
That little Jackdaw kept hopping about;
    Here and there
    Like a dog in a fair,
    Over comfits and cakes,
    And dishes and plates,
Cowl and cope, and rochet, and pall,
Mitre and crosier! he hopp'd upon all!
    With saucy air,
    He perch'd on the chair
Where, in state, the great Lord Cardinal sat

In the great Lord Cardinal's great red hat;
      And he peer'd in the face
      Of his Lordship's Grace,
With a satisfied look, as if he would say,
"We two are the greatest folks here today!"
      And the priests, with awe,
      As such freaks they saw,
Said, "The Devil must be in that little Jackdaw."

The feast was over, the board was clear'd,
The flawns and the custards had all disappear'd,
And six little Singing-boys — dear little souls!
In nice clean faces, and nice white stoles,
      Came, in order due,
      Two by two
Marching that great refectory through!
A nice little boy held a golden ewer,
Emboss'd and fill'd with water, as pure
As any that flows between Rheims and Namur,
Which a nice little boy stood ready to catch
In a fine golden hand-basin made to match.
Two nice little boys, rather more grown,
Carried lavender-water, and eau de Cologne,
And a nice little boy had a nice cake of soap,
Worthy of washing the hands of the Pope.
      One little boy more
      A napkin bore,
Of the best white diaper, fringed with pink,
And a Cardinal's Hat mark'd in "permanent ink."

The great Lord Cardinal turns at the sight
Of these nice little boys dress'd all in white:

From his finger he draws
His costly turquoise;
And, not thinking at all about little Jackdaws,
Deposits it straight
By the side of his plate,
While the nice little boys on his Eminence wait;
Till, when nobody's dreaming of any such thing,
That little Jackdaw hops off with the ring!

———

There's a cry and a shout,
And a deuce of a rout,
And nobody seems to know what they're about,
But the monks have their pockets all turn'd inside out;
The friars are kneeling,
And hunting, and feeling
The carpet, the floor, and the walls, and the ceiling.
The Cardinal drew
Off each plum-color'd shoe,
And left his red stockings exposed to the view;
He peeps and he feels
In the toes and the heels;
They turn up the dishes — they turn up the plates —
They take up the poker and poke out the grates
— They turn up the rugs,
They examine the mugs —
But no! — no such thing;
— They can't find the ring!
And the Abbot declared that, "when nobody twigg'd it
Some rascal or other had popp'd in and prigg'd it!"

The Cardinal rose with a dignified look,
He call'd for his candle, his bell, and his book!

In holy anger and pious grief,
He solemnly cursed that rascally thief!
He cursed him at board, he cursed him in bed;
From the sole of his foot to the crown of his head;
He cursed him in sleeping, that every night
He should dream of the devil, and wake in a fright;
He cursed him in eating, he cursed him in drinking,
He cursed him in coughing, in sneezing, in winking;
He cursed him in sitting, in standing, in lying;
He cursed him in walking, in riding, in flying,
He cursed him in living, he cursed him dying! —
Never was heard such a terrible curse!
    But what gave rise
    To no little surprise,
Nobody seem'd one penny the worse!

    The day was gone,
    The night came on,
The Monks and the Friars they search'd till dawn;
    When the sacristan saw,
    On crumpled claw,
Come limping a poor little lame Jackdaw
    No longer gay,
    As on yesterday;
His feathers all seem'd to be turn'd the wrong way; —
His pinions droop'd — he could hardly stand —
His head was as bald as the palm of your hand:
    His eye so dim,
    So wasted each limb,
That, heedless of grammar, they all cried "That's him!
That's the scamp that has done this scandalous thing!
That's the thief that has got my Lord Cardinal's ring!"

The poor little Jackdaw,
When the monks he saw,
Feebly gave vent to the ghost of a caw;
And turn'd his bald head, as much as to say;
"Pray be so good as to walk this way!"
Slower and slower
He limped on before,
Till they came to the back of the belfry door,
Where the first thing they saw,
'Midst the sticks and the straw,
Was the ring in the nest of that little Jackdaw!

Then the great Lord Cardinal call'd for his book,
And off that terrible curse he took;
The mute expression
Served in lieu of confession,
And, being thus coupled with full restitution,
The Jackdaw got plenary absolution!
— When those words were heard,
That poor little bird
Was so changed in a moment, 'twas really absurd,
He grew sleek, and fat,
In addition to that,
A fresh crop of feathers came thick as a mat!
His tail waggled more
Even than before;
But no longer it wagged with an impudent air,
No longer he perch'd on the Cardinal's chair.
He hopp'd now about
With a gait devout;
At Matins, at Vespers, he never was out;
And, so far from any more pilfering deeds,

He always seem'd telling the Confessor's beads.
If anyone lied — or if anyone swore —
Or slumber'd in prayer-time and happen'd to snore,
    That good Jackdaw,
    Would give a great "Caw,"
As much as to say, "Don't do so any more!"
While many remark'd, as his manners they saw,
That they "never had known such a pious Jackdaw!"
    He long lived the pride
    Of that countryside,
And at last in the odor of sanctity died;
    When, as words were too faint,
    His merits to paint,
The Conclave determined to make him a Saint;
And on newly-made Saints and Popes, as you know,
It's the custom, at Rome, new names to bestow,
So they canonized him by the name of Jim Crow.
                Richard Harris Barham
                ("*Thomas Ingoldsby*")

THE VIZIER'S APOLOGY

Sing, Muse, of the anger of Haroun the Caliph
Aroused by complaints of the Sheik of Irak!
"The scoundrel!" he thundered, "We'll clap him in jail if
We don't drop him overboard, sewn in a sack!

"The villain has robbed the imperial coffer,
And witnesses charge him with every abuse;
And think of the fellow disdaining to offer
Our Clemency even a shred of excuse!"

"Perhaps 'twere as well," said the Minister, smiling,
"To stifle our anger and wait for a time.
Excuses, like charges, are framed for beguiling;
Besides, the Excuse may be worse than the Crime."

"What nonsense!" cried Haroun, the monarch effulgent,
"To hint that the Fault can be less than the Plea!"
"Perhaps," purred the Minister, blandly indulgent,
"I'll prove to Your Highness that such it may be."

The very next morning, superbly attended
By eunuchs in dozens and emirs in pairs,
With grandeur befitting the nobly descended,
The Caliph descended the glittering stairs;

When, daring unspeakable woes and disasters
And rage that devours its prey like pilaff,
The Minister reached through the marble pilasters
And wickedly pinched the imperial calf!

Aghast at an outrage so shockingly sinister
"Dog!" gasped the Autocrat, "What do you mean!"
"What a mistake!" wailed the profligate Minister:
"Pardon, your Highness — I thought 'twas the Queen!"

And then, by another experience wiser,
The Caliph with graciousness truly sublime
Admitted the fact that his faithful adviser
Had made an Excuse that was worse than the Crime.

Arthur Guiterman

THE LEGEND OF THE FIRST CAM–U–EL

AN ARABIAN APOLOGUE

Across the sands of Syria,
Or, possibly, Algeria,
Or some benighted neighborhood of barrenness and drouth,
There came the Prophet Sam-u-el
Upon the Only Cam-u-el —
A bumpy, grumpy Quadruped of discontented mouth.

The atmosphere was glutinous;
The Cam-u-el was mutinous;
He dumped the pack from off his back; with horrid grunts
and squeals
He made the desert hideous;
With strategy perfidious
He tied his neck in curlicues, he kicked his paddy heels.

Then said the gentle Sam-u-el,
"You rogue, I ought to lam you well!
Though zealously I've shielded you from every grief and woe,
It seems, to voice a platitude,
You haven't any gratitude.
I'd like to hear what cause you have for doing thus and so!"

To him replied the Cam-u-el,
"I beg your pardon, Sam-u-el.
I know that I'm a Reprobate, I know that I'm a Freak;
But, oh! this utter loneliness!
My too-distinguished Onliness!
Were there but other Cam-u-els I would not be unique."

The Prophet beamed beguilingly.
"Aha," he answered, smilingly,
"You feel the need of company?   I clearly understand.
We'll speedily create for you
The corresponding mate for you; —
Ho! presto, change-o, dinglebat" — he waved a potent hand.

And, lo! from out Vacuity
A second Incongruity,
To wit, a Lady Cam-u-el was born through magic art.
Her structure anatomical,
Her face and form *were* comical;
She was, in short, a Cam-u-el, the other's counterpart.

As Spaniards gaze on Aragon,
Upon that Female Paragon
So gazed the Prophet's Cam-u-el, that primal Desert Ship.
A connoisseur meticulous,
He found her that ridiculous
He grinned from ear to auricle *until he split his lip!*

Because of his temerity
That Cam-u-el's posterity
Must wear divided upper lips through all their solemn lives!
A prodigy astonishing
Reproachfully admonishing
Those wicked, heartless married men who ridicule their
wives.

Arthur Guiterman

THE PLAINT OF THE CAMEL

"Canary Birds feed on sugar and seed,
    Parrots have crackers to crunch;
And, as for the poodles, they tell me the noodles
    Have chicken and cream for their lunch.
        But there's never a question
        About MY digestion —
    ANYTHING does for me!

"Cats, you're aware, can repose in a chair,
    Chickens can roost upon rails;
Puppies are able to sleep in a stable,
    And oysters can slumber in pails.
        But no one supposes
        A poor Camel dozes —
    ANY PLACE does for me!

"Lambs are enclosed where it's never exposed,
    Coops are constructed for hens;
Kittens are treated to houses well heated,
    And pigs are protected by pens.
        But a Camel comes handy
        Wherever it's sandy —
    ANYWHERE does for me!

"People would laugh if you rode a giraffe,
    Or mounted the back of an ox;
It's nobody's habit to ride on a rabbit,
    Or try to bestraddle a fox.
        But as for a Camel, he's
        Ridden by families —
    ANY LOAD does for me!

"A snake is as round as a hole in the ground;
　　Weasels are wavy and sleek;
And no alligator could ever be straighter
　　Than lizards that live in a creek.
　　　But a Camel's all lumpy
　　　And bumpy and humpy —
　　ANY SHAPE does for me!"

　　　　　　　　　　　　　　　　Charles E. Carryl

THE SYCOPHANTIC FOX AND THE GULLIBLE
RAVEN

A raven sat upon a tree,
　　And not a word he spoke, for
His beak contained a piece of Brie,
　　Or, maybe, it was Roquefort:
　　　We'll make it any kind you please —
　　　At all events, it was a cheese.

Beneath the tree's umbrageous limb
　　A hungry fox sat smiling;
He saw the raven watching him,
　　And spoke in words beguiling.
　　　"*J'admire*," said he, "*ton beau plumage*,"
　　　(The which was simply persiflage.)

Two things there are, no doubt you know,
　　To which a fox is used:
A rooster that is bound to crow,
　　A crow that's bound to roost;
　　　And whichsoever he espies
　　　He tells the most unblushing lies.

"Sweet fowl," he said, "I understand
  You're more than merely natty,
I hear you sing to beat the band
  And Adelina Patti.
    Pray render with your liquid tongue
    A bit from 'Götterdämmerung.'"

This subtle speech was aimed to please
  The crow, and it succeeded:
He thought no bird in all the trees
  Could sing as well as he did.
    In flattery completely doused,
    He gave the "Jewel Song" from "Faust."

But gravitation's law, of course,
  As Isaac Newton showed it,
Exerted on the cheese its force,
  And elsewhere soon bestowed it.
    In fact, there is no need to tell
    What happened when to earth it fell.

I blush to add that when the bird
  Took in the situation
He said one brief, emphatic word
  Unfit for publication.
    The fox was greatly startled, but
    He only sighed and answered "Tut."

THE MORAL is: A fox is bound
  To be a shameless sinner.
And also: When the cheese comes round
  You know it's after dinner.

But (what is only known to few)
The fox is after dinner, too.

Guy Wetmore Carryl

STRICTLY GERM–PROOF

The Antiseptic Baby and the Prophylactic Pup
Were playing in the garden when the Bunny gamboled up;
They looked upon the Creature with a loathing undisguised—
It wasn't Disinfected and it wasn't Sterilized.

They said it was a Microbe and a Hotbed of Disease;
They steamed it in a vapor of a thousand-odd degrees;
They froze it in a freezer that was cold as Banished Hope
And washed it in permanganate with carbolated soap.

In sulphureted hydrogen they steeped its wiggly ears;
They trimmed its frisky whiskers with a pair of hard-boiled
        shears;
They donned their rubber mittens and they took it by the
        hand
And 'lected it a member of the Fumigated Band.

There's not a Micrococcus in the garden where they play;
They bathe in pure iodoform a dozen times a day;
And each imbibes his rations from a Hygienic Cup —
The Bunny and the Baby and the Prophylactic Pup.

Arthur Guiterman

THE PURPLE COW

Reflections on a Mythic Beast,
Who's Quite Remarkable, at Least.

I never saw a Purple Cow;
    I never Hope to See One;
But I can Tell you, Anyhow,
    I'd rather See than Be One.

CINQ ANS APRÈS

Confession: and a Portrait, Too,
Upon a Background that I Rue!

Ah, yes, I wrote the "Purple Cow" —
    I'm sorry, now, I Wrote it!
But I can Tell you, Anyhow,
    I'll Kill you if you Quote it!

                                Gelett Burgess

RÉSUMÉ

Razors pain you;
Rivers are damp;
Acids stain you;
And drugs cause cramp.
Guns aren't lawful;
Nooses give;
Gas smells awful;
You might as well live.

                                Dorothy Parker

PORTRAIT OF THE ARTIST

Oh, lead me to a quiet cell
    Where never footfall rankles,
And bar the window passing well,
    And gyve my wrists and ankles.

Oh, wrap my eyes with linen fair,
    With hempen cord go bind me,
And, of your mercy, leave me there,
    Nor tell them where to find me.

Oh, lock the portal as you go,
    And see its bolts be double....
Come back in half an hour or so,
    And I will be in trouble.

Dorothy Parker

SIMPLICITY

"Persicos odi, puer, apparatus ——"
HORACE: Book I, Ode 38

Lad, for overfancy clothing
I have but a healthy loathing
Nor can I see any reason
In the rose that's out of season.

I am one who deems it silly
To attempt to paint the lily;
Myrtle underneath the vine,
And some elderberry wine!

"PERSICOS ODI"

The pomp of the Persian I hold in aversion;
I hate their theatrical tricks;
Their garlicky wreathings and lindeny tree-things —
Nix.

Boy, me for the myrtle while under this fertile
Old grapevine I mellowly sink
As you and bibacious old Quintus Horatius
Drink.

Franklin P. Adams

THE SLUMP IN SYBARIS

"Lydia, dic, per omnes ——"
HORACE: BOOK I, ODE 8

O Lydia, tell me why it is, by all the gods above,
You seek to ruin Sybaris with your incandescent love?
He used to like the scorching sun, and brave the wind and
 rain,
But now he views the open road with undisguised disdain.

He used to sit a prancing steed, he used to dive and swim;
No more the Tiber laves him, and no more the horse for him.
He used to pack a vicious hook, he used to love a fight;
His arms no more are black with blows, of scars his arms are
 white.

Time was when none so far as he the javelin could hurl;
Now he that held the record once is silly for a girl!
Concealed he lies, as once of old the brave Achilles did;
By all the gods above you, what's the matter with him, Lyd?
Franklin P. Adams

WANG PENG, FAMOUS SOCIOLOGIST

Wang Peng, Famous Sociologist,
 Suggests to the Emperor the
 Only possible means of Im-
 Proving the People of
  The Empire

Having read the inscriptions
Upon the tombstones
Of the Great and the Little Cemeteries,

Wang Peng advised the Emperor
To kill all the living
And resurrect the dead.

Paul Eldridge

THE BLIND MEN AND THE ELEPHANT

(A HINDOO FABLE)

It was six men of Indostan
   To learning much inclined,
Who went to see the Elephant
   (Though all of them were blind),
That each by observation
   Might satisfy his mind.

The *First* approached the Elephant,
   And happening to fall
Against his broad and sturdy side,
   At once began to bawl:
"God bless me! but the Elephant
   Is very like a wall!"

The *Second*, feeling of the tusk,
   Cried, "Ho! what have we here
So very round and smooth and sharp?
   To me 'tis mighty clear
This wonder of an Elephant
   Is very like a spear!"

The *Third* approached the animal,
   And happening to take

The squirming trunk within his hands,
   Thus boldly up and spake:
"I see," quoth he, "the Elephant
   Is very like a snake!"

The *Fourth* reached out an eager hand,
   And felt about the knee.
"What most this wondrous beast is like
   Is mighty plain," quoth he;
"'Tis clear enough the Elephant
   Is very like a tree!"

The *Fifth*, who chanced to touch the ear,
   Said: "E'en the blindest man
Can tell what this resembles most;
   Deny the fact who can,
This marvel of an Elephant
   Is very like a fan!"

The *Sixth* no sooner had begun
   About the beast to grope,
Than, seizing on the swinging tail
   That fell within his scope,
"I see," quoth he, "the Elephant
   Is very like a rope!"

And so these men of Indostan
   Disputed loud and long,
Each in his own opinion
   Exceeding stiff and strong,
Though each was partly in the right,
   And all were in the wrong!

MORAL

So oft in theologic wars,
The disputants, I ween,
Rail on in utter ignorance
Of what each other mean,
And prate about an Elephant
Not one of them has seen!

John Godfrey Saxe

DOCTOR FELL

I do not love thee, Doctor Fell;
The reason why I cannot tell;
But this I know, and know full well:
I do not love thee, Doctor Fell.

Thomas Brown

THE OWL–CRITIC

"Who stuffed that white owl?"   No one spoke in the shop,
The barber was busy, and he couldn't stop;
The customers, waiting their turns, were all reading
The *Daily*, the *Herald*, the *Post*, little heeding
The young man who blurted out such a blunt question;
Not one raised a head, or even made a suggestion;
      And the barber kept on shaving.

"Don't you see, Mr. Brown,"
Cried the youth, with a frown,
"How wrong the whole thing is,
How preposterous each wing is,

How flattened the head is, how jammed down the neck is —
In short, the whole owl, what an ignorant wreck 'tis!
I make no apology;
I've learned owl-eology.
I've passed days and nights in a hundred collections,
And cannot be blinded to any deflections
Arising from unskillful fingers that fail
To stuff a bird right, from his beak to his tail.
Mister Brown! Mister Brown!
Do take that bird down,
Or you'll soon be the laughing-stock all over town!"
        And the barber kept on shaving.

"I've *studied* owls,
And other night-fowls,
And I tell you
What I know to be true;
An owl cannot roost
With his limbs so unloosed;
No owl in this world
Ever had his claws curled,
Ever had his legs slanted,
Ever had his bill canted,
Ever had his neck screwed
Into that attitude.
He can't *do* it, because
'Tis against all bird-laws.
Anatomy teaches,
Ornithology preaches,
An owl has a toe
That *can't* turn out so!
I've made the white owl my study for years,

And to see such a job almost moves me to tears!
Mr. Brown, I'm amazed
You should be so gone crazed
As to put up a bird
In that posture absurd!
To *look* at that owl really brings on a dizziness;
The man who stuffed *him* don't half know his business!"
          And the barber kept on shaving.

"Examine those eyes.
I'm filled with surprise
Taxidermists should pass
Off on you such poor glass;
So unnatural they seem
They'd make Audubon scream,
And John Burroughs laugh
To encounter such chaff.
Do take that bird down;
Have him stuffed again, Brown!"
          And the barber kept on shaving.

"With some sawdust and bark
I could stuff in the dark
An owl better than that.
I could make an old hat
Look more like an owl
Than that horrid fowl,
Stuck up there so stiff like a side of coarse leather.
In fact, about *him* there's not one natural feather."

Just then, with a wink and a sly normal lurch,
The owl, very gravely, got down from his perch.

Walked round, and regarded his fault-finding critic
(Who thought he was stuffed) with a glance analytic,
And then fairly hooted, as if he would say:
"Your learning's at fault *this* time, anyway;
Don't waste it again on a live bird, I pray.
I'm an owl; you're another.   Sir Critic, good-day!"
   And the barber kept on shaving.
       James Thomas Fields

BETWEEN TWO LOVES

 I gotta love for Angela,
  I love Carlotta, too.
 I no can marry both o' dem,
  So w'at I gona do?

 O! Angela ees pretta girl,
 She gotta hair so black, so curl,
 An' teeth so white as anytheeng.
 An' O! she gotta voice to seeng,
 Dat mak' your hearta feel eet must
 Jomp up an' dance or eet weel bust.
 An' alla time she seeng, her eyes
 Dey smila like Italia's skies,
 An' makin' flirtin' looks at you —
 But dat ees all w'at she can do.

 Carlotta ees no gotta song,
 But she ees twice so big an' strong
 As Angela, an' she no look
 So beautiful — but she can cook.
 You oughta see her carry wood!

I tal you w'at, eet do you good.
When she ees be som'body's wife
She worka hard, you bat my life!
She never gattin' tired, too —
But dat ees all w'at she can do.

O! my!   I weesh dat Angela
    Was strong for carry wood,
Or else Carlotta gotta song
    An' looka pretta good.
I gotta love for Angela,
    I love Carlotta, too.
I no can marry both o' dem,
    So w'at I gona do?

Thomas Augustine Daly

MIA CARLOTTA

Giuseppe, da barber, ees greata for "mash,"
He gotta da bigga, da blacka moustache,
Good clo'es an' good styla an' playnta good cash.

W'enevra Giuseppe ees walk on da street,
Da peopla dey talka, "How nobby! how neat!
How softa da handa, how smalla da feet."

He leefta hees hat an' he shaka hees curls,
An' smila weeth teetha so shiny like pearls;
Oh, many da heart of da seelly young girls
                    He gotta.
            Yes, playnta he gotta —
                    But notta
                    Carlotta!

Giuseppe, da barber, he maka da eye,
An' lika de steam engine puffa an' sigh,
For catcha Carlotta w'en she ees go by.

Carlotta she walka weeth nose in da air,
An' look through Giuseppe weeth far-away stare,
As eef she no see dere ees som'body dere.

Giuseppe, da barber, he gotta da cash,
He gotta da clo'es an' da bigga moustache,
He gotta da seely young girls for da "mash,"
        But notta —
    You bat my life, notta —
        Carlotta.
        I gotta!
                        Thomas Augustine Daly

POST–IMPRESSIONISM

I cannot tell you how I love
The canvases of Mr. Dove,
Which Saturday I went to see
In Mr. Thurber's gallery.

At first you fancy they are built
As patterns for a crazy-quilt,
But soon you see that they express
An ambient simultaneousness.

This thing which you would almost bet
Portrays a Spanish omelette,
Depicts instead, with wondrous skill,
A horse and cart upon a hill.

Now, Mr. Dove has too much art
To show the horse or show the cart;
Instead, he paints the *creak* and *strain*.
Get it?   No pike is half as plain.

This thing which would appear to show
A fancy vest scenario,
Is really quite another thing,
A flock of pigeons on the wing.

But Mr. Dove is much too keen
To let a single bird be seen;
To show the pigeons would not do
And so he simply paints the *coo*.

It's all as simple as can be;
He paints the things you cannot see,
Just as composers please the ear
With "programme" things you cannot hear.

Dove is the cleverest of chaps;
And, gazing at his rhythmic maps,
I wondered (and I'm wondering yet)
Whether he did them on a bet.

Leston Taylor

WRITTEN AFTER SWIMMING FROM
SESTOS TO ABYDOS

If, in the month of dark December,
   Leander, who was nightly wont
(What maid will not the tale remember?)
   To cross thy stream, broad Hellespont!

If, when the wintry tempest roar'd,
   He sped to Hero, nothing loath,
And thus of old thy current pour'd,
   Fair Venus! how I pity both!

For *me*, degenerate modern wretch,
   Though in the genial month of May,
My dripping limbs I faintly stretch,
   And think I've done a feat today.

But since he cross'd the rapid tide,
   According to the doubtful story,
To woo — and — Lord knows what beside,
   And swam for Love, as I for Glory;

'Twere hard to say who fared the best:
   Sad mortals! thus the Gods still plague you!
He lost his labor, I my jest;
   For he was drowned, and I've the ague.

                         Lord Byron

NO!

No sun — no moon!
No morn — no noon —
   No dawn — no dusk — no proper time of day —
No sky — no earthly view —
No distance looking blue —
   No road — no street — no "t'other side the way" —
No end to any Row —
No indications where the Crescents go —
No top to any steeple —

No recognitions of familiar people —
No courtesies for showing 'em —
No knowing 'em!
   No traveling at all — no locomotion,
   No inkling of the way — no notion —
   "No go"— by land or ocean —
No mail — no post —
No news from any foreign coast —
   No park — no ring — no afternoon gentility —
No company — no nobility —
   No warmth, no cheerfulness, no healthful ease,
   No comfortable feel in any member —
   No shade, no shine, no butterflies, no bees,
   No fruits, no flowers, no leaves, no birds, November!

Thomas Hood

FOR A PESSIMIST

He wore his coffin for a hat,
   Calamity his cape,
While on his face a death's head sat
   And waved a bit of crape.

Countée Cullen

TO THE TERRESTRIAL GLOBE

By a Miserable Wretch

Roll on, thou ball, roll on!
Through pathless realms of Space
   Roll on!
What though I'm in a sorry case?

What though I cannot meet my bills?
What though I suffer toothache's ills?
What though I swallow countless pills?
                Never *you* mind!
                    Roll on!

Roll on, thou ball, roll on!
Through seas of inky air
                    Roll on!
It's true I have no shirt to wear;
It's true my butcher's bill is due;
It's true my prospects all look blue —
But don't let that unsettle you:
                Never *you* mind!
                    Roll on!
                    [*It rolls on.*]
                    Sir William Schwenck Gilbert

THE FROG

Be kind and tender to the Frog
    And do not call him names,
As "Slimy-skin," or "Polly-wog,"
    Or likewise, "Uncle James,"
Or "Gape-a-grin," or "Toad-gone-wrong,"
    Or "Billy Bandy-knees":
The Frog is justly sensitive
    To epithets like these.

No animal will more repay
    A treatment kind and fair,
At least so lonely people say

Who keep a frog (and, by the way,
   They are extremely rare).

Hilaire Belloc

A HANDFUL OF LIMERICKS

FLIGHT

A fly and a flea in a flue
Were imprisoned, so what could they do?
   Said the fly, "Let us flee!"
   "Let us fly!" said the flea,
So they flew through a flaw in the flue.

Anonymous

ON DIGITAL EXTREMITIES

A Poem, And a gem it is!

I'd rather have Fingers than Toes;
I'd rather have Ears than a Nose;
   And as for my Hair,
   I'm glad it's All There;
I'll be Awfully Sad when it Goes!

Gelett Burgess

A Canner, exceedingly canny,
One morning remarked to his granny,
   "A canner can can
   Anything that he can;
But a canner can't can a can, can he?"

Carolyn Wells

There was a young fellow named Tait,
Who dined with his girl at 8:08;
 As Tait did not state,
 I cannot relate
What Tait and his tête-à-tête ate at 8:08.
Carolyn Wells

There was an old man of Tarentum,
Who gnashed his false teeth till he bent 'em:
 And when asked for the cost
 Of what he had lost,
Said, "I really can't tell, for I rent 'em!"
Anonymous

There was a young lady of Niger
Who smiled as she rode on a tiger;
 They returned from the ride
 With the lady inside,
And the smile on the face of the tiger.
Anonymous

The Well of Wisdom

OPPORTUNITY

This I beheld, or dreamed it in a dream: —
There spread a cloud of dust along a plain;
And underneath the cloud, or in it, raged
A furious battle, and men yelled, and swords
Shocked upon swords and shields.   A prince's banner
Wavered, then staggered backward, hemmed by foes.
A craven hung along the battle's edge,
And thought, "Had I a sword of keener steel —
That blue blade that the king's son bears — but this
Blunt thing!" he snapped and flung it from his hand,
And lowering crept away and left the field.
Then came the king's son, wounded, sore bestead,
And weaponless, and saw the broken sword,
Hilt-buried in the dry and trodden sand,
And ran and snatched it, and with battle-shout
Lifted afresh he hewed his enemy down,
And saved a great cause that heroic day.

Edward Rowland Sill

THE BLADES OF GRASS

In Heaven,
Some little blades of grass
Stood before God.
"What did you do?"
Then all save one of the little blades

Began eagerly to relate
The merits of their lives.
This one stayed a small way behind,
Ashamed.
Presently, God said,
"And what did you do?"
The little blade answered, "Oh, my Lord,
Memory is bitter to me,
For, if I did good deeds,
I know not of them."
Then God, in all his splendor,
Arose from his throne.
"Oh, best little blade of grass!" he said.

Stephen Crane

GOOD-BYE

Good-bye, proud world!   I'm going home:
Thou art not my friend, and I'm not thine.
Long through thy weary crowds I roam;
A river-ark on the ocean brine,
Long I've been tossed like the driven foam;
But now, proud world!   I'm going home.

Good-bye to Flattery's fawning face;
To Grandeur with his wise grimace;
To upstart Wealth's averted eye;
To supple Office, low and high;
To crowded halls, to court and street;
To frozen hearts and hasting feet;
To those who go, and those who come;
Good-bye, proud world!   I'm going home.

I am going to my own hearth-stone,
Bosomed in yon green hills alone —
A secret nook in a pleasant land,
Whose groves the frolic fairies planned;
Where arches green, the livelong day,
Echo the blackbird's roundelay,
And vulgar feet have never trod —
A spot that is sacred to thought and God.

O, when I am safe in my sylvan home,
I tread on the pride of Greece and Rome;
And when I am stretched beneath the pines,
Where the evening star so holy shines,
I laugh at the lore and the pride of man,
At the sophist schools, and the learned clan;
For what are they all, in their high conceit,
When man in the bush with God may meet?

Ralph Waldo Emerson

FOR A' THAT

Is there for honest poverty
    That hangs his head, an' a' that;
The coward slave, we pass him by —
    We dare be poor for a' that!
For a' that, an' a' that,
    Our toils obscure an' a' that,
The rank is but the guinea's stamp,
    The man's the gowd for a' that.

What though on hamely fare we dine,
    Wear hoddin gray, an' a' that?

Gie fools their silks, and knaves their wine —
  A man's a man for a' that.
For a' that, an' a' that,
  Their tinsel show, an' a' that,
The honest man, tho' e'er sae poor,
  Is king o' men for a' that.

Ye see yon birkie ca'd a lord,
  Wha struts, an' stares, an' a' that;
Tho' hundreds worship at his word,
  He's but a coof for a' that:
For a' that, an' a' that,
  His ribband, star, an' a' that,
The man o' independent mind,
  He looks an' laughs at a' that.

A prince can mak a belted knight,
  A marquis, duke, an' a' that!
But an honest man's aboon his might —
  Guid faith, he maunna fa' that!
For a' that, an' a' that,
  Their dignities an' a' that,
The pith o' sense, an' pride o' worth,
  Are higher rank than a' that.

Then let us pray that come it may
  (As come it will for a' that),
That Sense and Worth, o'er a' the earth.
  May bear the gree an' a' that!
For a' that, an' a' that,
  It's coming yet for a' that,
That man to man the world o'er,
  Shall brothers be for a' that.

                              Robert Burns

REMEMBER NOW THY CREATOR

Remember now thy Creator in the days of thy youth:
  While the evil days come not,
  Nor the years draw nigh,
    When thou shalt say, I have no pleasure in them:

While the sun,
  Or the light,
  Or the moon,
  Or the stars,
Be not darkened,
Nor the clouds return after the rain:

In the day when the keepers of the house shall tremble,
And the strong men shall bow themselves,
And the grinders cease because they are few,
And those that look out of the windows be darkened,
And the doors shall be shut in the streets;
When the sound of the grinding is low,
And he shall rise up at the voice of a bird,
And all the daughters of music shall be brought low;

Also when they shall be afraid of that which is high,
And fears shall be in the way;

And the almond tree shall flourish,
And the grasshopper shall be a burden,
And desire shall fail:

Because man goeth to his long home,
And the mourners go about the streets:

Or ever the silver cord be loosed,
Or the golden bowl be broken,
Or the pitcher be broken at the fountain,
Or the wheel broken at the cistern:

Then shall the dust return to the earth,
As it was;
And the spirit shall return unto God
Who gave it.

Ecclesiastes, 12

From THE WORLD

I saw Eternity the other night
Like a great ring of pure and endless light,
  All calm, as it was bright;
And round beneath it, Time in hours, days, years,
  Driv'n by the spheres,
Like a vast shadow moved, in which the world
  And all her train were hurled.

Henry Vaughan

EVOLUTION

Out of the dusk, a shadow,
    Then, a spark;
Out of the cloud a silence,
    Then, a lark;
Out of the heart a rapture,
    Then, a pain;
Out of the dead, cold ashes,
    Life again.

John B. Tabb

MIRACLES

From "Song of Myself"

I believe a leaf of grass is no less than the journey-work of the
    stars,
And the pismire is equally perfect, and a grain of sand, and
    the egg of the wren,
And the tree-toad is a chef-d'œuvre of the highest,
And the running blackberry would adorn the parlors of
    heaven,
And the narrowest hinge in my hand puts to scorn all
    machinery,
And the cow crunching with depress'd head surpasses any
    statue,
And a mouse is miracle enough to stagger sextillions of
    infidels.

Walt Whitman

THE BUILDER

Smoothing a cypress beam
    With a scarred hand,
I saw a carpenter
    In a far land.

Down past the flat roofs
    Poured the white sun;
But still he bent his back,
    The patient one.

And I paused surprised
    In that queer place

To find an old man
  With a haunting face.

"Who art thou, carpenter,
  Of the bowed head;
And what buildest thou?"
  "Heaven," he said.

Willard Wattles

THE WORLD IS TOO MUCH WITH US

The world is too much with us; late and soon,
Getting and spending, we lay waste our powers
Little we see in Nature that is ours;
We have given our hearts away, a sordid boon!
The Sea that bares her bosom to the moon;
The winds that will be howling at all hours,
And are up-gathered now like sleeping flowers;
For this, for everything, we are out of tune;
It moves us not. — Great God! I'd rather be
A Pagan suckled in a creed outworn;
So might I, standing on this pleasant lea,
Have glimpses that would make me less forlorn;
Have sight of Proteus rising from the sea;
Or hear old Triton blow his wreathèd horn.

William Wordsworth

"THE SPACIOUS FIRMAMENT ON HIGH"

The spacious firmament on high,
With all the blue ethereal sky,
And spangled heavens, a shining frame,

Their great Original proclaim.
The unwearied Sun, from day to day,
Does his Creator's power display;
And publishes to every land
The work of an Almighty hand.

Soon as the evening shades prevail,
The Moon takes up the wondrous tale;
And nightly to the listening Earth
Repeats the story of her birth:
Whilst all the stars that round her burn,
And all the Planets in their turn,
Confirm the tidings as they roll
And spread the truth from pole to pole.

What though, in solemn silence, all
Move round the dark terrestrial ball?
What though nor real voice nor sound
Amid their radiant orbs be found?
In Reason's ear they all rejoice,
And utter forth a glorious voice;
For ever singing as they shine,
"The Hand that made us is divine."

Joseph Addison

VOLUNTARIES

In an age of fops and toys,
Wanting wisdom, void of right,
Who shall nerve heroic boys
To hazard all in Freedom's fight —
Break sharply off their jolly games,

Forsake their comrades gay
And quit proud homes and youthful dames
For famine, toil, and fray?
Yet on the nimble air benign
Speed nimbler messages,
That waft the breath of grace divine
To hearts in sloth and ease.
So nigh is grandeur to our dust,
So near is God to man,
When Duty whispers low, *Thou must*,
The youth replies, *I can*.

Ralph Waldo Emerson

THE TWENTY-THIRD PSALM

The Lord is my shepherd; I shall not want.

He maketh me to lie down in green pastures: he leadeth me beside the still waters.

He restoreth my soul: he leadeth me in the paths of righteousness for his name's sake.

Yea, though I walk through the valley of the shadow of death, I will fear no evil: for thou art with me; thy rod and thy staff they comfort me.

Thou preparest a table before me in the presence of mine enemies: thou anointest my head with oil; my cup runneth over.

Surely goodness and mercy shall follow me all the days of my life: and I will dwell in the house of the Lord for ever.

ODE ON A GRECIAN URN

Thou still unravished bride of quietness,
Thou foster-child of Silence and slow Time,

Sylvan historian, who canst thus express
  A flowery tale more sweetly than our rhyme:
What leaf-fringed legend haunts about thy shape
  Of deities or mortals, or of both
    In Tempe or the dales of Arcady?
  What men or gods are these?   What maidens loth?
What mad pursuit?   What struggle to escape?
    What pipes and timbrels?   What wild ecstasy?

Heard melodies are sweet, but those unheard
  Are sweeter; therefore, ye soft pipes, play on;
Not to the sensual ear, but, more endeared,
  Pipe to the spirit ditties of no tone:
Fair youth, beneath the trees, thou canst not leave
  Thy song, nor ever can those trees be bare;
    Bold lover, never, never canst thou kiss,
Though winning near the goal — yet, do not grieve;
    She cannot fade, though thou hast not thy bliss,
  For ever wilt thou love, and she be fair!

Ah, happy, happy boughs! that cannot shed
  Your leaves, nor ever bid the Spring adieu;
And, happy melodist, unwearièd,
  For ever piping songs for ever new;
More happy love! more happy, happy love!
  For ever warm and still to be enjoyed,
    For ever panting and for ever young;
All breathing human passion far above,
    That leaves a heart high-sorrowful and cloyed,
  A burning forehead, and a parching tongue.

Who are these coming to the sacrifice?
  To what green altar, O mysterious priest,

Lead'st thou that heifer lowing at the skies,
    And all her silken flanks with garlands drest?
What little town by river or sea shore,
    Or mountain-built, with peaceful citadel,
        Is emptied of its folk, this pious morn?
And, little town, thy streets for evermore
    Will silent be; and not a soul to tell
        Why thou art desolate, can e'er return.

O Attic shape! fair attitude! with brede
    Of marble men and maidens overwrought,
With forest branches and the trodden weed;
    Thou, silent form, dost tease us out of thought
As doth eternity.   Cold Pastoral!
    When old age shall this generation waste,
        Thou shalt remain, in midst of other woe
    Than ours, a friend to man, to whom thou say'st,
"Beauty is truth, truth beauty — that is all
        Ye know on earth, and all ye need to know."
                                        John Keats

CHARITY

In men whom men condemn as ill
I find so much of goodness still,
In men whom men pronounce divine
I find so much of sin and blot,
I do not dare to draw a line
Between the two, where God has not.
                                Joaquin Miller

TO NIGHT

Mysterious Night! when our first parent knew
Thee from report divine, and heard thy name,
Did he not tremble for this lovely frame,
This glorious canopy of light and blue?
Yet 'neath the curtain of translucent dew,
Bathed in the rays of the great setting flame,
Hesperus with the host of heaven came,
And lo! creation widened on man's view.
Who could have thought such darkness lay concealed
Within thy beams, O Sun! or who could find,
While fly, and leaf, and insect stood revealed,
That to such countless orbs thou mad'st us blind!
  Why do we, then, shun Death with anxious strife? —
  If Light can thus deceive, wherefore not Life?

Joseph Blanco White

OUTWITTED

He drew a circle that shut me out —
Heretic, rebel, a thing to flout.
But Love and I had the wit to win:
We drew a circle that took him in!

Edwin Markham

PREPAREDNESS

For all your days prepare,
  And meet them ever alike:
When you are the anvil, bear —
  When you are the hammer, strike.

Edwin Markham

IMMIGRANTS

"These foreigners with strange and avid faces
Crowding our shores, marring our pleasant places,
They must be curbed...."   So mused King Powhatan,
Hundred per-cent, red-blood American.

Nancy Byrd Turner

I SAW A MAN

I saw a man pursuing the horizon;
Round and round they sped.
I was disturbed at this;
I accosted the man.
"It is futile," I said,
"You can never —"

"You lie," he cried,
And ran on.

Stephen Crane

EACH IN HIS OWN TONGUE

A fire-mist and a planet,
    A crystal and a cell,
A jelly-fish and a saurian,
    And caves where the cave-men dwell;
Then a sense of law and beauty
    And a face turned from the clod —
Some call it Evolution,
    And others call it God.

A haze on the far horizon,
  The infinite, tender sky,
The ripe, rich tint of the cornfields
  And the wild geese sailing high;
And all over upland and lowland
  The charm of the goldenrod —
Some of us call it Autumn,
  And others call it God.

Like tides on a crescent sea-beach,
  When the moon is new and thin,
Into our hearts high yearnings
  Come welling and surging in;
Come from the mystic ocean
  Whose rim no foot has trod —
Some of us call it Longing,
  And others call it God.

A picket frozen on duty,
  A mother starved for her brood,
Socrates drinking the hemlock,
  And Jesus on the rood;
And millions who, humble and nameless,
  The straight, hard pathway plod —
Some call it Consecration,
  And others call it God.

William Herbert Carruth

QUATORZAIN

Most men know love but as a part of life;
They hide it in some corner of the breast,

Even from themselves; and only when they rest
In the brief pauses of that daily strife,
Wherewith the world might else be not so rife,
They draw it forth (as one draws forth a toy
To soothe some ardent kiss-exacting boy)
And hold it up to sister, child, or wife.
Ah me! why may not love and life be one?
Why walk we thus alone, when by our side,
Love, like a visible god, might be our guide?
How would the marts grow noble! and the street,
Worn like a dungeon-floor by weary feet,
Seem then a golden court-way of the Sun!

                                        Henry Timrod

IN HARBOR

I think it is over, over
I think it is over at last;
Voices of foeman and lover,
    The sweet and the bitter, have passed;
Life, like a tempest of ocean,
Hath outblown its ultimate blast:
There's but a faint sobbing seaward
While the calm of the tide deepens leeward,
And behold! like the welcoming quiver
Of heart-pulses throbbed through the river,
    Those lights in the harbor at last,
    The heavenly harbor at last!

I feel it is over! over!
    For the winds and the waters surcease;
Ah, few were the days of the rover
    That smiled in the beauty of peace!

And distant and dim was the omen
That hinted redress or release: —
From the ravage of life, and its riot,
What marvel I yearn for the quiet
    Which bides in the harbor at last,
For the lights, with their welcoming quiver,
That throb through the sanctified river,
    Which girdle the harbor at last,
    This heavenly harbor at last?

                                Paul Hamilton Hayne

HATE

My enemy came nigh;
And I
Stared fiercely in his face:
My lips went writhing back in a grimace,
And stern I watched him from a narrowed eye:

Then, as I turned away,
My enemy,
That bitter-heart, and savage, said to me:

— Some day, when this is past;
When all the arrows that we have are cast;
We may ask one another why we hate?
And fail to find a story to relate:
It may seem to us, then, a mystery
That we could hate each other —
Thus said he; and did not turn away;
Waiting to hear what I might have to say!

But I fled quickly: fearing, if I stayed,
I might have kissed him, as I would a maid.

James Stephens

IDENTITY

Somewhere — in desolate wind-swept space —
    In Twilight-land — in No-man's land —
Two hurrying Shapes met face to face,
    And bade each other stand.

"And who are you?" cried one agape,
    Shuddering in the gloaming light.
"I know not," said the second Shape,
    "I only died last night!"

Thomas Bailey Aldrich

WORTH MAKES THE MAN

Honor and shame from no condition rise;
Act well your part, there all the honor lies.
Fortune in men has some small difference made,
One flaunts in rags, one flutters in brocade;
The cobbler aproned, and the parson gowned;
The friar hooded, and the monarch crowned.
"What differ more," you cry, "than crown and cowl!"
I'll tell you, friend! a wise man and a fool.
You'll find, if once the monarch acts the monk,
Or, cobbler-like, the parson will be drunk,
Worth makes the man, and want of it the fellow;
The rest is all but leather or prunella.

Alexander Pope
(*From An Essay on Man*)

OF CHINA AND HER WISDOM

QUAM TSI T'UNG FINDS VIOLENCE WEAKER THAN SERENITY

The moth,
Enraged,
Beats against the lamp,
His wings forming
Countless tiny fans,
And falls at last
A fragile pinch of gray ashes.
The lamp burns on,
Tranquilly.

KU MUNG MOURNS THE PASSING OF HIS YEARS

The rose is dangling
On its broken stem —
Its petals are dropping
One by one —
Who shall gather them together
To make a rose again?

MI TI ADVISES A YOUNG POET NOT TO DESPAIR

At the right moment,
The Earth smiles —
Between her lips,
Slightly parted,
A daisy trembles
In sheer delight.

CHOU CHING ADVISES PRACTICALITY TO A POET

The stars are radiant queens,
Walking majestically across Infinity,

But the edges of their azure cloaks
Trail in the muddy pools of the Earth.

Ti Fu Rebukes a Vain Man

The branches laden with fruit
Bend humbly to the ground.

Wing Mu Si Speaks of the Vanity of Man's Illusions

The souls of men
Are birds with beaks of glass,
Which break, knocking
At the adamantine gates
Of Paradise.

Paul Eldridge

OUT-OF-DOORS

I hear the wings, the winds, the river pass,
And toss the fretful book upon the grass.
Poor book, it could not cure my soul of aught —
It has itself the old disease of thought.

Walter Conrad Arensberg

"TIME, YOU OLD GIPSY MAN"

Time, you old gipsy man,
Will you not stay,
Put up your caravan
Just for one day?

All things I'll give you
Will you be my guest,

Bells for your jennet
Of silver the best,
Goldsmiths shall beat you
A great golden ring,
Peacocks shall bow to you,
Little boys sing,
Oh, and sweet girls will
Festoon you with may,
Time, you old gipsy,
Why hasten away?

Last week in Babylon,
Last night in Rome,
Morning, and in the crush
Under Paul's dome;
Under Paul's dial
You tighten your rein —
Only a moment,
And off once again;
Off to some city
Now blind in the womb,
Off to another
Ere that's in the tomb.

Time, you old gipsy man,
Will you not stay,
Put up your caravan
Just for one day?

Ralph Hodgson

FAME

As I came down into the Place of Spain,
Above the motors tooting in the streets

I heard a voice that asked, "Well, who was Keats?"
In the best accent of Nebraska's plain.
A thin but rigid female, who in vain
Perused her Baedeker's close-printed sheets,
Answered: "An Irish Poet," scattering sweets
Of information to the Vast Inane.

Who was he?   A voice, forgotten in some quarters
Apparently.   The mortal lyric cry
Stilled by the house where the man came to die;
A lost identity of long ago;
Music and love quenched by the many waters.
Who was he?   Do the critics really know?

Leonard Bacon

VOICES

O there were lights and laughter
  And the motions to and fro
Of people as they enter
  And people as they go . . .

And there were many voices
  Vying at the feast,
But mostly I remember
  Yours — who spoke the least.

Witter Bynner

THE EAGLE AND THE MOLE

Avoid the reeking herd,
Shun the polluted flock,

Live like that stoic bird,
The eagle of the rock.

The huddled warmth of crowds
Begets and fosters hate;
He keeps, above the clouds,
His cliff inviolate.

When flocks are folded warm,
And herds to shelter run,
He sails above the storm,
He stares into the sun.

If in the eagle's track
Your sinews cannot leap,
Avoid the lathered pack,
Turn from the steaming sheep.

If you would keep your soul
From spotted sight or sound,
Live like the velvet mole;
Go burrow underground.

And there hold intercourse
With roots of trees and stones,
With rivers at their source,
And disembodied bones.

Elinor Wylie

POLONIUS' ADVICE TO LAERTES

And these few precepts in thy memory
See thou character.   Give thy thoughts no tongue,

Nor any unproportion'd thought his act.
Be thou familiar, but by no means vulgar.
The friends thou hast, and their adoption tried,
Grapple them to thy soul with hoops of steel;
But do not dull thy palm with entertainment
Of each new-hatch'd, unfledg'd comrade.   Beware
Of entrance to a quarrel; but, being in,
Bear't that the opposed may beware of thee.
Give every man thine ear, but few thy voice:
Take each man's censure, but reserve thy judgment.
Costly thy habit as thy purse can buy,
But not expressed in fancy; rich, not gaudy:
For the apparel oft proclaims the man,
And they in France of the best rank and station
Are most select and generous chief in that.
Neither a borrower nor a lender be;
For loan oft loses both itself and friend,
And borrowing dulls the edge of husbandry.
This above all: to thine own self be true;
And it must follow, as the night the day,
Thou canst not then be false to any man.
Farewell: my blessing season this in thee!

William Shakespeare

IF I SHOULD DIE TONIGHT

If I should die tonight
My friends would look upon my quiet face,
Before they laid it in its resting-place,
And deem that death had left it almost fair,
And laying snow-white flowers against my hair,
Would smooth it down with tearful tenderness,

And fold my hands with lingering caress —
Poor hands so empty and so cold tonight!

        If I should die tonight
My friends would call to mind with loving thought
Some kindly deed the icy hand had wrought,
Some gentle word the frozen lips had said,
Errands on which the willing feet had sped.
The memory of my selfishness and pride,
My hasty words, would all be put aside,
And so I should be loved and mourned tonight.

        If I should die tonight
Even hearts estranged would turn once more to me,
Recalling other days remorsefully.
The eyes that chill me with averted glance
Would look upon me as of yore, perchance,
Would soften in the old familiar way;
For who would war with dumb, unconscious clay?
So I might rest, forgiven of all tonight.

        O, friends, I pray tonight
Keep not your kisses for my dead, cold brow:
The way is lonely, let me feel them now.
Think gently of me; I am travel-worn,
My faltering feet are pierced with many a thorn.
Forgive, O hearts estranged, forgive, I plead!
When dreamless rest is mine I shall not need
The tenderness for which I long tonight.

Arabella Eugenia Smith

IF

If you can keep your head when all about you
    Are losing theirs and blaming it on you;
If you can trust yourself when all men doubt you,
    But make allowance for their doubting too;
If you can wait and not be tired by waiting,
    Or being lied about, don't deal in lies,
Or being hated don't give way to hating,
    And yet don't look too good, nor talk too wise;

If you can dream — and not make dreams your master;
    If you can think — and not make thoughts your aim;
If you can meet with Triumph and Disaster
    And treat those two impostors just the same;
If you can bear to hear the truth you've spoken
    Twisted by knaves to make a trap for fools,
Or watch the things you gave your life to, broken,
    And stoop and build 'em up with worn out tools;

If you can make one heap of all your winnings
    And risk it on one turn of pitch-and-toss,
And lose, and start again at your beginnings
    And never breathe a word about your loss;
If you can force your heart and nerve and sinew
    To serve your turn long after they are gone,
And so hold on when there is nothing in you
    Except the Will which says to them: "Hold on!"

If you can talk with crowds and keep your virtue,
    Or walk with Kings — nor lose the common touch;
If neither foes nor loving friends can hurt you;
    If all men count with you, but none too much;

If you can fill the unforgiving minute
With sixty seconds' worth of distance run,
Yours is the Earth and everything that's in it,
And — which is more — you'll be a Man, my son!
Rudyard Kipling

FLOWER IN THE CRANNIED WALL

Flower in the crannied wall,
I pluck you out of crannies,
I hold you here, root and all, in my hand,
Little flower — but if I could understand
What you are, root and all, and all in all,
I should know what God and man is.
Alfred Lord Tennyson

THE SLAVE

They set the slave free, striking off his chains . . .
Then he was as much of a slave as ever.

He was still chained to servility,
He was still manacled to indolence and sloth,
He was still bound by fear and superstition,
By ignorance, suspicion, and savagery . . .
His slavery was not in the chains,
But in himself. . . .

They can only set free men free . . .
And there is no need of that:
Free men set themselves free.
James Oppenheim

FAITH

O world, thou choosest not the better part!
It is not wisdom to be only wise,
And on the inward vision close the eyes;
But it is wisdom to believe the heart.
Columbus found a world and had no chart,
Save one that faith deciphered in the skies;
To trust the soul's invincible surmise
Was all his science and his only art.
Our knowledge is a torch of smoky pine
That lights the pathway but one step ahead
Across a void of mystery and dread.
Bid, then, the tender light of faith to shine
By which alone the mortal heart is led
Unto the thinking of the thought divine.

George Santayana

A BALLAD OF TREES AND THE MASTER

Into the woods my Master went,
Clean forspent, forspent.
Into the woods my Master came,
Forspent with love and shame.
But the olives they were not blind to Him;
The little gray leaves were kind to Him;
The thorn tree had a mind to Him
When into the woods He came.

Out of the woods my Master went,
And He was well content.
Out of the woods my Master came,
Content with death and shame.

When Death and Shame would woo Him last,
From under the trees they drew Him last:
'Twas on a tree they slew Him — last,
When out of the woods He came.

Sidney Lanier

WORK

Let me but do my work from day to day,
    In field or forest, at the desk or loom,
    In roaring market-place or tranquil room;
Let me but find it in my heart to say,
When vagrant wishes beckon me astray,
    "This is my work; my blessing, not my doom;
    Of all who live, I am the one by whom
This work can best be done in the right way."

Then shall I see it not too great, nor small,
    To suit my spirit and to prove my powers;
    Then shall I cheerful greet the laboring hours,
And cheerful turn, when the long shadows fall
At eventide, to play and love and rest,
Because I know for me my work is best.

Henry van Dyke

DAYS

Daughters of Time, the hypocritic Days,
Muffled and dumb like barefoot dervishes,
And marching single in an endless file,
Bring diadems and fagots in their hands.
To each they offer gifts after his will,
Bread, kingdoms, stars, and sky that holds them all.

I, in my pleachèd garden, watched the pomp,
Forgot my morning wishes, hastily
Took a few herbs and apples, and the Day
Turned and departed silent.   I, too late,
Under her solemn fillet saw the scorn.

Ralph Waldo Emerson

STUPIDITY STREET

I saw with open eyes
Singing birds sweet
Sold in the shops
For the people to eat,
Sold in the shops of
Stupidity Street.

I saw in a vision
The worm in the wheat,
And in the shops nothing
For people to eat;
Nothing for sale in
Stupidity Street.

Ralph Hodgson

PEDIGREE

The pedigree of honey
Does not concern the bee;
A clover, any time, to him
Is aristocracy.

Emily Dickinson

VICTORY IN DEFEAT

Defeat may serve as well as victory
To shake the soul and let the glory out.
When the great oak is straining in the wind,
The boughs drink in new beauty, and the trunk
Sends down a deeper root on the windward side.
Only the soul that knows the mighty grief
Can know the mighty rapture.   Sorrows come
To stretch out spaces in the heart for joy.

Edwin Markham

Under the Open Sky

THE MERRY GUIDE

Once in the wind of morning
  I ranged the thymy wold;
The world-wide air was azure
  And all the brooks ran gold.

There through the dews beside me
  Behold a youth that trod,
With feathered cap on forehead,
  And poised a golden rod.

With mien to match the morning
  And gay delightful guise
And friendly brows and laughter
  He looked me in the eyes.

Oh whence, I asked, and whither?
  He smiled and would not say,
And looked at me and beckoned
  And laughed and led the way.

And with kind looks and laughter
  And nought to say beside
We two went on together,
  I and my happy guide.

Across the glittering pastures
  And empty upland still

And solitude of shepherds
  High in the folded hill.

By hanging woods and hamlets
  That gaze through orchards down
On many a windmill turning
  And far-discovered town,

With gay regards of promise
  And sure unslackened stride
And smiles and nothing spoken
  Led on my merry guide.

By blowing realms of woodland
  With sunstruck vanes afield
And cloud-led shadows sailing
  About the windy weald,

By valley-guarded granges
  And silver waters wide,
Content at heart I followed
  With my delightful guide.

And like the cloudy shadows
  Across the country blown
We two fare on forever,
  But not we two alone.

With the great gale we journey
  That breathes from gardens thinned,
Borne in the drift of blossoms
  Whose petals throng the wind;

Buoyed on the heaven-heard whisper
    Of dancing leaflets whirled
From all the woods that autumn
    Bereaves in all the world.

And midst the fluttering legion
    Of all that ever died
I follow, and before us
    Goes the delightful guide,

With lips that brim with laughter
    But never once respond,
And feet that fly on feathers,
    And serpent-circled wand.

                              A. E. Housman

LOVELIEST OF TREES

Loveliest of trees, the cherry now
Is hung with bloom along the bough,
And stands about the woodland ride
Wearing white for Eastertide.

Now, of my threescore years and ten,
Twenty will not come again,
And take from seventy springs a score,
It only leaves me fifty more.

And since to look at things in bloom
Fifty springs are little room,
About the woodlands I will go
To see the cherry hung with snow.

                              A. E. Housman

IMMORTAL

The last thin acre of stalks that stood
　　Was never the end of the wheat.
Always something fled to the wood,
　　As if the field had feet.

In front of the sickle something rose —
　　Mouse, or weasel, or hare;
We struck and struck, but our worst blows
　　Dangled in the air.

Nothing could touch the little soul
　　Of the grain.   It ran to cover,
And nobody knew in what warm hole
　　It slept till the winter was over,

And early seeds lay cold in the ground.
　　Then — but nobody saw —
It burrowed back with never a sound,
　　And awoke the thaw.

Mark Van Doren

VERMONT

Wide and shallow, in the cowslip marshes,
Floods the freshet of the April snow;
Late drifts linger in the hemlock gorges,
Through the brakes and mosses trickling slow,
　　Where the mayflower,
Where the painted trillium, leaf and blow.

Foliaged deep, the cool midsummer maples
Shade the porches of the long white street.

Trailing wide, Olympian elms lean over
Tiny churches, where the cross-roads meet;
  Fields of fireflies
Wheel all night like stars above the wheat.

Blaze the mountains in the windless Autumn,
Frost-clear, blue-nooned, apple-ripening days;
Faintly fragrant, in the farther valleys,
Smoke of many bonfires swell the haze:
  Fair-bound cattle
Plod with lowing up the meadowy ways.

Roaring snows, down-sweeping from the uplands,
Bury the still valleys, drift them deep.
Low along the mountains, lake-blue shadows,
Sea-blue shadows, in the snowdrifts sleep.
  High above them
Blinding crystal is the sunlit steep.

                          Sarah N. Cleghorn

THE BLACKBIRD

The nightingale has a lyre of gold,
The lark's is a clarion call,
And the blackbird plays but a boxwood flute,
But I love him best of all.

For his song is all of the joy of life,
And we in the mad, spring weather,
We two have listened till he sang
Our hearts and lips together.

                              W. E. Henley

ELLEN HANGING CLOTHES

The maid is out in the clear April light
Our store of linen hanging up to dry;
On clump of box, on the small grass there lie
Bits of thin lace, and broidery blossom-white.
And something makes tall Ellen — gesture, look —
Or else but that most ancient, simple thing,
Hanging the clothes upon a day in spring,
A Greek girl cut out of some old lovely book.
The wet white flaps; a tune just come in mind,
The sound brims the still house.   Our flags are out,
Blue by the box, blue by the kitchen stair;
Betwixt the two she trips across the wind,
Her warm hair blown all cloudy-wise about,
Slim as the flags, and every whit as fair.

Lizette Woodworth Reese

KENTUCKY MOUNTAINEER

Spring in Kentucky hills will soon awaken;
The sap will run in every vein of tree,
Green will come to the land bleak and forsaken;
Warm silver wind will catch the honey bee.
Blood-root will whiten on the barren hill;
Wind-flowers will grow beneath the oaks and nod
To silver April wind against their will.
Bitterns will break the silence of the hills
And meadow's grass sup dew under the moons,
Pastures will green and bring back whippoorwills
And butterflies that break from stout cocoons.
Spring in Kentucky hills, and I shall be

A free soil-man to walk beneath the trees
And listen to the wind among the leaves —
And count the stars and do as I ... please.

   .   .   .   .

Last night the rain thumped on the clapboard roof
Like feet of house rats running over tin.
I laid awake beneath this sheltering roof
And listened to a cold wind blowing in
The trees outside and blowing through a crack
Into my room — stirring the covers on my bed.
I slept upstairs in a Kentucky shack.
Last night some verse kept running through my head
And I got up and lit the smoke-globed lamp.
I took a sheet of paper from the stack.
I wrote about a mouse and brown oat stack —
The room was mighty cold and dark and damp.
I threw the poem out into the rain.
Its destiny was darkness and the rain.

   .   .   .   .

I came the Womack Road from Sandy Bridge
When red shoe-makes were nodding with the dew.
The sun rose even with the Seaton Ridge;
Under the leaves a golden ray came through.
A man with horse and buggy passed me by,
A jar-fly sang upon the weedy hill;
A mallard duck flew over with a cry,
A crow flew by with something in its bill.
I went the Womack Road from Sandy Bridge
When red shoe-makes were drinking back the dew.
The moon rose even with the Seaton Ridge;
Under the leaves a silver ray came through.

I could pick blackberries along the way,
For moonlight on the fields was bright as day.

.   .   .   .

Farewell to Springtime in Kentucky hills;
Farewell to dogwood blossoms and percoon;
To blood-root in the wind and daffodils;
To wild plum blossoms and white April moon.
Farewell to walnut trees beside the river;
Farewell to April's sky-blue singing brooks;
Farewell to young thin April leaves that quiver;
Farewell to white clouds mirrored in the brooks.
Farewell to Spring wheat waving in the wind
And rank potatoes bursting from the ground;
Farewell to shower-clouds watery-thinned
And to the far-off cowbell's lonely sound.
Farewell to April and bright bull-tongue plows;
Farewell to green pastures and spotted cows.

Jesse Stuart

HOME–THOUGHTS, FROM ABROAD

O, to be in England
Now that April's there,
And whoever wakes in England
Sees, some morning, unaware,
That the lowest boughs and the brushwood sheaf
Round the elm-tree bole are in tiny leaf,
While the chaffinch sings on the orchard bough
In England — now!

And after April, when May follows,
And the whitethroat builds, and all the swallows!

Hark, where my blossom'd pear-tree in the hedge
Leans to the field and scatters on the clover
Blossoms and dewdrops — at the bent spray's edge —
That's the wise thrush; he sings each song twice over,
Lest you should think he never could recapture
The first fine careless rapture!
And though the fields look rough with hoary dew,
All will be gay when noontide wakes anew
The buttercups, the little children's dower
— Far brighter than this gaudy melon-flower!

Robert Browning

TO A LADY SEEN FROM THE TRAIN

O why do you walk through the fields in gloves,
    Missing so much and so much?
O fat white woman whom nobody loves,
Why do you walk through the fields in gloves,
When the grass is soft as the breast of doves
    And shivering-sweet to the touch?
O why do you walk through the fields in gloves,
    Missing so much and so much?

Frances Cornford

FIREFLIES IN THE GARDEN

Here come real stars to fill the upper skies,
And here on earth come emulating flies,
That though they never equal stars in size,
(And they were never really stars at heart)
Achieve at times a very star-like start.
Only, of course, they can't sustain the part.

Robert Frost

FIRST RAIN

When Eve walked in her garden,
With Adam by her side,
And God was still the warden,
And she was still a bride,

How great was her amazement
To see when twilight died,
The first moon at the casement
Of evening, open wide!

But greater than her wonder
At star or bird or tree,
Or afterward at thunder,
Or delicate deer or bee,

Was her flushed awe one morning,
When down the clouded air
With freshened winds for warning,
Came water — everywhere!

Zoë Akins

SWIMMERS

I took the crazy short-cut to the bay;
Over a fence or two and through a hedge,
Jumping a private road, along the edge
Of backyards full of drying wash it lay.
I ran, electric with elation,
Sweating, impetuous, and wild
For a swift plunge in the sea that smiled,

Quiet and luring, half a mile away.
This was the final thrill, the last sensation
That capped four hours of violence and laughter:
To have, with casual friends and casual jokes,
Hard sport, a cold swim and fresh linen after...
And now, the last set being played and over,
I hurried past the ruddy lakes of clover;
I swung my racket at astonished oaks,
My arm still tingling from aggressive strokes.
Tennis was over for the day —
I took the leaping short-cut to the bay.

Then the swift plunge into the cool, green dark —
The windy waters rushing past me, through me;
Filled with a sense of some heroic lark,
Exulting in a vigor clean and roomy.
Swiftly I rose to meet the feline sea
That sprang upon me with a hundred claws,
And grappled, pulled me down and played with me.
Then, tense and breathless in the tightening pause
When one wave grows into a toppling acre,
I dived headlong into the foremost breaker;
Pitting against a cold and turbulent strife
The feverish intensity of life.

Out of the foam I lurched and rode the wave,
Swimming, hand over hand, against the wind;
I felt the sea's vain pounding, and I grinned
Knowing I was its master, not its slave.
Oh, the proud total of those lusty hours —
The give and take of rough and vigorous tussles
With happy sinews and rejoicing muscles;

The knowledge of my own miraculous powers,
Feeling the force in one small body bent
To curb and tame this towering element.

Back on the curving beach I stood again,
Facing the bath-house, when a group of men,
Stumbling beneath some sort of weight, went by.
I could not see the hidden thing they carried;
I only heard: "He never gave a cry" —
"Who's going to tell her?" — "Yes, and they just mar-
        ried" —
"Such a good swimmer, too." ... And then they passed;
Leaving the silence throbbing and aghast.

A moment there my buoyant heart hung slack,
And then the glad, barbaric blood came back
Singing a livelier tune; and in my pulse
Beat the great wave that surges and exults. ...
Why I was there and whither I must go
I did not care.   Enough for me to know
The same unresting struggle and the glowing
Beauty of spendthrift hours, bravely showing
Life, an adventure perilous and gay;
And Death, a long and vivid holiday.

                                    Louis Untermeyer

THE BAREFOOT BOY

Blessings on thee, little man,
Barefoot boy, with cheek of tan!
With thy turned-up pantaloons,
And thy merry whistled tunes;

With thy red lip, redder still
Kissed by strawberries on the hill;
With the sunshine on thy face,
Through thy torn brim's jaunty grace;
From my heart I give thee joy —
I was once a barefoot boy!
Prince thou art — the grown-up man
Only is republican,
Let the million-dollared ride!
Barefoot, trudging at his side,
Thou hast more than he can buy
In the reach of ear and eye —
Outward sunshine, inward joy:
Blessings on thee, barefoot boy!

Oh for boyhood's painless play,
Sleep that wakes in laughing day,
Health that mocks the doctor's rules,
Knowledge never learned of schools,
Of the wild bee's morning chase,
Of the wild-flower's time and place,
Flight of fowl and habitude
Of the tenants of the wood;
How the tortoise bears his shell,
How the woodchuck digs his cell,
And the ground-mole sinks his well;
How the robin feeds her young,
How the oriole's nest is hung;
Where the whitest lilies blow,
Where the freshest berries grow,
Where the ground-nut trails its vine,
Where the wood-grape's clusters shine;

Of the black wasp's cunning way,
Mason of his walls of clay,
And the architectural plans
Of gray hornet artisans!
For, eschewing books and tasks,
Nature answers all he asks;
Hand in hand with her he walks,
Face to face with her he talks,
Part and parcel of her joy —
Blessings on the barefoot boy!

Oh for boyhood's time of June,
Crowding years in one brief moon,
When all things I heard and saw,
Me, their master, waited for.
I was rich in flowers and trees,
Humming-birds and honey-bees;
For my sport the squirrel played,
Plied the snouted mole his spade;
For my taste the blackberry cone
Purpled over hedge and stone;
Laughed the brook for my delight
Through the day and through the night,
Whispering at the garden wall,
Talked with me from fall to fall;
Mine the sand-rimmed pickerel pond,
Mine the walnut slopes beyond,
Mine, on bending orchard trees,
Apples of Hesperides!
Still as my horizon grew,
Larger grew my riches too;
All the world I saw or knew

Seemed a complex Chinese toy,
Fashioned for a barefoot boy!

Oh for festal dainties spread,
Like my bowl of milk and bread;
Pewter spoon and bowl of wood,
On the door-stone, gray and rude!
O'er me, like a regal tent,
Cloudy-ribbed, the sunset bent,
Purple-curtained, fringed with gold,
Looped in many a wind-swung fold;
While for music came the play
Of the pied frogs' orchestra;
And, to light the noisy choir,
Lit the fly his lamp of fire.
I was monarch: pomp and joy
Waited on the barefoot boy!

Cheerily, then, my little man,
Live and laugh, as boyhood can!
Though the flinty slopes be hard,
Stubble-speared the new-mown sward,
Every morn shall lead thee through
Fresh baptisms of the dew;
Every evening from thy feet
Shall the cool wind kiss the heat:
All too soon these feet must hide
In the prison cells of pride,
Lose the freedom of the sod,
Like a colt's for work be shod,
Made to tread the mills of toil,
Up and down in ceaseless moil:

Happy if their track be found
Never on forbidden ground;
Happy if they sink not in
Quick and treacherous sands of sin.
Ah! that thou couldst know thy joy,
Ere it passes, barefoot boy!
                              John Greenleaf Whittier

A DAY IN JUNE

And what is so rare as a day in June?
    Then, if ever, come perfect days;
Then Heaven tries earth if it be in tune,
    And over it softly her warm ear lays;
Whether we look, or whether we listen,
We hear life murmur, or see it glisten;
    Every clod feels a stir of might,
        An instinct within it that reaches and towers,
And, groping blindly above it for light,
    Climbs to a soul in grass and flowers;
The flush of life may well be seen
    Thrilling back over hills and valleys;
The cowslip startles in meadows green,
    The buttercup catches the sun in its chalice,
And there's never a leaf nor a blade too mean
    To be some happy creature's palace;
The little bird sits at his door in the sun,
    Atilt like a blossom among the leaves,
And lets his illumined being o'errun
    With the deluge of summer it receives;
His mate feels the eggs beneath her wings,
And the heart in her dumb breast flutters and sings.

He sings to the wide world, and she to her nest —
In the nice ear of Nature which song is the best?

Now is the high-tide of the year,
  And whatever of life hath ebbed away
Comes flooding back with a ripply cheer,
  Into every bare inlet and creek and bay;
Now the heart is so full that a drop overfills it,
We are happy now because God wills it;
No matter how barren the past may have been,
'Tis enough for us now that the leaves are green;
We sit in the warm shade and feel right well
How the sap creeps up and the blossoms swell;
We may shut our eyes, but we cannot help knowing
That skies are clear and grass is growing;
The breeze comes whispering in our ear,
That dandelions are blossoming near,
  That maize has sprouted, that streams are flowing,
That the river is bluer than the sky,
That the robin is plastering his house hard by;
And if the breeze kept the good news back,
For other couriers we should not lack;
  We could guess it all by yon heifer's lowing, —
And hark! how clear bold chanticleer,
Warmed with the new wine of the year,
  Tells all in his lusty crowing!

Joy comes, grief goes, we know not how;
Everything is happy now,
  Everything is upward striving;
'Tis as easy now for the heart to be true
As for grass to be green or skies to be blue —

'Tis the natural way of living:
Who knows whither the clouds have fled?
    In the unscarred heaven they leave no wake;
And the eyes forget the tears they have shed,
    The heart forgets its sorrow and ache;
The soul partakes the season's youth,
    And the sulphurous rifts of passion and woe
Lie deep 'neath a silence pure and smooth,
    Like burnt-out craters healed with snow.

James Russell Lowell

JUNE

Broom out the floor now, lay the fender by,
And plant this bee-sucked bough of woodbine there,
And let the window down.   The butterfly
Floats in upon the sunbeam, and the fair
Tanned face of June, the nomad gipsy, laughs
Above her widespread wares, the while she tells
The farmers' fortunes in the fields, and quaffs
The water from the spider-peopled wells.

The hedges are all drowned in green grass seas,
And bobbing poppies flare like Elmor's light,
While siren-like the pollen-stained bees
Drone in the clover depths.   And up the height
The cuckoo's voice is hoarse and broke with joy.
And on the lowland crops the crows make raid,
Nor fear the clappers of the farmer's boy,
Who sleeps, like drunken Noah, in the shade.

And loop this red rose in that hazel ring
That snares your little ear, for June is short

And we must joy in it and dance and sing,
And from her bounty draw her rosy worth.
Ay! soon the swallows will be flying south,
The wind wheel north to gather in the snow,
Even the roses split on youth's red mouth
Will soon blow down the road all roses go.

Francis Ledwidge

COCK-CROW

Out of the wood of thoughts that grows by night
To be cut down by the sharp axe of light —
Out of the night, two cocks together crow,
Cleaving the darkness with a silver blow:
And bright before my eyes twin trumpeters stand,
Heralds of splendor, one at either hand,
Each facing each as in a coat of arms:
The milkers lace their boots up at the farms.

Edward Thomas

ADLESTROP

Yes.   I remember Adlestrop —
The name, because one afternoon
Of heat the express-train drew up there
Unwontedly.   It was late June.

The steam hissed.   Someone cleared his throat.
No one left and no one came
On the bare platform.   What I saw
Was Adlestrop — only the name

And willows, willow-herb, and grass,
And meadowsweet, and haycocks dry,

No whit less still and lonely fair
Than the high cloudlets in the sky.

And for that minute a blackbird sang
Close by, and round him, mistier,
Farther and farther, all the birds
Of Oxfordshire and Gloucestershire.

Edward Thomas

SHADE

The kindliest thing God ever made,
His hand of very healing laid
Upon a fevered world, is shade.

His glorious company of trees
Throw out their mantles, and on these
The dust-stained wanderer finds ease.

Green temples, closed against the beat
Of noontime's blinding glare and heat,
Open to any pilgrim's feet.

The white road blisters in the sun;
Now half the weary journey done,
Enter and rest, O weary one!

And feel the dew of dawn still wet
Beneath thy feet, and so forget
The burning highway's ache and fret.

This is God's hospitality,
And whoso rests beneath a tree
Hath cause to thank Him gratefully.

Theodosia Garrison

THE DAFFODILS

I wandered lonely as a cloud
That floats on high o'er vales and hills,
When all at once I saw a crowd,
A host, of golden daffodils;
Beside the lake, beneath the trees,
Fluttering and dancing in the breeze.

Continuous as the stars that shine
And twinkle in the Milky Way,
They stretched in never-ending line
Along the margin of a bay:
Ten thousand saw I at a glance,
Tossing their heads in sprightly dance.

The waves beside them danced; but they
Outdid the sparkling waves in glee:
A poet could not but be gay
In such a jocund company:
I gazed — and gazed — but little thought
What wealth the show to me had brought:

For oft, when on my couch I lie
In vacant or in pensive mood,
They flash upon that inward eye
Which is the bliss of solitude;
And then my heart with rapture fills,
And dances with the daffodils.

William Wordsworth

ODE TO A NIGHTINGALE

My heart aches, and a drowsy numbness pains
   My sense, as though of hemlock I had drunk,
Or emptied some dull opiate to the drains
   One minute past, and Lethe-wards had sunk:
'Tis not through envy of thy happy lot,
   But being too happy in thine happiness —
      That thou, light-wingèd Dryad of the trees,
      In some melodious plot
   Of beechen green, and shadows numberless,
      Singest of summer in full-throated ease.

O for a draught of vintage! that hath been
   Cool'd a long age in the deep-delvèd earth,
Tasting of Flora and the country green,
   Dance, and Provençal song, and sunburnt mirth!
O for a beaker full of the warm South,
   Full of the true, the blushful Hippocrene,
      With beaded bubbles winking at the brim,
      And purple-stainèd mouth;
   That I might drink, and leave the world unseen,
And with thee fade away into the forest dim:

Fade far away, dissolve, and quite forget,
   What thou among the leaves hast never known,
The weariness, the fever, and the fret
   Here, where men sit and hear each other groan;
Where palsy shakes a few, sad, last gray hairs,
   Where youth grows pale, and spectre-thin, and dies;
      Where but to think is to be full of sorrow
      And leaden-eyed despairs,

Where Beauty cannot keep her lustrous eyes,
  Or new Love pine at them beyond tomorrow.

Away! away! for I will fly to thee,
  Not charioted by Bacchus and his pards,
But on the viewless wings of Poesy,
  Though the dull brain perplexes and retards:
Already with thee! tender is the night,
    And haply the Queen-Moon is on her throne,
      Cluster'd around by all her starry Fays;
        But here there is no light,
Save what from heaven is with the breezes blown
  Through verdurous glooms and winding mossy ways.

I cannot see what flowers are at my feet,
  Nor what soft incense hangs upon the boughs,
But, in embalmèd darkness, guess each sweet
  Wherewith the seasonable month endows
The grass, the thicket, and the fruit-tree wild;
    White hawthorn, and the pastoral eglantine;
      Fast fading violets cover'd up in leaves;
        And mid-May's eldest child,
The coming musk-rose, full of dewy wine,
  The murmurous haunt of flies on summer eves.

Darkling I listen; and, for many a time
  I have been half in love with easeful Death,
Call'd him soft names in many a musèd rhyme,
  To take into the air my quiet breath;
Now more than ever seems it rich to die,
    To cease upon the midnight with no pain,
      While thou art pouring forth thy soul abroad
      In such an ecstasy!

Still wouldst thou sing, and I have ears in vain —
    To thy high requiem become a sod.

Thou wast not born for death, immortal Bird!
    No hungry generations tread thee down;
The voice I hear this passing night was heard
    In ancient days by emperor and clown:
Perhaps the self-same song that found a path
    Through the sad heart of Ruth, when, sick for home,
        She stood in tears amid the alien corn;
            The same that oft-times hath
        Charmed magic casements, opening on the foam
    Of perilous seas, in faery lands forlorn.

Forlorn! the very word is like a bell
    To toll me back from thee to my sole self!
Adieu! the fancy cannot cheat so well
    As she is famed to do, deceiving elf.
Adieu! adieu! thy plaintive anthem fades
    Past the near meadows, over the still stream,
        Up the hill-side; and now 'tis buried deep
            In the next valley-glades:
        Was it a vision, or a waking dream?
        Fled is that music: — Do I wake or sleep?

                                        John Keats

NIGHTINGALES

Beautiful must be the mountains whence ye come,
And bright in the fruitful valleys the streams, wherefrom
            Ye learn your song:
Where are those starry woods? O might I wander there,
Among the flowers, which in that heavenly air
            Bloom the year long.

Nay, barren are those mountains and spent the streams:
Our song is the voice of desire, that haunts our dreams,
   A throe of the heart,
Whose pining visions dim, forbidden hopes profound,
No dying cadence nor long sigh can sound
   For all our art.

Alone, aloud in the raptured ear of men
We pour our dark nocturnal secret; and then,
   As night is withdrawn
From these sweet-springing meads and bursting boughs of May
Dream, while the innumerable choir of day
   Welcome the dawn.

         Robert Bridges

WOOD SONG

I heard a wood thrush in the dusk
 Twirl three notes and make a star —
My heart that walked with bitterness
 Came back from very far.

Three shining notes were all he had,
 And yet they made a starry call —
I caught life back against my breast
 And kissed it, scars and all.

         Sara Teasdale

THIS QUIET DUST WAS GENTLEMEN AND LADIES

This quiet Dust was Gentlemen and Ladies
 And Lads and Girls;

Was laughter and ability and sighing,
   And frocks and curls.
This passive place a Summer's nimble mansion,
   Where Bloom and Bees
Fulfilled their Oriental Circuit,
   Then ceased like these.

Emily Dickinson

AN ABANDONED TOW-PATH

In idle dalliance now it welcomes weeds;
   Grasshoppers dance along its unused ways;
A rainbow blur of flowers tells of seeds
   The wind had caught in care-free yesterdays.
And resting close beside it, almost dry,
   A greenish ghost of what was once a stream
Sags low within its muddy bed, as lie
   The broken things whose life is but a dream.

In memory alone it suffers pain;
   Informal insect choirs and elfin brass
Intone a dirge for all who wax and wane,
   A requiem for all who thrive and pass.
Sometimes, beneath the moon, it wakes to see
The rotted locks draw open noiselessly.

Elias Lieberman

MENDING WALL

Something there is that doesn't love a wall,
That sends the frozen-ground-swell under it,
And spills the upper boulders in the sun;
And makes gaps even two can pass abreast.

The work of hunters is another thing:
I have come after them and made repair
Where they have left not one stone on a stone,
But they would have the rabbit out of hiding,
To please the yelping dogs.   The gaps I mean,
No one has seen them made or heard them made,
But at spring mending-time we find them there.
I let my neighbor know beyond the hill;
And on a day we meet to walk the line
And set the wall between us once again.
We keep the wall between us as we go.
To each the boulders that have fallen to each.
And some are loaves and some so nearly balls
We have to use a spell to make them balance:
"Stay where you are until our backs are turned!"
We wear our fingers rough with handling them.
Oh, just another kind of outdoor game,
One on a side.   It comes to little more:
There where it is we do not need the wall:
He is all pine and I am apple-orchard.
My apple trees will never get across
And eat the cones under his pines, I tell him.
He only says, "Good fences make good neighbors."
Spring is the mischief in me, and I wonder
If I could put a notion in his head:
"*Why* do they make good neighbors?   Isn't it
Where there are cows?   But here there are no cows.
Before I built a wall I'd ask to know
What I was walling in or walling out,
And to whom I was like to give offense.
Something there is that doesn't love a wall,
That wants it down!"   I could say "elves" to him,

But it's not elves exactly, and I'd rather
He said it for himself.   I see him there,
Bringing a stone grasped firmly by the top
In each hand, like an old-stone savage armed.
He moves in darkness, as it seems to me,
Not of woods only and the shade of trees.
He will not go behind his father's saying,
And he likes having thought of it so well
He says again, "Good fences make good neighbors."

Robert Frost

TO EARTHWARD

Love at the lips was touch
As sweet as I could bear;
And once that seemed too much;
I lived on air

That crossed me from sweet things,
The flow of — was it musk
From hidden grapevine springs
Down hill at dusk?

I had the swirl and ache
From sprays of honeysuckle
That when they're gathered shake
Dew on the knuckle.

I craved strong sweets, but those
Seemed strong when I was young;
The petal of the rose
It was that stung.

Now no joy but lacks salt
That is not dashed with pain
And weariness and fault;
I crave the stain

Of tears, the aftermark
Of almost too much love,
The sweet of bitter bark
And burning clove.

When stiff and sore and scarred
I take away my hand
From leaning on it hard
In grass and sand,

The hurt is not enough:
I long for weight and strength
To feel the earth as rough
To all my length.

Robert Frost

SILVER

Slowly, silently, now the moon
Walks the night in her silver shoon;
This way, and that, she peers and sees
Silver fruit upon silver trees;
One by one the casements catch
Her beams beneath the silvery thatch;
Couched in his kennel, like a log,
With paws of silver sleeps the dog;
From their shadowy cote the white breasts peep

Of doves in a silver-feathered sleep;
A harvest mouse goes scampering by,
With silver claws, and a silver eye;
And moveless fish in the water gleam,
By silver reeds in a silver stream.

Walter de la Mare

THE CIRCUS–POSTERED BARN

When Dobbin and Robin, unharnessed from the plow,
Stamp smoking to their stalls,
They pass beneath white horses with long manes
Shining upon the walls,
White horses airily leaping through great hoops
Along applauding tracks
Or carrying princesses in rosy tights
Upon their backs.

And Daisy, Madge and Buttercup
Raise their soft eyes,
Where through the darkness of the web-hung stable
Hippopotami arise,
Shaking the water from their enormous shoulders
Floundering in savage mud,
Showing those muzzles huge enough to ponder
An epic cud.

And Tom beside a rat-hole in the boarding
Meets the still stare
Of eyes fiercer than his eyes and a large lithe body
Above him there —
Despondent grow the inmates of the barnyard;

Not one achieves
The super-powers of those super-mammals
Beneath the eaves!

Elizabeth Coatsworth

THE GRAND CANYON

By Zeus!
Shout word of this
To the eldest dead!   Titans,
Gods, Heroes, come who have once more
A home!

Adelaide Crapsey

GARGANTUA

Gargantuan ranges of blue-dappled hills
Roll down titanic coasts of cobalt shires,
And inland dreams a sunstruck city's ghost
And herds of mooncalves graze near towered byres.
Down, down the hills a bull-voiced waterfall
Plunges from cloudy cliffs that climb so high,
It shudders like an organ from a hall
Up stairs that wind into the windy sky.
And there are bestial footprints in the sand
That twist up rusty roadways red as snakes
Onto an upland paved with level floors
Of copper water stagnant in iron lakes.
And hooded peaks vault into clouded wonder,
From whence the island's voice drifts out to sea,
Reverberating words of blatant thunder,
Dull as a demon's glee.

Its hills sequester meadows, walled with fire,
On which like evil prayers the sphinxes lie,
With flame-like plumes that bloom upon their wings,
While red clouds wither by —
The eagle's shadow drifts along its cliffs
And in the evening from a mountain's dome,
Remote as thought, there blurs the sound of drums
That call the giants home.

Hervey Allen

OREAD

Whirl up, sea —
Whirl your pointed pines.
Splash your great pines
On our rocks.
Hurl your green over us —
Cover us with your pools of fir.

H. D.
(*Hilda Doolittle*

WILD PLUM

They are unholy who are born
    To love wild plum at night,
Who once have passed it on a road
    Glimmering and white.

It is as though the darkness had
    Speech of silver words,
Or as though a cloud of stars
    Perched like ghostly birds.

They are unpitied from their birth
    And homeless in men's sight,

Who love, better than the earth,
  Wild plum at night.

Orrick Johns

LEISURE

What is this life if, full of care,
We have no time to stand and stare?

No time to stand beneath the boughs
And stare as long as sheep or cows.

No time to see when woods we pass,
Where squirrels hide their nuts in grass.

No time to see, in broad daylight,
Streams full of stars, like skies at night.

No time to turn at Beauty's glance,
And watch her feet, how they can dance.

No time to wait till her mouth can
Enrich that smile her eyes began.

A poor life this if, full of care,
We have no time to stand and stare.

W. H. Davies

THE SOUND OF TREES

  I wonder about the trees:
  Why do we wish to bear
  Forever the noise of these

More than another noise
So close to our dwelling place?
We suffer them by the day
Till we lose all measure of pace
And fixity in our joys,
And acquire a listening air.
They are that that talks of going
But never gets away;
And that talks no less for knowing,
As it grows wiser and older,
That now it means to stay.
My feet tug at the floor
And my head sways to my shoulder
Sometimes when I watch trees sway
From the window or the door.
I shall set forth for somewhere,
I shall make the reckless choice,
Some day when they are in voice
And tossing so as to scare
The white clouds over them on.
I shall have less to say,
But I shall be gone.

Robert Frost

SONG OF THE CHATTAHOOCHEE

Out of the hills of Habersham,
Down the valleys of Hall,
I hurry amain to reach the plain,
Run the rapid and leap the fall,
Split at the rock and together again,
Accept my bed, or narrow or wide,

And flee from folly on every side
With a lover's pain to attain the plain
 Far from the hills of Habersham,
 Far from the valleys of Hall.

All down the hills of Habersham,
 All through the valleys of Hall,
The rushes cried, *Abide, abide,*
The willful waterweeds held me thrall,
The laving laurel turned my tide,
The ferns and the fondling grass said, *Stay,*
The dewberry dipped for to work delay,
And the little reeds sighed, *Abide, abide,*
 Here in the hills of Habersham,
 Here in the valleys of Hall.

High o'er the hills of Habersham,
 Veiling the valleys of Hall,
The hickory told me manifold
Fair tales of shade, the poplar tall
Wr ght me her shadowy self to hold,
The chestnut, the oak, the walnut, the pine,
Overleaning, with flickering meaning and sign,
Said, *Pass not, so cold, these manifold*
 Deep shades of the hills of Habersham,
 These glades in the valleys of Hall.

And oft in the hills of Habersham,
 And oft in the valleys of Hall,
The white quartz shone, and the smooth brook-stone
Did bar me of passage with friendly brawl,
And many a luminous jewel lone

— Crystals clear or a-cloud with mist,
Ruby, garnet, and amethyst —
Made lures with the lights of streaming stone
    In the clefts of the hills of Habersham,
    In the beds of the valleys of Hall.

But oh, not the hills of Habersham,
    And oh, not the valleys of Hall,
Avail: I am fain for to water the plain.
Downward the voices of duty call —
Downward, to toil and be mixed with the main,
The dry fields burn, and the mills are to turn,
And a myriad flowers mortally yearn,
And the lordly main from beyond the plain
    Calls o'er the hills of Habersham,
    Calls through the valleys of Hall.

Sidney Lanier

THE CATARACT OF LODORE

How does the water come down at Lodore?
    From its sources which well
    In the tarn on the fell;
        From its fountains
        In the mountains,
            Its rills
            And its gills;
        Through moss and through brake,
            It runs and it creeps
            For awhile, till it sleeps
        In its own little lake.
    And thence at departing,
    Awakening and starting,

It runs through the reeds,
And away it proceeds
Through meadow and glade,
In sun and in shade,
And through the wood shelter,
    Among crags in its flurry,
        Helter-skelter,
        Hurry-skurry.
Here it comes sparkling,
And there it lies darkling;
Now smoking and frothing
Its tumult and wrath in;
Till, in this rapid race
On which it is bent,
It reaches the place
Of its steep descent.
The cataract strong
Then plunges along;
Striking and raging,
As if a war waging
Its caverns and rocks among:
Rising and leaping.
Sinking and creeping,
Swelling and sweeping,
Showering and springing,
Flying and flinging,
Writhing and ringing,
Eddying and whisking,
Spouting and frisking,
Turning and twisting,
Around and around
With endless rebound:

Smiting and fighting,
A sight to delight in,
Confounding,
Astounding,
Dizzying and deafening the earth with its sound:
Collecting, projecting,
Receding and speeding,
And shocking and rocking,
And darting and parting,
And threading and spreading,
And whizzing and hissing,
And dripping and skipping,
And hitting and spitting,
And shining and twining,
And rattling and battling,
And shaking and quaking,
And pouring and roaring,
And waving and raving,
And tossing and crossing,
And flowing and going,
And running and stunning,
And foaming and roaming,
And dinning and spinning,
And dropping and hopping,
And working and jerking,
And guggling and struggling,
And heaving and cleaving,
And moaning and groaning;
And glittering and flittering,
And gathering and feathering,
And whitening and brightening,
And quivering and shivering,

And hurrying and skurrying,
And thundering and floundering;
Dividing and gliding and sliding;
And falling and brawling and sprawling,
And driving and riving and striving,
And sprinkling and twinkling and wrinkling,
And sounding and bounding and rounding,
And bubbling and troubling and doubling,
And grumbling and rumbling and tumbling;
And clattering and battering and shattering;
Retreating and beating and meeting and sheeting,
Delaying and straying and playing and spraying,
Advancing and prancing and glancing and dancing,
Recoiling, turmoiling, and toiling and boiling,
And gleaming and streaming and steaming and beaming,
And rushing and flushing and brushing and pushing,
And flapping and rapping and clapping and slapping,
And curling and whirling and purling and twirling,
And thumping and plumping and bumping and jumping,
And dashing and flashing and splashing and clashing;
      And so never ending,
      But always descending,
Sounds and motions for ever and ever are blending,
      All at once and all o'er,
      With a mighty uproar;
All this way the water comes down at Lodore!
                              Robert Southey

AUGUST

Why should this Negro insolently stride
Down the red noonday on such noiseless feet?
Piled in his barrow, tawnier than wheat,

Lie heaps of smouldering daisies, somber-eyed,
Their copper petals shriveled up with pride,
Hot with a superfluity of heat,
Like a great brazier borne along the street
By captive leopards, black and burning pied.

Are there no water-lilies, smooth as cream,
With long stems dripping crystal?   Are there none
Like those white lilies, luminous and cool,
Plucked from some hemlock-darkened northern stream
By fair-haired swimmers, diving where the sun
Scarce warms the surface of the deepest pool?

                                      Elinor Wylie

MADONNA OF THE EVENING FLOWERS

All day long I have been working,
Now I am tired.
I call: "Where are you?"
But there is only the oak tree rustling in the wind.
The house is very quiet,
The sun shines in on your books,
On your scissors and thimble just put down,
But you are not there.
Suddenly I am lonely:
Where are you?
I go about searching.

Then I see you,
Standing under a spire of pale blue larkspur,
With a basket of roses on your arm.
You are cool, like silver,

And you smile.
I think the Canterbury bells are playing little tunes,
You tell me that the peonies need spraying,
That the columbines have overrun all bounds,
That the pyrus japonica should be cut back and rounded.
You tell me these things.
But I look at you, heart of silver,
White heart-flame of polished silver,
Burning beneath the blue steeples of the larkspur,
And I long to kneel instantly at your feet,
While all about us peal the loud, sweet *Te Deums* of the
        Canterbury bells.

Amy Lowell

LILACS

Lilacs,
False blue,
White,
Purple,
Color of lilac,
Your great puffs of flowers
Are everywhere in this my New England.
Among your heart-shaped leaves
Orange orioles hop like music-box birds and sing
Their little weak soft songs;
In the crooks of your branches
The bright eyes of song sparrows sitting on spotted eggs
Peer restlessly through the light and shadow
Of all Springs.
Lilacs in dooryards
Holding quiet conversations with an early moon;

Lilacs watching a deserted house
Settling sideways into the grass of an old road;
Lilacs, wind-beaten, staggering under a lopsided shock of
    bloom
Above a cellar dug into a hill.
You are everywhere.
You were everywhere.
You tapped the window when the preacher preached his
    sermon,
And ran along the road beside the boy going to school.
You stood by pasture-bars to give the cows good milking,
You persuaded the housewife that her dish pan was of silver
And her husband an image of pure gold.
You flaunted the fragrance of your blossoms
Through the wide doors of Custom Houses —
You, and sandal-wood, and tea,
Charging the noses of quill-driving clerks
When a ship was in from China.
You called to them: "Goose-quill men, goose-quill men,
May is a month for flitting,"
Until they writhed on their high stools
And wrote poetry on their letter-sheets behind the propped-
    up ledgers.
Paradoxical New England clerks,
Writing inventories in ledgers, reading the "Song of Solo-
    mon" at night,
So many verses before bed-time,
Because it was the Bible.
The dead fed you
Amid the slant stones of graveyards.
Pale ghosts who planted you
Came in the night-time

And let their thin hair blow through your clustered stems.
You are of the green sea,
And of the stone hills which reach a long distance.
You are of elm-shaded streets with little shops where they
      sell kites and marbles,
You are of great parks where everyone walks and nobody
      is at home.
You cover the blind sides of greenhouses
And lean over the top to say a hurry-word through the glass
To your friends, the grapes, inside.

Lilacs,
False blue,
White,
Purple,
Color of lilac,
You have forgotten your Eastern origin,
The veiled women with eyes like panthers,
The swollen, aggressive turbans of jeweled Pashas.
Now you are a very decent flower.
A reticent flower,
A curiously clear-cut, candid flower,
Standing beside clean doorways,
Friendly to a house-cat and a pair of spectacles,
Making poetry out of a bit of moonlight
And a hundred or two sharp blossoms.

Maine knows you,
Has for years and years;
New Hampshire knows you,
And Massachusetts
And Vermont.

Cape Cod starts you along the beaches to Rhode Island;
Connecticut takes you from a river to the sea.
You are brighter than apples,
Sweeter than tulips,
You are the great flood of our souls
Bursting above the leaf-shapes of our hearts,
You are the smell of all summers,
The love of wives and children,
The recollection of the gardens of little children,
You are State Houses and Charters
And the familiar treading of the foot to and fro on a road
     it knows.
May is lilac here in New England,
May is thrush singing "Sun up!" on a tip-top ash-tree,
May is white clouds behind pine-trees
Puffed out and marching upon a blue sky.
May is green as no other,
May is much sun through small leaves,
May is soft earth,
And apple-blossoms,
And windows open to a South wind.
May is a full light wind of lilac
From Canada to Narragansett Bay.

Lilacs,
False blue,
White,
Purple,
Color of lilac.
Heart-leaves of lilac all over New England,
Roots of lilac under all the soil of New England,
Lilac in me because I am New England,

Because my roots are in it,
Because my leaves are of it,
Because my flowers are for it,
Because it is my country
And I speak to it of itself
And sing of it with my own voice
Since certainly it is mine.

Amy Lowell

ODE TO THE WEST WIND

I

O wild West Wind, thou breath of Autumn's being,
Thou, from whose unseen presence the leaves dead
Are driven, like ghosts from an enchanter fleeing,

Yellow, and black, and pale, and hectic red,
Pestilence-stricken multitudes: O thou,
Who chariotest to their dark wintry bed

The wingèd seeds, where they lie cold and low,
Each like a corpse within its grave, until
Thine azure sister of the Spring shall blow

Her clarion o'er the dreaming earth, and fill
(Driving sweet buds like flocks to feed in air)
With living hues and odors plain and hill:

Wild Spirit, which art moving everywhere;
Destroyer and preserver; hear, oh, hear!

II

Thou on whose stream, mid the steep sky's commotion,
Loose clouds like earth's decaying leaves are shed,
Shook from the tangled boughs of Heaven and Ocean,

Angels of rain and lightning: there are spread
On the blue surface of thine airy surge,
Like the bright hair uplifted from the head

Of some fierce Mænad, even from the dim verge
Of the horizon to the zenith's height,
The locks of the approaching storm.   Thou dirge

Of the dying year, to which this closing night
Will be the dome of a vast sepulchre,
Vaulted with all thy congregated might

Of vapors, from whose solid atmosphere
Black rain, and fire, and hail will burst: oh, hear!

III

Thou who didst waken from his summer dreams
The blue Mediterranean, where he lay,
Lulled by the coil of his crystalline streams,

Beside a pumice isle in Baiæ's bay,
And saw in sleep old palaces and towers
Quivering within the wave's intenser day,

All overgrown with azure moss and flowers,
So sweet, the sense faints picturing them! thou
For whose path the Atlantic's level powers

Cleave themselves into chasms, while far below
The sea-blooms and the oozy woods which wear
The sapless foliage of the ocean, know

Thy voice, and suddenly grow gray with fear,
And tremble and despoil themselves: oh, hear!

IV

If I were a dead leaf thou mightest bear;
If I were a swift cloud to fly with thee;
A wave to pant beneath thy power, and share

The impulse of thy strength, only less free
Than thou, O uncontrollable!   If even
I were as in my boyhood, and could be

The comrade of thy wanderings over heaven,
As then, when to outstrip thy skyey speed
Scarce seemed a vision; I would ne'er have striven

As thus with thee in prayer in my sore need.
Oh, lift me as a wave, a leaf, a cloud!
I fall upon the thorns of life!   I bleed!

A heavy weight of hours has chained and bowed
One too like thee: tameless, and swift, and proud.

V

Make me thy lyré, even as the forest is:
What if my leaves are falling like its own!
The tumult of thy mighty harmonies

Will take from both a deep, autumnal tone,
Sweet though in sadness.   Be thou, Spirit fierce,
My spirit!   Be thou me, impetuous one!

Drive my dead thoughts over the universe
Like withered leaves to quicken a new birth!
And, by the incantation of this verse,

Scatter, as from an unextinguished hearth
Ashes and sparks, my words among mankind!
Be through my lips to unawakened earth

The trumpet of a prophecy!   O Wind,
If Winter comes, can Spring be far behind?

Percy Bysshe Shelley

TO AUTUMN

Season of mists and mellow fruitfulness,
　　Close bosom-friend of the maturing sun;
Conspiring with him how to load and bless
　　With fruit the vines that round the thatch-eaves run;
To bend with apples the moss'd cottage-trees,
　　And fill all fruit with ripeness to the core;
　　　　To swell the gourd, and plump the hazel-shells
With a sweet kernel; to set budding more,
　　And still more, later flowers for the bees,
　　Until they think warm days will never cease,
　　　　For Summer has o'er-brimm'd their clammy cells.

Who hath not seen thee oft amid thy store?
　　Sometimes whoever seeks abroad may find

Thee sitting careless on a granary floor,
　Thy hair soft-lifted by the winnowing wind;
Or on a half-reap'd furrow sound asleep,
　Drows'd with the fume of poppies, while thy hook
　　Spares the next swath and all its twinèd flowers:
And sometimes like a gleaner thou dost keep
　Steady thy laden head across a brook;
　Or by a cider-press, with patient look,
　　Thou watchest the last oozings hours by hours.

Where are the songs of Spring?　Ay, where are they?
　Think not of them, thou hast thy music too, —
While barred clouds bloom the soft-dying day,
　And touch the stubble-plains with rosy hue;
Then in a wailful choir the small gnats mourn
　Among the river sallows, borne aloft
　　Or sinking as the light wind lives or dies;
And full-grown lambs loud bleat from hilly bourn;
　Hedge-crickets sing; and now with treble soft
　The red-breast whistles from a garden-croft;
　　And gathering swallows twitter in the skies.

John Keats

A VAGABOND'S SONG

There is something in the autumn that is native to my blood,
Touch of manner, hint of mood;
And my heart is like a rhyme,
With the yellow and the purple and the crimson keeping time.

The scarlet of the maples can shake me like a cry
Of bugles going by.
And my lonely spirit thrills
To see the frosty asters like smoke upon the hills.

There is something in October sets the gipsy blood astir;
We must rise and follow her,
When from every hill of flame,
She calls and calls each vagabond by name.

Bliss Carman

THE SOLITARY REAPER

Behold her, single in the field,
   Yon solitary Highland Lass!
Reaping and singing by herself;
   Stop here, or gently pass!
Alone she cuts and binds the grain,
And sings a melancholy strain;
O listen! for the Vale profound
Is overflowing with the sound.

No Nightingale did ever chaunt
   More welcome notes to weary bands
Of travelers in some shady haunt,
   Among Arabian sands:
A voice so thrilling ne'er was heard
In spring-time from the Cuckoo-bird,
Breaking the silence of the seas
Among the farthest Hebrides.

Will no one tell me what she sings? —
   Perhaps the plaintive numbers flow
For old, unhappy, far-off things,
   And battles long ago:
Or is it some more humble lay,
Familiar matter of today?

Some natural sorrow, loss or pain,
That has been, and may be again?

Whate'er the theme, the Maiden sang
    As if her song could have no ending;
I saw her singing at her work,
    And o'er the sickle bending; —
I listened, motionless and still;
And, as I mounted up the hill
The music in my heart I bore,
Long after it was heard no more.

                        William Wordsworth

SCYTHE SONG

Mowers, weary and brown and blithe,
    What is the word methinks ye know
Endless over-word that the scythe
    Sings to the blades of the grass below?
Scythes that swing in the grass and clover,
    Something, still, they say as they pass;
What is the word that, over and over,
    Sings the scythe to the flowers and grass?

Hush, ah, hush, the scythes are saying,
    Hush, and heed not, and fall asleep;
Hush, they say to the grasses swaying;
    Hush, they sing to the clover deep!
Hush — 'tis the lullaby Time is singing —
    Hush and heed not for all things pass,
Hush, ah, hush! and the scythes are swinging
    Over the clover, over the grass!

                        Andrew Lang

WHEN THE FROST IS ON THE PUNKIN

When the frost is on the punkin and the fodder's in the shock,
And you hear the kyouck and gobble of the struttin' turkey-
    cock,
And the clackin' of the guineys, and the cluckin' of the hens,
And the rooster's hallylooyer as he tiptoes on the fence;
O, it's then the time a feller is a-feelin' at his best,
With the risin' sun to greet him from a night of peaceful rest,
As he leaves the house, bareheaded, and goes out to feed the
    stock,
When the frost is on the punkin and the fodder's in the shock.

They's something kindo' harty-like about the atmusfere
When the heat of summer's over and the coolin' fall is here —
Of course we miss the flowers, and the blossoms on the trees,
And the mumble of the hummin'-birds and buzzin' of the
    bees;
But the air's so appetizin'; and the landscape through the
    haze
Of a crisp and sunny morning of the airly autumn days
Is a pictur' that no painter has the colorin' to mock —
When the frost is on the punkin and the fodder's in the shock.

The husky, rusty russel of the tossels of the corn,
And the raspin' of the tangled leaves as golden as the morn;
The stubble in the furries — kindo' lonesome-like, but still
A-preachin' sermuns to us of the barns they growed to fill;
The strawstack in the medder, and the reaper in the shed;
The hosses in theyr stalls below — the clover overhead! —
O, it sets my hart a-clickin' like the tickin' of a clock,
When the frost is on the punkin and the fodder's in the shock.

Then your apples all is gethered, and the ones a feller keeps
Is poured around the cellar-floor in red and yaller heaps;
And your cider-makin's over, and your wimmern-folks is
    through
With theyr mince and apple-butter, and theyr souse and
    sausage too!
I don't know how to tell it — but ef such a thing could be
As the angels wantin' boardin', and they'd call around on
    me —
I'd want to 'commodate 'em — all the whole-indurin' flock—
When the frost is on the punkin and the fodder's in the shock.

James Whitcomb Riley

HOME–COMING

When I stepped homeward to my hill
    Dusk went before with quiet tread;
The bare laced branches of the trees
    Were as a mist about its head.

Upon its leaf-brown breast, the rocks
    Like great gray sheep lay silent-wise;
Between the birch trees' gleaming arms
    The faint stars trembled in the skies.

The white brook met me halfway up
    And laughed as one that knew me well,
To whose more clear than crystal voice
    The frost had joined a crystal spell.

The skies lay like pale-watered deep.
    Dusk ran before me to its strand

And cloudily leaned forth to touch
The moon's slow wonder with her hand.

Léonie Adams

RIVER SKATER

Bound to a boy's swift feet, hard blades of steel
   Ring out a brutal rhythm from black ice.
A gawky skater with a godlike heel,
   He cuts a clear and convolute device,
A foliated script, nor looks around
   To see what letters twine where he has come,
But, all delighted with the savage sound,
   His body beats from such a solid drum,
He springs into a faster pace, and then,
   Far down the pastures, paper-white and pure,
You see his figure slanted like a pen,
   Writing his own and winter's signature.

Winifred Welles

TO A SNOW-FLAKE

What heart could have thought you? —
Past our devisal
(O filigree petal!)
Fashioned so purely,
Fragilely, surely,
From what Paradisal
Imagineless metal,
Too costly for cost?
Who hammered you, wrought you,
From argentine vapor? —

"God was my shaper.
Passing surmisal,
He hammered, He wrought me,
From curled silver vapor
To lust of His mind;
Thou could'st not have thought me!
So purely, so palely,
Tinily, surely,
Mightily, frailly,
Insculped and embossed,
With His hammer of wind,
And His graver of frost."

Francis Thompson

THE SNOW-STORM

Announced by all the trumpets of the sky,
Arrives the snow, and, driving o'er the fields,
Seems nowhere to alight: the whited air
Hides hills and woods, the river, and the heaven,
And veils the farmhouse at the garden's end.
The sled and traveler stopped, the courier's feet
Delayed, all friends shut out, the housemates sit
Around the radiant fireplace, enclosed
In a tumultuous privacy of storm.

Come see the north wind's masonry.
Out of an unseen quarry evermore
Furnished with tile, the fierce artificer
Curves his white bastions with projected roof
Round every windward stake, or tree, or door.
Speeding, the myriad-handed, his wild work

So fanciful, so savage, nought cares he
For number or proportion.   Mockingly,
On coop or kennel he hangs Parian wreaths;
A swan-like form invests the hidden thorn;
Fills up the farmer's lane from wall to wall,
Maugre the farmer's sighs; and, at the gate,
A tapering turret overtops the work.
And when his hours are numbered, and the world
Is all his own, retiring, as he were not,
Leaves, when the sun appears, astonished Art
To mimic in slow structures, stone by stone,
Built in an age, the mad wind's night-work,
The frolic architecture of the snow.

Ralph Waldo Emerson

VELVET SHOES

Let us walk in the white snow
    In a soundless space;
With footsteps quiet and slow,
    At a tranquil pace,
    Under veils of white lace.

I shall go shod in silk,
    And you in wool,
White as a white cow's milk,
    More beautiful
    Than the breast of a gull.

We shall walk through the still town
    In a windless peace;
We shall step upon white down,
    Upon silver fleece,
    Upon softer than these.

We shall walk in velvet shoes:
 Wherever we go
Silence will fall like dews
 On white silence below.
 We shall walk in the snow.

      Elinor Wylie

STOPPING BY WOODS ON A SNOWY EVENING

Whose woods these are I think I know.
His house is in the village though;
He will not see me stopping here
To watch his woods fill up with snow.

The little horse must think it queer
To stop without a farmhouse near
Between the woods and frozen lake
The darkest evening of the year.

He gives his harness bells a shake
To ask if there is some mistake.
The only other sound's the sweep
Of easy wind and downy flake.

The woods are lovely, dark and deep.
But I have promises to keep,
And miles to go before I sleep,
And miles to go before I sleep.

      Robert Frost

WINTER REVERY

Now let the garden sleep.
Bank the red coals of your impatience

Under the ash of prunings and raked leaves
And swing your eager glance
By the late rising, early setting sun's
Short and remoter arc.   This is no hour to sweep
The quiet, self-sufficient dark with flame.
Earth has forgotten fire, to light indifferent grown.
Night and the North alone attend her now.
Colder than ocean, cold as stone her blood,
Her pulses slow in long, libational rhythm.
Therefore if you would haunt the garden paths,
Ally, not alien, go in winter's way:
Not one superfluous candle in your eyes,
Nor heat of haste searing the ground with footprints.
Rather in shoes heavy with gathered snow
Or padded with thick cling of sodden leaves,
Your breath a cloud of chilly vapor,
Drift through the barren quiet like a sleepy mist
That coldly mingles with an austere dream.

Sara Bard Field

All Manner of Creatures

THE DOG

When Adam quitted the Garden,
　　Along with his buxom wife,
For to delve and swink and swither
　　And earn his way in life,
The Animals sidled about him
　　To grunt and whine good-bye —
But little enough their grief was,
　　However they piped the eye.

A tear from the rhino trickled,
　　But he did not really care.
The hippo mumbled politely,
　　Grumbled the hypocrite bear.
One hump of the camel quivered
　　As a chin that shakes with grief,
But his other hump was perky
　　Like it really felt relief.
The walrus sniveled dankly
　　In a quite perfunctory way,
And the bull was patently anxious
　　To get back to his hay.
And the porcupine and narwhal,
　　The wallaby and giraffe,
Parodied sorrow so broadly
　　They made the penguin laugh.

"Which of you brutes so mournful,"
  The watching Angel said,
"Will follow Man from Eden
  To toil for daily bread?
And which of you beasts so tearful
  Will give him more than tears,
Faithful to his footsteps
  Through all his outcast years?
Come forward," said the Angel,
"Before the barriers close,
You friend of all his friendships,
  And foeman of his foes!"

The sly little seal, he sniggered,
  Chuckled the kangaroo,
The chimpanzee pulled a razzberrie
  And winked at the cockatoo,
His thumb on his proboscis
  The mangy ape did place,
And flickered his ribald digits
  Right in Adam's face.
And they shuffled and lurched and ambled,
  Each to his separate den —
And that was the honest measure
  Of what they felt for men.

The Angel smiled in knowledge,
  He permitted himself a tear,
And if he weren't an Angel
  I'd say that he sneered a sneer —
(They see so much, these Angels,
  As they ramble here and there,

That we must try and forgive them
   If now and again they wear
That manner of sad amusement,
   That faintly cynical air).

But a pup there was that lingered
   In most abject unease;
He lay too broken-hearted
   Even to bite his fleas.
His tail swished desolation,
   And its swish was his only sound;
A splay-foot pup with a belly
   That grieved along the ground;
His ears were the dragging cypress
   And his eyes were love profound.

He looked not at the Angel,
   But of a sudden he rose
And he ran and nuzzled Adam,
   And his soul was in his nose —
He scampered out of the Garden
   Before the gates could close,
The friend of all our friendships
   And the foeman of our foes.

                    Don Marquis

DOG AT NIGHT

At first he stirs uneasily in sleep
And, since the moon does not run off, unfolds
Protesting paws.   Grumbling that he must keep
Both eyes awake, he whimpers; then he scolds

And, rising to his feet, demands to know
The stranger's business.   You who break the dark
With insolent light, who are you? Where do you go?
But nothing answers his indignant bark.
The moon ignores him, walking on as though
Dogs never were.   Stiffened to fury now,
His small hairs stand upright, his howls come fast,
And terrible to hear is his bow-wow
That tears the night.   Stirred by this bugle-blast,
The farmer's bitch grows active; without pause
Summons her mastiff and the hound that lies
Three fields away to rally to the cause.
And the next county wakes.   And miles beyond
Throats tear themselves and brassy lungs respond
With threats, entreaties, bellowings, and cries,
Chasing the white intruder down the skies.

Louis Untermeyer

THE TOM–CAT

At midnight in the alley
    A Tom-cat comes to wail,
And he chants the hate of a million years
    As he swings his snaky tail.

Malevolent, bony, brindled,
    Tiger and devil and bard,
His eyes are coals from the middle of Hell
    And his heart is black and hard.

He twists and crouches and capers
    And bares his curved sharp claws,

And he sings to the stars of the jungle nights
  Ere cities were, or laws.

Beast from a world primeval,
  He and his leaping clan,
When the blotched red moon leers over the roofs
  Give voice to their scorn of man.

He will lie on a rug tomorrow
  And lick his silky fur,
And veil the brute in his yellow eyes
  And play he's tame, and purr.

But at midnight in the alley
  He will crouch again and wail,
And beat the time for his demon's song
  With the swing of his demon's tail.

                    Don Marquis

THE BAD KITTENS

You may call, you may call,
But the little black cats won't hear you,
The little black cats are maddened
  By the bright green light of the moon,
They are whirling and running and hiding,
They are wild who were once so confiding,
They are crazed when the moon is riding —
  You will not catch the kittens soon.
They care not for saucers of milk,
They think not of pillows of silk,
Your softest, crooningest call

Is less than the buzzing of flies.
They are seeing more than you see,
They are hearing more than you hear,
And out of the darkness they peer
    With a goblin light in their eyes.

Elizabeth Coatsworth

AN ALLEY CAT

Mangy and gaunt I walk the tiles tonight,
And mangy comes my lady to her tryst;
And nine lives back (nine hundred some have guessed)
With prouder mien we rambled, ranging light.
Sacred and sleek, on roofs of amethyst
And eaves of ivory we wandered, while
A lotus-colored moon swung up the Nile,
And Memphis slumbered in a silver mist.

O it was heaven just to sit and be
Antiphonal beneath some royal room
Until, for all our sacredness, we heard
Loud hieroglyphic curses flowing free,
And marked a sandal hurtling through the gloom
Hot from the hand of Rameses the Third.

Nancy Byrd Turner

HORSE

His bridle hung around the post.
The sun and the leaves made spots come down;
I looked close at him through the fence;
The post was drab and he was brown.

His nose was long and hard and still,
And on his lip were specks like chalk.
But once he opened up his eyes,
And he began to talk.

He didn't talk out with his mouth;
He didn't talk with words or noise.
The talk was there along his nose;
It seemed and then it was.

He said the day was hot and slow,
And he said he didn't like the flies;
They made him have to shake his skin,
And they got drowned in his eyes.

He said that drab was just about
The same as brown, but he was not
A post, he said, to hold a fence.
"I'm horse," he said, "that's what!"

And then he shut his eyes again.
As still as they had been before.
He said for me to run along
And not to bother him any more.

Elizabeth Madox Roberts

SAY THIS OF HORSES

Across the ages they come thundering
  On faithful hoofs, the horses man disowns.
Their velvet eyes are wide with wondering;
  They whinny down the wind in silver tones

Vibrant with all the bugles of old wars;
   Their nostrils quiver with the summer scent
Of grasses in deep fields lit by pale stars
   Hung in a wide and silent firmament.
And in their hearts they keep the dreams of earth
   Their patient plodding furrowed to the sun
Unnumbered springs before the engine's birth
   Doomed them to sadness and oblivion.
Across the swift new day I watch them go
   Driven by wheel and gear and dynamo.

Say this of horses: engines leave behind
   No glorious legacy of waving manes
And wild proud hearts, and heels before the wind.
   No heritage of ancient Arab strains
Blazes within a cylinder's cold spark;
   An engine labors with a sullen fire,
Hoarding no dreams of acres sweet and dark:
   No love for man has ever surged through wire!
Along the farthest slopes I hear the rumble
   Of these last hoofs — tomorrow they will be still;
Then shall the strength of countless horses crumble
   The staunchest rock and level the highest hill;
And man who made machines to gain an hour
   Shall lose himself before their ruthless power.
                  Minnie Hite Moody

FOUR LITTLE FOXES

Speak gently, Spring, and make no sudden sound;
For in my windy valley, yesterday, I found
New-born foxes squirming on the ground...
             Speak gently.

Walk softly, March, forbear the bitter blow;
Her feet within a trap, her blood upon the snow,
The four little foxes saw their mother go...
             Walk softly.

Go lightly, Spring, oh, give them no alarm;
When I covered them with boughs to shelter them from
      harm,
The thin blue foxes suckled at my arm...
             Go lightly.

Step softly, March, with your rampant hurricane;
Nuzzling one another, and whimpering with pain,
The new little foxes are shivering in the rain...
             Step softly.

Lew Sarett

CRYSTAL MOMENT

Once or twice this side of death
Things can make one hold his breath.

From my boyhood I remember
A crystal moment of September.

A wooded island rang with sounds
Of church bells in the throats of hounds.

A buck leaped out and took the tide
With jewels flowing past each side.

With his high head like a tree
He swam within a yard of me.

I saw the golden drop of light
In his eyes turned dark with fright.

I saw the forest's holiness
On him like a fierce caress.

Fear made him lovely past belief,
My heart was trembling like a leaf.

He leaned towards the land and life
With need above him like a knife.

In his wake the hot hounds churned,
They stretched their muzzles out and yearned.

They bayed no more, but swam and throbbed,
Hunger drove them till they sobbed.

Pursued, pursuers reached the shore
And vanished.   I saw nothing more.

So they passed, a pageant such
As only gods could witness much,

Life and death upon one tether
And running beautiful together.
                    Robert P. Tristram Coffin

TIGER

Tiger! Tiger! burning bright
In the forests of the night,
What immortal hand or eye
Could frame thy fearful symmetry?

In what distant deeps or skies
Burnt the fire of thine eyes?
On what wings dare he aspire?
What the hand dare seize the fire?

And what shoulder, and what art,
Could twist the sinews of thy heart?
And when thy heart began to beat,
What dread hand? and what dread feet?

What the hammer? what the chain?
In what furnace was thy brain?
What the anvil? what dread grasp
Dare its deadly terrors clasp?

When the stars threw down their spears,
And watered heaven with their tears,
Did He smile His work to see?
Did He who made the Lamb make thee?

Tiger! Tiger! burning bright
In the forests of the night,
What immortal hand or eye
Dare frame thy fearful symmetry?

William Blake

MONKEYS

Two little creatures
With faces the size of
A pair of pennies
Are clasping each other:

"Ah, do not leave me,"
One says to the other,
In the high monkey-
Cage in the beast shop.

There are no people
To gape at them now,
For people are loth to
Peer in the dimness;
Have they not builded
Streets and playhouses,
Sky-signs and bars
To lose the loneliness
Shaking the hearts]
Of the two little monkeys?

Yes.   But who watches
The penny-small faces
Can hear the voices:
"Ah, do not leave me;
Suck I will give you,
Warmth and clasping,
And if you slip from
This beam, I can never
Find you again."

Dim is the evening,
And chill is the weather;
There, drawn from their colored
Hemisphere,
The apes liliputian
With faces the size of

A pair of pennies,
And voices as low as
The flow of my blood.

Padraic Colum

TO A MOUSE

Wee, sleekit cow'rin, tim'rous beastie,
O, what a panic's in thy breastie!
Thou need na start awa sae hasty,
     Wi' bickering brattle!
I wad be laith to rin an' chase thee,
     Wi' murd'ring pattle!

I'm truly sorry man's dominion
Has broken Nature's social union,
An' justifies that ill opinion,
     Which makes thee startle
At me, thy poor, earth-born companion
     An' fellow-mortal!

I doubt na, whyles, but thou may thieve;
What then? poor beastie, thou maun live!
A daimen icker in a thrave
     'S a sma' request;
I'll get a blessin' wi' the lave,
     And never miss't!

Thy wee bit housie, too, in ruin!
Its silly wa's the win's are strewin'!
An' naething, now, to big a new ane,
     O' foggage green!

An' bleak December's winds ensuin'
    Baith snell an' keen!

Thou saw the fields laid bare an' waste,
An' weary winter comin' fast,
An' cozie here, beneath the blast,
    Thou thought to dwell —
Till, crash! the cruel coulter passed
    Out through thy cell.

That wee bit heap o' leaves an' stibble
Has cost thee mony a weary nibble!
Now thou's turned out, for a' thy trouble,
    But house or hald,
To thole the winter's sleety dribble,
    An' cranreuch cauld!

But, Mousie, thou art no thy lane,
In proving foresight may be vain:
The best-laid schemes o' mice an' men
    Gang aft agley,
An' lea'e us naught but grief an' pain,
    For promised joy!

Still thou art blest, compared wi' me!
The present only toucheth thee:
But, och! I backward cast my e'e
    On prospects drear!
An' forward, though I canna see,
    I guess an' fear!

Robert Burns

THE HEDGEHOG

Hedgehog, hail the happy day
That fashioned you against decay.
You were a cog in Nature's plan
Before Man's doubtful race began,
And though in stature a Tom Thumb,
Not destined early to succumb,
No crass inferiority
Marked your godmother's legacy.
With spines of salvation bounded,
All your foes you may defy,
Into a tight fortress rounded
Take your ease beneath the sky.
Meekly you lap bread and milk,
Countenance as bland as silk;
Yet, by the same mysterious token,
Crush and crack an adder open,
Raising your troop of spiteful bristles
Thick as an avenue of thistles.

Laura Benét

THE WORM

Dickie found a broken spade
And said he'd dig himself a well,
And then Charles took a piece of tin,
And I was digging with a shell.

Then Will said he would dig one too;
We shaped them out and made them wide,
And I dug up a piece of clod
That had a little worm inside.

We watched him pucker up himself
And stretch himself to walk away.
He tried to go inside the dirt,
But Dickie made him wait and stay.

His shining skin was soft and wet.
I poked him once to see him squirm,
And then Will said, "I wonder if
He knows that he's a worm."

And then we sat back on our feet
And wondered for a little bit,
And we forgot to dig our wells
A while, and tried to answer it.

And while we tried to find it out
He puckered in a little wad.
And then he stretched himself again
And went back home inside the clod.

Elizabeth Madox Roberts

ON A FLY DRINKING OUT OF HIS CUP

Busy, curious, thirsty fly!
Drink with me and drink as I:
Freely welcome to my cup,
Couldst thou sip and sip it up:
Make the most of life you may,
Life is short and wears away.

Both alike are mine and thine
Hastening quick to their decline:

Thine's a summer, mine's no more,
Though repeated to threescore.
Threescore summers, when they're gone,
Will appear as short as one!

William Oldys

THE TREE-TOAD

A tiny bell the tree-toad has,
    I wonder if he knows
The charm it is to hear him
    Ringing as he goes.

He can't have gone the journeys
    He tells me to go on,
Here in the darkness
    Of the cool, cropped lawn.

He cannot know the thrill
    Of the soft spring wind,
Or the wonder, when you walk,
    What will come behind.

He hasn't seen the places
    I'd break my heart to win,
Nor heard the city calling
    When the cold comes in.

He sings away contented,
    And doesn't leave his tree,
But he sets my blood agoing
    Where his song will never be.

Orrick Johns

CHIPMUNK

When he runs hunting the chipmunk stretches
To a stripe over the wood's ground;
He has the sun's style of flickering; he matches
The half-shadowy places where nuts are found.

The chipmunk is compressed while the grim
Wing-beat of a hawk passes;
He is a chunk of turf, and his whiskers tremble on him
In the manner of grasses.

Marie de L. Welch

PYTHON

A lithe beautiful fear
Thrusts through the parted canes.
I should have known it near
By the blind blood in my veins.

Here is one way of death,
Though with no threat for me.
Now I have caught my breath,
Now that my brain can see,

Amber pours over the ground,
Darkness of amber too:
Blue of the gulf profound,
Superb and bitter blue

Sharp on the lacquered black.
Gold-corniced groping head,
Bold-swerving diamond back,
Why wish such beauty dead?

Why thwart such will to live?
Better to think twice.
It is I who am fugitive
From Paradise.

Grace Hazard Conkling

THE SPIDER

With six small diamonds for his eyes
He walks upon the Summer skies,
Drawing from his silken blouse
The lacework of his dwelling house.

He lays his staircase as he goes
Under his eight thoughtful toes
And grows with the concentric flower
Of his shadowless, thin bower.

His back legs are a pair of hands,
They can spindle out the strands
Of a thread that is so small
It stops the sunlight not at all.

He spins himself to threads of dew
Which will harden soon into
Lines that cut like slender knives
Across the insects' airy lives.

He makes no motion but is right,
He spreads out his appetite
Into a network, twist on twist,
This little ancient scientist.

He does not know he is unkind,
He has a jewel for a mind
And logic deadly as dry bone,
This small son of Euclid's own.

Robert P. Tristram Coffin

NOSEGAY FOR A YOUNG GOAT

With what smug elegance the small goat minces
    Over the rocks to me; inquisitive,
Yet quite sedate, he fearlessly evinces
    Interest in what my outstretched hand may give.

His horns are dainty curves, his beard points trimly.
    He has an eye that's both demure and shrewd.
And yet for all he moves his lips so primly,
    Spoken aloud, his language might be lewd.

It makes me smile to see so much that's charming,
    So grave, naïve, and innocent a grace,
An air so decorous and so disarming,
    Combined with that uncouth and crafty face.

Winifred Welles

THE EAGLE

He clasps the crag with crooked hands;
Close to the sun in lonely lands,
Ring'd with the azure world, he stands.

The wrinkled sea beneath him crawls;
He watches from his mountain walls,
And like a thunderbolt he falls.

Alfred Lord Tennyson

TO A PHOEBE BIRD

Under the eaves, out of the wet,
  You nest within my reach;
You never sing for me and yet
  You have a golden speech.

You sit and quirk a rapid tail,
  Wrinkle a ragged crest,
Then pirouette from tree to rail
  And vault from rail to nest.

And when in frequent, dainty fright
  You grayly slip and fade,
And when at hand you realight
  Demure and unafraid,

And when you bring your brood its fill
  Of iridescent wings
And green legs dewy in your bill,
  Your silence is what sings.

Not of a feather that enjoys
  To prate or praise or preach,
O phoebe, with so little noise,
  What eloquence you teach!
                              Witter Bynner

THE WHITE ROOSTER

Ah, God! To have a breast like that
To throw at day,
Thrust for the hands of dawn
To quiver and flare upon.

And a hook of gold to end you,
And a bloody flag sewn in your head,
And all yourself an arch,
And your soul a white cascade.

With yellow spirals,
Step, step, stalk,
And clutch reluctant loam,
Hard kernels and brown hens
In the brazen blue of noon.

Ah, God!   Stab upward with your noise;
Tear at the sky.
With the day gone molten down his throat
And his spine a tilted flame,
What singer could not make one song
As fine as fire?

George O'Neil

THE HENS

The night was coming very fast;
It reached the gate as I ran past.

The pigeons had gone to the tower of the church,
And all the hens were on their perch.

Up in the barn, and I thought I heard
A piece of a little purring word.

I stopped inside, waiting and staying,
To try to hear what the hens were saying.

They were asking something, that was plain,
Asking it over and over again.

One of them moved and turned around,
Her feathers made a ruffled sound,

A ruffled sound, like a bushful of birds,
And she said her little asking words.

She pushed her head close into her wing,
But nothing answered anything.

Elizabeth Madox Roberts

THE SWAN

Under a wall of bronze,
Where beeches dip and trail
Thin branches in the water,
With red-tipped head and wings,
A beaked ship under sail,
There glides a great black swan.

Under the autumn trees
He goes. The branches quiver,
Dance in the wraith-like water,
Which ripples beneath the sedge
With the slackening furrow that glides
In his wake when he is gone:
The beeches bow dark heads.

Into the windless dusk,
Where in mist great towers stand

Guarding a lonely strand
That is bodiless and dim,
He speeds with easy stride;
And I would go beside,
Till the low brown hills divide
At last, for me and him.

John Gould Fletcher

TO A WILD GOOSE OVER DECOYS

O lonely trumpeter, coasting down the sky,
Like a winter leaf blown from the bur-oak tree
By whipping winds, and flapping silverly
Against the sun — I know your lonely cry.

I know the worn wild heart that bends your flight
And circles you above this beckoning lake,
Eager of neck, to find the honking drake
Who speaks of reedy refuge for the night.

I know the sudden rapture that you fling
In answer to our friendly gander's call —
Halloo! Beware decoys! — or you will fall
With a silver bullet whistling in your wing!

Beat on your weary flight across the blue!
Beware, O traveler, of our gabbling geese!
Beware this weedy counterfeit of peace! —
Oh, I was once a passing bird like you.

Lew Sarett

THE FISH-HAWK

On the large highway of the awful air that flows
   Unbounded between sea and heaven, while twilight
      screened
The majestic distances, he moved and had repose;
   On the huge wind of the Immensity he leaned
His steady body in long lapse of flight, and rose

Gradual, through broad gyres of ever-climbing rest,
   Up the clear stair of the eternal sky; and stood
Throned on the summit! Slowly, with his widening breast,
   Widened around him the enormous Solitude,
From the gray rim of ocean to the glowing west.

Headlands and capes forlorn of the far coast, the land
   Rolling her barrens toward the south, he, from his throne
Upon the gigantic wind, beheld: he hung — he fanned
   The abyss for mighty joy, to feel beneath him strown
Pale pastures of the sea, with heaven on either hand,

The world with all her winds and waters, earth and air,
   Field, folds, and moving clouds. The awful and adored
Arches and endless aisles of vacancy, the fair
   Void of sheer heights and hollows hailed him as her lord
And lover in the highest, to whom all heaven lay bare!

Till from that tower of ecstasy, that baffled height,
   Stooping, he sank; and slowly on the world's wide way
Walked, with great wing on wing, the merciless proud Might,
   Hunting the huddles and lone reaches for his prey
Down the dim shore — and faded in the crumbling light.

Slowly the dusk covered the land.   Like a great hymn
The sound of moving winds and waters was; the sea
Whispered a benediction, and the west grew dim
Where evening lifted her clear candles quietly . . .
Heaven, crowded with stars, trembled from rim to rim.
John Hall Wheelock

LITTLE THINGS

Little things that run and quail
And die in silence and despair;

Little things that fight and fail
And fall on earth and sea and air;

All trapped and frightened little things,
The mouse, the coney, hear our prayer

As we forgive those done to us,
The lamb, the linnet, and the hare,

Forgive us all our trespasses,
Little creatures everywhere.
James Stephens

TO A WATERFOWL

Whither, midst falling dew,
While glow the heavens with the last steps of day,
Far, through their rosy depths, dost thou pursue
Thy solitary way?

Vainly the fowler's eye
Might mark thy distant flight to do thee wrong,
As, darkly seen against the crimson sky,
    Thy figure floats along.

Seek'st thou the plashy brink
Of weedy lake, or marge of river wide,
Or where the rocking billows rise and sink
    On the chafed ocean-side?

There is a Power whose care
Teaches thy way along that pathless coast ---
The desert and illimitable air —
    Lone wandering, but not lost.

All day thy wings have fanned,
At that far height, the cold, thin atmosphere,
Yet stoop not, weary, to the welcome land,
    Though the dark night is near.

And soon that toil shall end;
Soon shalt thou find a summer home, and rest,
And scream among thy fellows; reeds shall bend,
    Soon, o'er thy sheltered nest.

Thou'rt gone, the abyss of heaven
Hath swallowed up thy form; yet, on my heart
Deeply has sunk the lesson thou hast given,
    And shall not soon depart.

He who, from zone to zone,
Guides through the boundless sky thy certain flight,
In the long way that I must tread alone,
    Will lead my steps aright.

William Cullen Bryant

Challenge to Courage

LINCOLN, THE MAN OF THE PEOPLE

When the Norn Mother saw the Whirlwind Hour,
Greatening and darkening as it hurried on,
She left the Heaven of Heroes and came down
To make a man to meet the mortal need.
She took the tried clay of the common road —
Clay warm yet with the genial heat of Earth,
Dashed through it all a strain of prophecy,
Tempered the heap with thrill of human tears,
Then mixt a laughter with the serious stuff.
Into the shape she breathed a flame to light
That tender, tragic, ever-changing face;
And laid on him a sense of the Mystic Powers,
Moving — all husht — behind the mortal veil.
Here was a man to hold against the world,
A man to match the mountains and the sea.

The color of the ground was in him, the red earth;
The smack and tang of elemental things:
The rectitude and patience of the cliff;
The good-will of the rain that loves all leaves;
The friendly welcome of the wayside well;
The courage of the bird that dares the sea;
The gladness of the wind that shakes the corn;
The pity of the snow that hides all scars;
The secrecy of streams that make their way
Under the mountain to the rifted rock;
The tolerance and equity of light

That gives as freely to the shrinking flower
As to the great oak flaring to the wind —
To the grave's low hill as to the Matterhorn
That shoulders out the sky.   Sprung from the West,
He drank the valorous youth of a new world.
The strength of virgin forests braced his mind,
The hush of spacious prairies stilled his soul.
His words were oaks in acorns; and his thoughts
Were roots that firmly gript the granite truth.
Up from log cabin to the Capitol,
One fire was on his spirit, one resolve —
To send the keen ax to the root of wrong,
Clearing a free way for the feet of God,
The eyes of conscience testing every stroke,
To make his deed the measure of a man.
He built the rail-pile and he built the State,
Pouring his splendid strength through every blow:
The grip that swung the ax in Illinois
Was on the pen that set a people free.

So came the Captain with the mighty heart;
And when the judgment thunders split the house,
Wrenching the rafters from their ancient rest,
He held the ridgepole up, and spikt again
The rafters of the Home.   He held his place —
Held the long purpose like a growing tree —
Held on through blame and faltered not at praise,
Towering in calm rough-hewn sublimity.
And when he fell in whirlwind, he went down
As when a lordly cedar, green with boughs,
Goes down with a great shout upon the hills,
And leaves a lonesome place against the sky.
                                        Edwin Markham

O CAPTAIN! MY CAPTAIN!

O Captain! my Captain! our fearful trip is done,
The ship has weather'd every rack, the prize we sought is
    won,
The port is near, the bells I hear, the people all exulting,
While follow eyes the steady keel, the vessel grim and daring;
        But O heart! heart! heart!
          O the bleeding drops of red,
            Where on the deck my Captain lies,
            Fallen cold and dead.

O Captain! my Captain! rise up and hear the bells;
Rise up — for you the flag is flung — for you the bugle trills,
For you bouquets and ribbon'd wreaths — for you the
    shores a-crowding,
For you they call, the swaying mass, their eager faces turning;
        Here Captain! dear father!
          This arm beneath your head!
            It is some dream that on the deck,
            You've fallen cold and dead.

My Captain does not answer, his lips are pale and still,
My father does not feel my arm, he has no pulse nor will,
The ship is anchor'd safe and sound, its voyage closed and
    done,
From fearful trip the victor ship comes in with object won;
      Exult O shores, and ring O bells!
        But I with mournful tread,
          Walk the deck my Captain lies,
          Fallen cold and dead.

                  Walt Whitman

"I THINK CONTINUALLY OF THOSE ——"

I think continually of those who were truly great.
Who, from the womb, remembered the soul's history
Through corridors of light where the hours are suns
Endless and singing.   Whose lovely ambition
Was that their lips, still touched with fire,
Should tell of the Spirit clothed from head to foot in song.
And who hoarded from the Spring branches
The desires falling across their bodies like blossoms.

What is precious is never to forget
The essential delight of the blood drawn from ageless springs
Breaking through rocks in worlds before our earth.
Never to deny its pleasure in the morning simple light
Nor its grave evening demand for love.
Never to allow gradually the traffic to smother
With noise and fog the flowering of the spirit.

Near the snow, near the sun, in the highest fields
See how these names are fêted by the waving grass
And by the streamers of white cloud
And whispers of wind in the listening sky.
The names of those who in their lives fought for life
Who wore at their hearts the fire's center.
Born of the sun they traveled a short while toward the sun,
And left the vivid air signed with their honor.

                                        Stephen Spender

THE EAGLE THAT IS FORGOTTEN

(JOHN P. ALTGELD.   Born December 30, 1847; died March 12, 1902)

Sleep softly . . . eagle forgotten . . . under the stone.
Time has its way with you there, and the clay has its own.

"We have buried him now," thought your foes, and in secret
    rejoiced.
They made a brave show of their mourning, their hatred un-
    voiced.
They had snarled at you, barked at you, foamed at you day
    after day.
Now you were ended.   They praised you, . . . and laid you
    away.

The others that mourned you in silence and terror and truth,
The widow bereft of her crust, and the boy without youth,
The mocked and the scorned and the wounded, the lame and
    the poor
That should have remembered forever, . . . remember no
    more.

Where are those lovers of yours, on what name do they call
The lost, that in armies wept over your funeral pall?
They call on the names of a hundred high-valiant ones,
A hundred white eagles have risen the sons of your sons,
The zeal in their wings is a zeal that your dreaming began
The valor that wore out your soul in the service of man.

Sleep softly, . . . eagle forgotten, . . . under the stone,
Time has its way with you there and the clay has its own.

Sleep on, O brave-hearted, O wise man, that kindled the
     flame —
To live in mankind is far more than to live in a name,
To live in mankind, far, far more . . . than to live in a name.

Vachel Lindsay

DO YOU FEAR THE WIND?

Do you fear the force of the wind,
The slash of the rain?
Go face them and fight them,
Be savage again.
Go hungry and cold like the wolf,
   Go wade like the crane:
The palms of your hands will thicken,
The skin of your cheek will tan;
You'll grow ragged and weary and swarthy,
   But you'll walk like a man!

Hamlin Garland

COURAGE

Courage is armor
A blind man wears;
The calloused scar
Of outlived despairs:
Courage is Fear
That has said its prayers.

Karle Wilson Baker

THE KINGS

A man said unto his angel:
"My spirits are fallen thro',
And I cannot carry this battle;
O brother! what shall I do?

"The terrible Kings are on me,
With spears that are deadly bright,
Against me so from the cradle
Do fate and my fathers fight."

Then said to the man his angel:
"Thou wavering, foolish soul,
Back to the ranks! What matter
To win or to lose the whole,

"As judged by the little judges
Who hearken not well, nor see?
Not thus, by the outer issue,
The Wise shall interpret thee.

"Thy will is the very, the only,
The solemn event of things;
The weakest of hearts defying
Is stronger than all these Kings.

"Tho' out of the past they gather,
Mind's Doubt and Bodily Pain,
And pallid Thirst of the Spirit
That is kin to the other twain,

"And Grief, in a cloud of banners,
  And ringleted Vain Desires,
  And Vice, with the spoils upon him
  Of thee and thy beaten sires,

"While Kings of eternal evil
  Yet darken the hills about,
  Thy part is with broken saber
  To rise on the last redoubt;

"To fear not sensible failure,
  Nor covet the game at all,
  But fighting, fighting, fighting,
  Die, driven against the wall!"

Louise Imogen Guiney

PANDORA'S SONG

FROM THE FIRE-BRINGER

Of wounds and sore defeat
I made my battle stay;
Wingèd sandals for my feet
I wove of my delay;
Of weariness and fear,
I made my shouting spear;
Of loss, and doubt, and dread,
And swift oncoming doom
I made a helmet for my head
And a floating plume.
From the shutting mist of death,
From the failure of the breath,
I made a battle-horn to blow

Across the vales of overthrow.
O hearken, love, the battle-horn!
The triumph clear, the silver scorn!
O hearken where the echoes bring,
Down the gray disastrous morn,
Laughter and rallying!

William Vaughn Moody

UNREST

A fierce unrest seethes at the core
    Of all existing things:
It was the eager wish to soar
    That gave the gods their wings.

From what flat wastes of cosmic slime,
    And stung by what quick fire,
Sunward the restless races climb! —
    Men risen out of mire!

There throbs through all the worlds that are
    This heart-beat hot and strong
And shaken systems, star by star,
    Awake and glow in song.

But for the urge of this unrest
    These joyous spheres are mute;
But for the rebel in his breast
    Had man remained a brute.

When baffled lips demanded speech,
    Speech trembled into birth —
(One day the lyric word shall reach
    From earth to laughing earth.) —

When man's dim eyes demanded light,
　　The light he sought was born —
His wish, a Titan, scaled the height
　　And flung him back the morn!

From deed to dream, from dream to deed,
　　From daring hope to hope,
The restless wish, the instant need,
　　Still lashed him up the slope!
　　　.　　.　　.　　.　　.　　.

I sing no governed firmament,
　　Cold, ordered, regular —
I sing the stinging discontent
　　That leaps from star to star!

Don Marquis

THE FALCONER OF GOD

I flung my soul to the air like a falcon flying.
I said, "Wait on, wait on, while I ride below!
　　I shall start a heron soon
　　In the marsh beneath the moon ——
A strange white heron rising with silver on its wings,
　　　Rising and crying
　　Wordless, wondrous things;
　The secret of the stars, of the world's heart-strings
　　The answer to their woe,
Then stoop thou upon him, and grip and hold him so!"

My wild soul waited on as falcons hover.
I beat the reedy fens as I trampled past.

I heard the mournful loon
In the marsh beneath the moon.
And then, with feathery thunder, the bird of my desire
    Broke from the cover
    Flashing silver fire.
High up among the stars I saw his pinions spire.
    The pale clouds gazed aghast
As my falcon stooped upon him, and gript and held him fast.

My soul dropped through the air — with heavenly plun-
    der?——
Gripping the dazzling bird my dreaming knew?
    Nay! but a piteous freight,
    A dark and heavy weight
Despoiled of silver plumage, its voice forever stilled ——
    All of the wonder
    Gone that ever filled
Its guise with glory.   O bird that I have killed,
    How brilliantly you flew
Across my rapturous vision when first I dreamed of you!

Yet I fling my soul on high with new endeavor,
And I ride the world below with a joyful mind.
    I shall start a heron soon
    In the marsh beneath the moon —
A wondrous silver heron its inner darkness fledges!
    I beat forever
    The fens and the sedges.
    The pledge is still the same — for all disastrous pledges,
    All hopes resigned!
My soul still flies above me for the quarry it shall find!
                                        William Rose Benét

THE LAST ALLY

He fought for his soul.   The stubborn fighting
Mastered his strength.
"Endless indeed this long requiting!"
He cried at length.
"Six times have I come where my first hope jeered
And laughed me to scorn.
O now I fear as I never feared
To fall forsworn!"

"Ah, when they fight upright and at me
I give them then
Blows as shrewd as those combat me;
But now, again,
They struggle and writhe like fiends escaping.
Underhand
They flicker and strike.   My wounds are gaping.
I reel to stand.

"Six battles' span; by this gasping breath,
No pantomime!
'Tis all that I can.   I am sick to death.
A seventh time?
Not for all crowns and thrones hereafter!" ...
He stared wide-eyed:
Like a knight in glittering armor, Laughter
Stood up at his side.

                                        William Rose Benét

ELDORADO

Gaily bedight,
A gallant knight,
In sunshine and in shadow,
Had journeyed long,
Singing a song,
In search of Eldorado.

But he grew old —
This knight so bold —
And o'er his heart a shadow
Fell as he found
No spot of ground
That looked like Eldorado.

And, as his strength
Failed him at length,
He met a pilgrim shadow —
"Shadow," said he,
"Where can it be —
This land of Eldorado?"

"Over the Mountains
Of the Moon,
Down the Valley of the Shadow,
Ride, boldly ride,"
The shade replied —
"If you seek for Eldorado!"

Edgar Allan Poe

THE MOUSE THAT GNAWED
THE OAK-TREE DOWN

The mouse that gnawed the oak-tree down
Began his task in early life.
He kept so busy with his teeth
He had no time to take a wife.

He gnawed and gnawed through sun and rain
When the ambitious fit was on,
Then rested in the sawdust till
A month of idleness had gone.

He did not move about to hunt
The coteries of mousie-men.
He was a snail-paced, stupid thing
Until he cared to gnaw again.

The mouse that gnawed the oak-tree down,
When that tough foe was at his feet —
Found in the stump no angel-cake
Nor buttered bread, nor cheese nor meat —

The forest-roof let in the sky.
"This light is worth the work," said he.
"I'll make this ancient swamp more light,"
And started on another tree.

Vachel Lindsay

INVICTUS

Out of the night that covers me,
Black as the Pit from pole to pole,
I thank whatever gods may be
For my unconquerable soul.

In the fell clutch of circumstance
I have not winced nor cried aloud.
Under the bludgeonings of chance
My head is bloody, but unbowed.

Beyond this place of wrath and tears
Looms but the Horror of the shade,
And yet the menace of the years
Finds, and shall find, me unafraid.

It matters not how strait the gate,
How charged with punishments the scroll,
I am the master of my fate:
I am the captain of my soul.

W. E. Henley

AT MAGNOLIA CEMETERY

Sleep sweetly in your humble graves,
    Sleep, martyrs of a fallen cause;
Though yet no marble column craves
    The pilgrim here to pause.

In seeds of laurel in the earth
    The blossom of your fame is blown,
And somewhere, waiting for its birth,
    The shaft is in the stone.

Meanwhile, behalf the tardy years
    Which keep in trust your storied tombs,
Behold! your sisters bring their tears,
    And these memorial blooms.

Small tributes! but your shades will smile
    More proudly on these wreaths today,
Than when some cannon-moulded pile
    Shall overlook this bay.

Stoop, angels, hither from the skies!
    There is no holier spot of ground
Than where defeated valor lies,
    By mourning beauty crowned.

Henry Timrod

THE KINGS GO BY

The Kings go by with jeweled crowns,
Their horses gleam, their banners shake, their spears
    are many.
The sack of many-peopled towns
Is all their dream:
The way they take
Leaves but a ruin in the brake
And, in the furrow that the ploughmen make,
A stampless penny; a tale, a dream.

The merchants reckon up their gold,
Their letters come, their ships arrive, their freights
    are glories:
The profits of their treasures sold
They tell and sum;
Their foremen drive
The servants starved to half-alive
Whose labors do not make the earth a hive
Of stinking stories; a tale, a dream.

The priests are singing in their stalls,
Their singing lifts, their incense burns, their praying clamors;
Yet God is as the sparrow falls;
The ivy drifts,
The votive urns
Are all left void when Fortune turns,
The god is but a marble for the kerns
To break with hammers; a tale, a dream.

O Beauty, let me know again
The green earth cold, the April rain,
The quiet waters figuring sky,
The one star risen.
So shall I pass into the feast
Not touched by King, merchant, or priest,
Know the red spirit of the beast,
Be the green grain;
Escape from prison.

John Masefield

COMRADES

Comrades, pour the wine tonight
For the parting is with dawn!
Oh, the clink of cups together,
With the daylight coming on!
Greet the morn
With a double horn,
When strong men drink together!

Comrades, gird your swords tonight,
For the battle is with dawn!

Oh, the clash of shields together,
With the triumph coming on!
Greet the foe,
And lay him low,
When strong men fight together!

Comrades, watch the tides tonight,
For the sailing is with dawn!
Oh, to face the spray together,
With the tempest coming on!
Greet the sea
With a shout of glee,
When strong men roam together!

Comrades, give a cheer tonight,
For the dying is with dawn!
Oh, to meet the stars together,
With the silence coming on!
Greet the end
As a friend a friend,
When strong men die together!

Richard Hovey

CRY OF THE PEOPLE

Tremble before thy chattels,
Lords of the scheme of things!
Fighters of all earth's battles,
Ours is the might of kings!
Guided by seers and sages,
The world's heart-beat for a drum,
Snapping the chains of ages,
Out of the night we come!

Lend us no ear that pities!
Offer no almoner's hand!
Alms for the builders of cities!
When will you understand?
Down with your pride of birth
And your golden gods of trade!
A man is worth to his mother, Earth,
All that a man has made!

We are the workers and makers!
We are no longer dumb!
Tremble, O Shirkers and Takers!
Sweeping the earth — we come!
Ranked in the world-wide dawn,
Marching into the day!
The night is gone and the sword is drawn
And the scabbard is thrown away!

                                  John G. Neihardt

ULYSSES

It little profits that an idle king,
By this still hearth, among these barren crags,
Matched with an agèd wife, I mete and dole
Unequal laws unto a savage race,
That hoard, and sleep, and feed, and know not me.
I cannot rest from travel; I will drink
Life to the lees.   All times I have enjoyed
Greatly, have suffered greatly, both with those
That loved me, and alone; on shore, and when
Through scudding drifts the rainy Hyades
Vexed the dim sea.   I am become a name;

For always roaming with a hungry heart
Much have I seen and known, — cities of men
And manners, climates, councils, governments,
Myself not least, but honored of them all;
And drunk delight of battle with my peers,
Far on the ringing plains of windy Troy.
I am a part of all that I have met;
Yet all experience is an arch wherethrough
Gleams that untraveled world whose margin fades
For ever and for ever when I move.
How dull it is to pause, to make an end,
To rust unburnished, not to shine in use,
As though to breathe were life.   Life piled on life
Were all too little, and of one to me
Little remains; but every hour is saved
From that eternal silence, something more,
A bringer of new things; and vile it were
For some three suns to store and hoard myself,
And this gray spirit yearning in desire
To follow knowledge like a sinking star,
Beyond the utmost bound of human thought.
This is my son, mine own Telemachus,
To whom I leave the scepter and the isle —
Well-loved of me, discerning to fulfill
This labor, by slow prudence to make mild
A rugged people, and through soft degrees
Subdue them to the useful and the good.
Most blameless is he, centered in the sphere
Of common duties, decent not to fail
In offices of tenderness, and pay
Meet adoration to my household gods,
When I am gone. He works his work, I mine.

There lies the port; the vessel puffs her sail;
There gloom the dark, broad seas.   My mariners,
Souls that have toiled, and wrought, and thought with me —
That ever with a frolic welcome took
The thunder and the sunshine, and opposed
Free hearts, free foreheads — you and I are old;
Old age hath yet his honor and his toil;
Death closes all — but something ere the end,
Some work of noble note, may yet be done
Not unbecoming men that strove with Gods.
The lights begin to twinkle from the rocks;
The long day wanes; the slow moon climbs; the deep
Moans round with many voices.   Come, my friends,
'Tis not too late to seek a newer world.
Push off, and sitting well in order, smite
The sounding furrows; for my purpose holds
To sail beyond the sunset, and the baths
Of all the western stars, until I die.
It may be that the gulfs will wash us down:
It may be we shall touch the Happy Isles
And see the great Achilles, whom we knew.
Though much is taken, much abides; and though
We are not now that strength which in old days
Moved earth and heaven, that which we are, we are,
One equal temper of heroic hearts,
Made weak by time and fate, but strong in will
To strive, to seek, to find, and not to yield.

                                        Alfred Lord Tennyson

SAY NOT THE STRUGGLE NOUGHT AVAILETH

Say not the struggle nought availeth,
   The labor and the wounds are vain,
The enemy faints not, nor faileth,
   And as things have been they remain.

If hopes were dupes, fears may be liars;
   It may be, in yon smoke concealed,
Your comrades chase e'en now the fliers,
   And, but for you, possess the field.

For while the tired waves, vainly breaking,
   Seem here no painful inch to gain,
Far back, through creeks and inlets making,
   Comes silent, flooding in, the main.

And not by eastern windows only,
   When daylight comes, comes in the light,
In front, the sun climbs slow, how slowly,
   But westward, look, the land is bright.

                  Arthur Hugh Clough

CROSSING THE BAR

Sunset and evening star,
   And one clear call for me!
And may there be no moaning of the bar,
   When I put out to sea,

But such a tide as moving seems asleep,
   Too full for sound and foam,

When that which drew from out the boundless deep
    Turns again home.

Twilight and evening bell,
    And after that the dark!
And may there be no sadness of farewell,
    When I embark;

For though from out our bourne of Time and Place
    The flood may bear me far,
I hope to see my Pilot face to face
When I have crossed the bar.

Alfred Lord Tennyson

EPILOGUE

From ASOLANDO

At the midnight in the silence of the sleep-time,
    When you set your fancies free,
Will they pass to where — by death, fools think, impris-
        oned —
Low he lies who once so loved you, whom you loved so,
                — Pity me?

Oh to love so, be so loved, yet so mistaken!
    What had I on earth to do
With the slothful, with the mawkish, the unmanly?
Like the aimless, helpless, hopeless, did I drivel
                — Being — who?

One who never turned his back but marched breast forward,
    Never doubted clouds would break,

Never dreamed, though right were worsted, wrong would
    triumph,
Held we fall to rise, are baffled to fight better,
        Sleep to wake.

No, at noonday in the bustle of man's work-time
  Greet the unseen with a cheer!
Bid him forward, breast and back as either should be,
"Strive and thrive!" cry "Speed — fight on, fare ever
        There as here!"

Robert Browning

Man and Warfare

CAESAR REMEMBERS

Caesar, that proud man,
   Sat in his tent,
Weary with victory,
   With striving spent.

Where the gray Chilterns
   Coiled and slept
That hard-lipped Emperor
   Vigil kept.

In the thin starlight
   His glimmering hordes
Fought with the hard earth —
   Spades for swords.

Out on the hill-slopes
   His helmèd host
Piled stark ramparts
   Rimmed with frost.

But Caesar cared not
   For dyke and wall,
Faint and remote
   Came the bugles' call;

Soft in the shadows
   He saw, and heard,

A Roman garden,
A Roman bird.

"Worlds to conquer!
But Caesar fails
To add one song
To the nightingale's!"

Soft in the shadows
The tired man heard
A woman's laughter,
A woman's word.

Caesar, shivering,
Heard repeat
Spades on the hillside,
Sentries' feet.

William Kean Seymour

I HEARD A SOLDIER

I heard a soldier sing some trifle
Out in the sun-dried veldt alone:
He lay and cleaned his grimy rifle
Idly, behind a stone.

"If after death, love, comes a waking,
And in their camp so dark and still
The men of dust hear bugles breaking
Their halt upon the hill,

"To me the slow and silver pealing
That then the last high trumpet pours,

Shall softer than the dawn come stealing,
  For, with its call, comes yours!"

What grief of love had he to stifle,
  Basking so idly by his stone,
That grimy soldier with his rifle
  Out in the veldt, alone?

Herbert Trench

BACK

They ask me where I've been,
And what I've done and seen.
But what can I reply
Who know it wasn't I,
But someone just like me,
Who went across the sea,
And with my head and hands
Killed men in foreign lands . . .
Though I must bear the blame
Because he bore my name?

Wilfrid Wilson Gibson

DOES IT MATTER?

Does it matter? — losing your legs? . . .
For people will always be kind,
And you need not show that you mind
When the others come in after hunting
To gobble their muffins and eggs.

Does it matter? — losing your sight? . . .
There's such splendid work for the blind;

And people will always be kind,
As you sit on the terrace remembering
And turning your face to the light.

Do they matter? — those dreams from the pit? ...
You can drink and forget and be glad,
And people won't say that you're mad;
For they'll know that you've fought for your country,
And no one will worry a bit.

Siegfried Sassoon

GRASS

Pile the bodies high at Austerlitz and Waterloo.
Shovel them under and let me work —
       I am the grass; I cover all.

And pile them high at Gettysburg
And pile them high at Ypres and Verdun.
Shovel them under and let me work.
Two years, ten years, and passengers ask the conductor:
       What place is this?
       Where are we now?

       I am the grass.
       Let me work.

Carl Sandburg

THE MAN HE KILLED

"Had he and I but met
   By some old ancient inn,
We should have sat us down to wet
   Right many a nipperkin!

"But ranged as infantry,
    And staring face to face,
I shot at him as he at me,
    And killed him in his place.

"I shot him dead because —
    Because he was my foe,
Just so: my foe of course he was;
    That's clear enough; although

"He thought he'd 'list, perhaps,
    Off-hand like — just as I —
Was out of work — had sold his traps —
    No other reason why.

"Yes; quaint and curious war is!
    You shoot a fellow down
You'd treat if met where any bar is,
    Or help to half-a-crown."

                                    Thomas Hardy

                    be still

always remembering always remembering
deep in the well the spring bubbles
slowly but always
remembering talking to you and me
inconsequential things Jim's marriage
the high rent of apartments
the symphony last night and
the scandal in the papers always
remembering how the air fluttered and whined

shaking the body fear was a quick fever
springing from the ambush of the mind
like a ravenous beast tearing the trembling nerves
and the feet moved like slow clouds always
remembering looking quiet and peaceful
with the brain torn and quivering
spilled on the green turf the eyes stark-staring
and a twitch of the graying body always
remembering as if set with concrete the
angular planes of thought projecting
through the normal periphery always
remembering the monstrous red-eyed rats
beside the ragged ghostly columns of Vailly watching
in the terrifying moonlight
the lonely walkers while the shells screamed
put your arms around me love this is
a fragrant pleasant flesh so quick it
can be limp and nauseous not now the guns but always
remembering how the sky shook red-gashed all night
and the steel death was a gray rain splashing fire
the liquid slosh of the gas shells warbling
like ill-omened birds and the sudden
ripping fingers in the throat choking always
remembering father why do you sit in bed like that
you frighten me be still my child be still it's
nothing but a dream nothing but a dream

William Closson Emory

THE CONSCRIPT

Indifferent, flippant, earnest, but all bored,
The doctors sit in the glare of electric light

Watching an endless stream of naked white
Bodies of men for whom their hasty award
Means life or death maybe, or the living death
Of mangled limbs, blind eyes, or a darkened brain;
And the chairman, as his monocle falls again,
Pronounces each doom with easy indifferent breath.

Then suddenly I shudder as I see
A young man stand before them wearily,
Cadaverous as one already dead;
But still they stare untroubled as he stands
With arms outstretched and drooping thorn-crowned head,
The nail-marks glowing in his feet and hands.

Wilfrid Wilson Gibson

I HAVE A RENDEZVOUS WITH DEATH

I have a rendezvous with Death
At some disputed barricade,
When Spring comes back with rustling shade
And apple-blossoms fill the air —
I have a rendezvous with Death
When Spring brings back blue days and fair.

It may be he shall take my hand
And lead me into his dark land
And close my eyes and quench my breath —
It may be I shall pass him still.
I have a rendezvous with Death
On some scarred slope of battered hill,
When Spring comes round again this year
And the first meadow-flowers appear.

God knows 'twere better to be deep
Pillowed in silk and scented down,
Where Love throbs out in blissful sleep,
Pulse nigh to pulse, and breath to breath,
Where hushed awakenings are dear ...
But I've a rendezvous with Death
At midnight in some flaming town,
When Spring trips north again this year,
And I to my pledged word am true,
I shall not fail that rendezvous.

Alan Seeger

DREAMERS

Soldiers are citizens of death's gray land,
  Drawing no dividend from time's tomorrows.
In the great hour of destiny they stand,
  Each with his feuds, and jealousies, and sorrows.
Soldiers are sworn to action; they must win
  Some flaming, fatal climax with their lives.
Soldiers are dreamers; when the guns begin
  They think of firelit homes, clean beds, and wives.

I see them in foul dugouts, gnawed by rats,
  And in the ruined trenches, lashed with rain,
Dreaming of things they did with balls and bats,
  And mocked by hopeless longing to regain
Bank-holidays, and picture shows, and spats,
  And going to the office in the train.

Siegfried Sassoon

ON READING THE WAR DIARY OF
A DEFUNCT AMBASSADOR

So that's your Diary — that's your private mind
Translated into shirt-sleeved History.   That
Is what diplomacy has left behind
For after-ages to peruse, and find
What passed beneath your elegant silk-hat.

You were a fine old gentleman: compact
Of shrewdness, charm, refinement, and finesse.
Impeccable in breeding, taste, and dress,
No diplomatic quality you lacked —
No tittle of ambassadorial tact.

I can imagine you among "the guns,"
Urbanely peppering partridge, grouse, or pheasant —
Guest of those infinitely privileged ones
Whose lives are padded, petrified, and pleasant.
I visualize you feeding off gold plate
And gossiping on grave affairs of State.

Now you're defunct; your gossip's gravely printed;
The world discovers where you lunched and dined
On such and such a day; and what was hinted
By ministers and generals far behind
The all-important conflict, carnage-tinted.

The world can read the rumors that you gleaned
From various Fronts; the well-known Names you met;
Each conference you attended and convened;
And (at appropriate moments) what you ate.

Thus (if the world's acute) it can derive
Your self, exact, uncensored, and alive.

The world will find no pity in your pages;
No exercise of spirit worthy of mention;
Only a public-funeral grief-convention;
And all the circumspection of the ages.
But I, for one, am grateful, overjoyed,
And unindignant that your punctual pen
Should have been so constructively employed
In manifesting to unprivileged men
The visionless officialized fatuity
That once kept Europe safe for Perpetuity.

Siegfried Sassoon

THE ANTHEM FOR DOOMED YOUTH

What passing-bells for these who died as cattle?
Only the monstrous anger of the guns.
Only the stuttering rifles' rapid rattle
Can patter out their hasty orisons.
No mockeries for them; no prayers or bells,
Nor any voice of mourning save the choirs —
The shrill demented choirs of wailing shells;
And bugles calling for them from sad shires.

What candles may be held to speed them all?
Not in the hands of boys, but in their eyes
Shall shine the holy glimmers of good-byes.
The pallor of girls' brows shall be their pall;
Their flowers the tenderness of patient minds.
And each slow dusk a drawing-down of blinds.

Wilfred Owen

AFTER BLENHEIM

It was a summer evening,
  Old Kaspar's work was done,
And he before his cottage door
  Was sitting in the sun,
And by him sported on the green
His little grandchild Wilhelmine.

She saw her brother Peterkin
  Roll something large and round,
Which he beside the rivulet
  In playing there had found;
He came to ask what he had found
That was so large, and smooth, and round.

Old Kaspar took it from the boy,
  Who stood expectant by;
And then the old man shook his head,
  And with a natural sigh,
" 'Tis some poor fellow's skull," said he,
"Who fell in the great victory.

"I find them in the garden,
  For there's many here about;
And often when I go to plow,
  The plowshare turns them out!
For many thousand men," said he,
"Were slain in that great victory."

"Now tell us what 'twas all about,"
  Young Peterkin, he cries;

And little Wilhelmine looks up
  With wonder-waiting eyes;
"Now tell us all about the war,
  And what they fought each other for."

"It was the English," Kaspar said,
  "Who put the French to rout;
But what they fought each other for
  I could not well make out;
But everybody said," quoth he,
"That 'twas a famous victory.

"My father lived at Blenheim then,
  Yon little stream hard by;
They burnt his dwelling to the ground,
  And he was forced to fly;
So with his wife and child he fled,
Nor had he where to rest his head.

"With fire and sword the country round
  Was wasted far and wide,
And many a childing mother then,
  And new-born baby died;
But things like that, you know, must be
At every famous victory.

"They say it was a shocking sight
  After the field was won;
For many thousand bodies here
  Lay rotting in the sun;
But things like that, you know, must be
After a famous victory.

"Great praise the Duke of Marlbro' won,
    And our good Prince Eugene."
"Why, 'twas a very wicked thing!"
    Said little Wilhelmine.
"Nay ... nay ... my little girl," quoth he,
"It was a famous victory.

"And everybody praised the Duke
    Who this great fight did win."
"But what good came of it at last?"
    Quoth little Peterkin.
"Why, that I cannot tell," said he,
"But 'twas a famous victory."

                                    Robert Southey

AFTERMATH

Have you forgotten yet? ...
For the world's events have rumbled on since those gagged
        days,
Like traffic checked awhile at the crossing of city ways:
And the haunted gap in your mind has filled with thoughts
        that flow
Like clouds in the lit heavens of life; and you're a man
        reprieved to go,
Taking your peaceful share of time, with joy to spare.
But the past is just the same — and War's a bloody game. ...
Have you forgotten yet? ...
*Look down, and swear by the slain of the War that you'll never
    forget.*

Do you remember the dark months you held the sector at
    Mametz —
The nights you watched and wired and dug and piled
    sandbags on parapets?

Do you remember the rats; and the stench
Of corpses rotting in front of the front-line trench —
And dawn coming, dirty-white, and chill with a hopeless
    rain?
Do you ever stop and ask, "Is it all going to happen again?"

Do you remember that hour of din before the attack —
And the anger, the blind compassion that seized and shook
    you then
As you peered at the doomed and haggard faces of your men?
Do you remember the stretcher-cases lurching back
With dying eyes and lolling heads — those ashen-gray
Masks of the lads who once were keen and kind and gay?

Have you forgotten yet? . . .
Look up, and swear by the green of the Spring that you'll never
    forget.

                               Siegfried Sassoon

Remarkable Sonnets

SONNETS

Man has his unseen friend, his unseen twin,
His straitened spirit's possibility,
The palace unexplored he thinks an inn,
The glorious garden which he wanders by.
It is beside us while we clutch at clay
To daub ourselves that we may never see.
Like the lame donkey lured by moving hay
We chase the shade but let the real be.
Yet, when confusion in our heaven brings stress,
We thrust on that unseen, get stature from it,
Cast to the devil's challenge the man's yes,
And stream our fiery hour like a comet,
And know for that fierce hour a friend behind,
With sword and shield, the second to the mind.

* * *

What am I, Life? A thing of watery salt
Held in cohesion by unresting cells,
Which work they know not why, which never halt,
Myself unwitting where their Master dwells.
I do not bid them, yet they toil, they spin;
A world which uses me as I use them,
Nor do I know which end or which begin
Nor which to praise, which pamper, which condemn.
So, like a marvel in a marvel set,
I answer to the vast, as wave by wave
The sea of air goes over, dry or wet,
Or the full moon comes swimming from her cave,

Or the great sun comes north, this myriad I
Tingles, not knowing how, yet wondering why.

* * *

Ah, we are neither heaven nor earth, but men;
Something that uses and despises both,
That takes its earth's contentment in the pen,
Then sees the world's injustice and is wroth,
And flinging off youth's happy promise, flies
Up to some breach, despising earthly things,
And, in contempt of hell and heaven, dies,
Rather than bear some yoke of priests or kings.
Our joys are not of heaven nor earth, but man's,
A woman's beauty or a child's delight,
The trembling blood when the discoverer scans
The sought-for world, the guessed-at satellite;
The ringing scene, the stone at point to blush
For unborn men to look at and say "Hush."

* * *

O little self, within whose smallness lies
All that man was, and is, and will become,
Atom unseen that comprehends the skies
And tells the tracks by which the planets roam.
That, without moving, knows the joys of wings,
The tiger's strength, the eagle's secrecy,
And in the hovel can consort with kings,
Or clothe a god with his own mystery.
O with what darkness do we cloak thy light,
What dusty folly gather thee for food,
Thou who alone art knowledge and delight,
The heavenly bread, the beautiful, the good
O living self, O god, O morning star,
Give us thy light, forgive us what we are.

John Masefield

NEW ENGLAND

Here where the wind is always north-north-east
And children learn to walk on frozen toes,
Wonder begets an envy of all those
Who boil elsewhere with such a lyric yeast
Of love that you will hear them at a feast
Where demons would appeal for some repose,
Still clamoring where the chalice overflows
And crying wildest who have drunk the least.

Passion is here a soilure of the wits,
We're told, and Love a cross for them to bear;
Joy shivers in the corner where she knits
And Conscience always has the rocking-chair,
Cheerful as when she tortured into fits
The first cat that was ever killed by Care.

Edwin Arlington Robinson

SONNET

Down to the Puritan marrow of my bones
There's something in this richness that I hate.
I love the look, austere, immaculate,
Of landscapes drawn in pearly monotones.
There's something in my very blood that owns
Bare hills, cold silver on a sky of slate,
A thread of water, churned to milky spate
Streaming through slanted pastures fenced with stones.
I love those skies, thin blue or snowy gray,
Those fields sparse-planted rendering meager sheaves;
That spring, briefer than apple-blossom's breath,

Summer, so much too beautiful to stay,
Swift autumn, like a bonfire of leaves,
And sleepy winter, like the sleep of death.

Elinor Wylie

THE DEAD

These hearts were woven of human joys and cares,
  Washed marvelously with sorrow, swift to mirth,
The years had given them kindness. Dawn was theirs,
  And sunset, and the colors of the earth.
These had seen movement, and heard music; known
  Slumber and waking; loved; gone proudly friended;
Felt the quick stir of wonder; sat alone;
  Touched flowers and furs and cheeks. All this is ended.

There are waters blown by changing winds to laughter
And lit by the rich skies, all day. And after,
  Frost, with a gesture, stays the waves that dance
And wandering loveliness. He leaves a white
  Unbroken glory, a gathered radiance,
A width, a shining peace, under the night.

Rupert Brooke

NATURE

As a fond mother, when the day is o'er,
  Leads by the hand her little child to bed,
  Half willing, half reluctant to be led,
  And leave his broken playthings on the floor,
Still gazing at them through the open door,
  Nor wholly reassured and comforted
  By promises of others in their stead,
  Which, though more splendid, may not please him more;

So Nature deals with us, and takes away
  Our playthings one by one, and by the hand
  Leads us to rest so gently, that we go
Scarce knowing if we wish to go or stay,
  Being too full of sleep to understand
  How far the unknown transcends the what we know.
                    Henry Wadsworth Longfellow

HOW DO I LOVE THEE?

How do I love thee?   Let me count the ways.
I love thee to the depth and breadth and height
My soul can reach, when feeling out of sight
For the ends of Being and Ideal Grace.
I love thee to the level of everyday's
Most quiet need, by sun and candlelight.
I love thee freely, as men strive for Right;
I love thee purely, as they turn from Praise.
I love thee with the passion put to use
In my old griefs, and with my childhood's faith.
I love thee with a love I seemed to lose
With my lost saints — I love thee with the breath,
Smiles, tears, of all my life! — and, if God choose,
I shall but love thee better after death.
                    Elizabeth Barrett Browning

SHAKESPEARE

Others abide our question.   Thou art free.
We ask and ask — Thou smilest and art still,
Out-topping knowledge.   For the loftiest hill

Who to the stars uncrowns his majesty,
Planting his steadfast footsteps in the sea,
Making the heaven of heavens his dwelling-place,
Spares but the cloudy border of his base
To the foiled searching of mortality:
And thou, who didst the stars and sunbeams know,
Self-schooled, self-scanned, self-honored, self-secure,
Didst tread on earth unguessed at — Better so!
All pains the immortal spirit must endure,
All weakness which impairs, all griefs which bow,
Find their sole voice in that victorious brow.

Matthew Arnold

OZYMANDIAS

I met a traveler from an antique land
Who said: "Two vast and trunkless legs of stone
Stand in the desert.   Near them, on the sand,
Half sunk, a shattered visage lies, whose frown,
And wrinkled lip, and sneer of cold command,
Tell that the sculptor well those passions read
Which yet survive, stamped on these lifeless things,
The hand that mocked them, and the heart that fed.
And on the pedestal these words appear —
'My name is Ozymandias, king of kings:
Look on my works, ye Mighty, and despair!'
Nothing beside remains.   Round the decay
Of that colossal wreck, boundless and bare
The lone and level sands stretch far away."

Percy Bysshe Shelley

BRIGHT STAR

Bright Star! would I were steadfast as thou art —
    Not in lone splendor hung aloft the night,
And watching, with eternal lids apart,
    Like Nature's patient, sleepless Eremite,
The moving waters at their priestlike task
    Of pure ablution round earth's human shores,
Or gazing on the new soft-fallen mask
    Of snow upon the mountains and the moors —
No — yet still steadfast, still unchangeable,
    Pillowed upon my fair love's ripening breast,
To feel for ever its soft fall and swell,
    Awake for ever in a sweet unrest,
Still, still to hear her tender-taken breath,
And so live ever — or else swoon to death.

John Keats

ENGLAND, 1802

I

O friend! I know not which way I must look
For comfort, being, as I am, oppressed,
To think that now our life is only dressed
For show; mean handy-work of craftsman, cook,
Or groom! — We must run glittering like a brook
In the open sunshine, or we are unblest:
The wealthiest man among us is the best:
No grandeur now in nature or in book
Delights us. Rapine, avarice, expense,
This is idolatry; and these we adore:

Plain living and high thinking are no more:
The homely beauty of the good old cause
Is gone; our peace, our fearful innocence,
   And pure religion breathing household laws.

II

Milton! thou should'st be living at this hour:
England hath need of thee: she is a fen
Of stagnant waters: altar, sword, and pen,
Fireside, the heroic wealth of hall and bower,
Have forfeited their ancient English dower
Of inward happiness.   We are selfish men;
Oh! raise us up, return to us again;
And give us manners, virtue, freedom, power.
Thy soul was like a Star, and dwelt apart;
Thou hadst a voice whose sound was like the sea:
Pure as the naked heavens, majestic, free,
So didst thou travel on life's common way,
In cheerful godliness; and yet thy heart
   The lowliest duties on herself did lay.

William Wordsworth

COMPOSED UPON WESTMINSTER BRIDGE,
SEPTEMBER 3, 1802

Earth has not anything to show more fair:
Dull would he be of soul who could pass by
A sight so touching in its majesty:
This City now doth, like a garment, wear
The beauty of the morning; silent, bare,
Ships, towers, domes, theaters, and temples lie

Open unto the fields, and to the sky;
All bright and glittering in the smokeless air.
Never did sun more beautifully steep
In his first splendor valley, rock, or hill;
Ne'er saw I, never felt, a calm so deep!
The river glideth at his own sweet will:
Dear God! the very houses seem asleep;
And all that mighty heart is lying still!

William Wordsworth

"SCORN NOT THE SONNET"

Scorn not the Sonnet; Critic, you have frowned,
Mindless of its just honors; with this key
Shakespeare unlocked his heart; the melody
Of this small lute gave ease to Petrarch's wound;
A thousand times this pipe did Tasso sound;
With it Camöens soothed an exile's grief;
The Sonnet glittered a gay myrtle leaf
Amid the cypress with which Dante crowned
His visionary brow: a glow-worm lamp,
It cheered mild Spenser, called from Faeryland
To struggle through dark ways; and, when a damp
Fell round the path of Milton, in his hand
The Thing became a trumpet; whence he blew
Soul-animating strains — alas, too few!

William Wordsworth

ON HIS BEING ARRIVED TO THE AGE OF TWENTY-THREE

How soon hath Time, the subtle thief of youth,
    Stolen on his wing my three and twentieth year!
    My hasting days fly on with full career,
    But my late spring no bud or blossom shew'th.
Perhaps my semblance might deceive the truth,
    That I to manhood am arrived so near;
    And inward ripeness doth much less appear,
    That some more timely-happy spirits endu'th.
Yet it be less or more, or soon or slow,
    It shall be still in strictest measure even
    To that same lot, however mean or high,
Toward which Time leads me, and the will of heaven:
    All is, if I have grace to use it so,
    As ever in my great Taskmaster's eye.

John Milton

ON HIS BLINDNESS

When I consider how my light is spent,
    Ere half my days in this dark world and wide,
    And that one talent which is death to hide
    Lodged in me useless, though my soul more bent
To serve therewith my Maker, and present
    My true account, lest he returning chide,
    "Doth God exact day-labor, light denied?"
    I fondly ask.　But patience, to prevent
That murmur, soon replies, "God doth not need
    Either man's work or his own gifts.　Who best
    Bear his mild yoke, they serve him best.　His state

Is kingly: thousands at his bidding speed,
   And post o'er land and ocean without rest;
   They also serve who only stand and wait."
                               John Milton

TRUE LOVE

Let me not to the marriage of true minds
Admit impediments.   Love is not love
Which alters when it alteration finds,
Or bends with the remover to remove.
O, no! it is an ever-fixèd mark,
That looks on tempests and is never shaken;
It is the star to every wandering bark,
Whose worth's unknown, although his height be taken.
Love's not Time's fool, though rosy lips and cheeks
Within his bending sickle's compass come;
Love alters not with his brief hours and weeks,
But bears it out even to the edge of doom.
   If this be error and upon me proved,
   I never writ, nor no man ever loved.
                            William Shakespeare
                            (Sonnet CXVI)

FRIENDSHIP

When to the sessions of sweet silent thought
I summon up remembrance of things past,
I sigh the lack of many a thing I sought,
And with old woes new wail my dear time's waste:
Then can I drown an eye, unused to flow,
For precious friends hid in death's dateless night,

And weep afresh love's long since canceled woe,
And moan the expense of many a vanished sight:
Then can I grieve at grievances foregone,
And heavily from woe to woe tell o'er
The sad account of fore-bemoanèd moan,
Which I new pay as if not paid before.
    But if the while I think on thee, dear friend,
    All losses are restored and sorrows end.

William Shakespeare
(Sonnet xxx)

WITH HOW SAD STEPS, O MOON

With how sad steps, O Moon, thou climb'st the skies!
How silently, and with how wan a face!
What, may it be that even in heavenly place
That busy archer his sharp arrows tries?
Sure, if that long-with-love-acquainted eyes
Can judge of love, thou feel'st a lover's case,
I read it in thy looks; thy languished grace,
To me, that feel the like, thy state descries.
Then, ev'n of fellowship, O Moon, tell me,
Is constant love deemed there but want of wit?
Are beauties there as proud as here they be?
Do they above love to be loved, and yet
Those lovers scorn whom that love doth possess?
Do they call virtue there ungratefulness?

Sir Philip Sidney
(*Astrophel and Stella*, xxxi)

Love and Memory

O, MY LUVE'S LIKE A RED, RED ROSE

O, my luve's like a red, red rose,
    That's newly sprung in June.
O, my luve's like the melodie
    That's sweetly play'd in tune.

As fair thou art, my bonnie lass,
    So deep in luve am I;
And I will luve thee still, my dear,
    Till a' the seas gang dry.

Till a' the seas gang dry, my dear,
    And the rocks melt wi' the sun!
And I will luve thee still, my dear,
    While the sands o' life shall run.

And fare thee weel, my only luve!
    And fare thee weel a while!
And I will come again, my luve,
    Tho' it were ten thousand mile.

Robert Burns

ALL THAT'S PAST

Very old are the woods;
    And the buds that break
Out of the briar's boughs,
    When March winds wake.

So old with their beauty are —
    Oh, no man knows
Through what wild centuries
    Roves back the rose.

Very old are the brooks;
    And the rills that rise
Where snow sleeps cold beneath
    The azure skies
Sing such a history
    Of come and gone,
Their every drop is as wise
    As Solomon.

Very old are we men;
    Our dreams are tales
Told in dim Eden
    By Eve's nightingales;
We wake and whisper awhile,
    But, the day gone by,
Silence and sleep like fields
    Of amaranth lie.

Walter de la Mare

NOD

Softly along the road of evening,
In a twilight dim with rose,
Wrinkled with age, and drenched with dew
Old Nod, the shepherd, goes.

His drowsy flock streams on before him,
Their fleeces charged with gold,

To where the sun's last beam leans low
On Nod the shepherd's fold.

The hedge is quick and green with briar,
From their sand the conies creep;
And all the birds that fly in heaven
Flock singing home to sleep.

His lambs outnumber a noon's roses,
Yet, when night's shadows fall,
His blind old sheep-dog, Slumber-soon,
Misses not one of all.

His are the quiet steeps of dreamland,
The waters of no-more-pain,
His ram's bell rings 'neath an arch of stars,
"Rest, rest, and rest again."

Walter de la Mare

FALLEN MAJESTY

Although crowds gathered once if she but showed her face,
And even old men's eyes grew dim, this hand alone,
Like some last courtier at a gypsy camping-place
Babbling of fallen majesty, records what's gone.

The lineaments, a heart that laughter has made sweet,
These, these remain, but I record what's gone.   A crowd
Will gather, and not know it walks the very street
Whereon a thing once walked that seemed a burning cloud.

William Butler Yeats

WHEN I WAS ONE-AND-TWENTY

When I was one-and-twenty
    I heard a wise man say,
"Give crowns and pounds and guineas
    But not your heart away;
Give pearls away and rubies
    But keep your fancy free."
But I was one-and-twenty,
    No use to talk to me.

When I was one-and-twenty
    I heard him say again,
"The heart out of the bosom
    Was never given in vain;
'Tis paid with sighs a plenty
    And sold for endless rue."
And I am two-and-twenty,
    And oh, 'tis true, 'tis true.

A. E. Housman

OH, WHEN I WAS IN LOVE WITH YOU

Oh, when I was in love with you,
    Then I was clean and brave,
And miles around the wonder grew
    How well did I behave.

And now the fancy passes by,
    And nothing will remain,
And miles around they'll say that I
    Am quite myself again.

A. E. Housman

FOR A DEAD LADY

No more with overflowing light
Shall fill the eyes that now are faded,
Nor shall another's fringe with night
Their woman-hidden world as they did.
No more shall quiver down the days
The flowing wonder of her ways,
Whereof no language may requite
The shifting and the many-shaded.

The grace, divine, definitive,
Clings only as a faint forestalling;
The laugh that love could not forgive
Is hushed, and answers to no calling;
The forehead and the little ears
Have gone where Saturn keeps the years;
The breast where roses could not live
Has done with rising and with falling.

The beauty, shattered by the laws
That have creation in their keeping,
No longer trembles at applause,
Or over children that are sleeping;
And we who delve in beauty's lore
Know all that we have known before
Of what inexorable cause
Makes Time so vicious in his reaping.

Edwin Arlington Robinson

A DREAM

My dead love came to me and said:
  "God gives me one hour's rest
To spend with thee on earth again;
  How shall we spend it best?"

"Why, as of old," I said; and so
  We quarreled as of old;
But, when I turned to make my peace,
  That one short hour was told.
                  Stephen Phillips

WYNKEN, BLYNKEN, AND NOD

Wynken, Blynken, and Nod one night
  Sailed off in a wooden shoe —
Sailed on a river of crystal light,
  Into a sea of dew.
"Where are you going, and what do you wish?"
  The old moon asked the three.
"We have come to fish for the herring fish
  That live in this beautiful sea;
  Nets of silver and gold have we!"
          Said Wynken,
          Blynken,
          And Nod.

The old moon laughed and sang a song,
  As they rocked in the wooden shoe,
And the wind that sped them all night long
  Ruffled the waves of dew.
The little stars were the herring fish
  That lived in that beautiful sea —

"Now cast your nets wherever you wish —
   Never afeard are we";
So cried the stars to the fishermen three:
          Wynken,
          Blynken,
          And Nod.

All night long their nets they threw
   To the stars in the twinkling foam —
Then down from the skies came the wooden shoe,
   Bringing the fishermen home;
'Twas all so pretty a sail it seemed
   As if it could not be,
And some folks thought 'twas a dream they'd dreamed
   Of sailing that beautiful sea —
   But I shall name you fishermen three:
          Wynken,
          Blynken,
          And Nod.

Wynken and Blynken are two little eyes,
   And Nod is a little head,
And the wooden shoe that sailed the skies
   Is a wee one's trundle-bed.
So shut your eyes while mother sings
   Of wonderful sights that be,
And you shall see the beautiful things
   As you rock in the misty sea,
   Where the old shoe rocked the fishermen three:
          Wynken,
          Blynken,
          And Nod.

Eugene Field

LITTLE BOY BLUE

The little toy dog is covered with dust,
But sturdy and staunch he stands;
And the little toy soldier is red with rust,
And his musket moulds in his hands.
Time was when the little toy dog was new,
And the soldier was passing fair;
And that was the time when our Little Boy Blue
Kissed them and put them there.

"Now, don't you go till I come," he said,
"And don't you make any noise!"
So, toddling off to his trundle-bed,
He dreamt of the pretty toys;
And, as he was dreaming, an angel song
Awakened our Little Boy Blue —
Oh! the years are many, the years are long
But the little toy friends are true!

Ay, faithful to Little Boy Blue they stand,
Each in the same old place —
Awaiting the touch of a little hand,
The smile of a little face;
And they wonder, as waiting the long years through
In the dust of that little chair,
What has become of our Little Boy Blue,
Since he kissed them and put them there.

Eugene Field

"TEARS, IDLE TEARS"

Tears, idle tears, I know not what they mean,
Tears from the depth of some divine despair

Rise in the heart, and gather to the eyes,
In looking on the happy Autumn fields,
And thinking of the days that are no more.

Fresh as the first beam glittering on a sail
That brings our friends up from the underworld,
Sad as the last which reddens over one
That sinks with all we love below the verge;
So sad, so fresh, the days that are no more.

Ah, sad and strange as in dark summer dawns
The earliest pipe of half-awakened birds
To dying ears, when unto dying eyes
The casement slowly grows a glimmering square;
So sad, so strange, the days that are no more.

Dear as remembered kisses after death,
And sweet as those by hopeless fancy feigned
On lips that are for others; deep as love,
Deep as first love, and wild with all regret;
O Death in Life, the days that are no more!
                              Alfred Lord Tennyson

BREAK, BREAK, BREAK

Break, break, break,
    On thy cold gray stones, O Sea!
And I would that my tongue could utter
    The thoughts that arise in me.

O well for the fisherman's boy,
    That he shouts with his sister at play!

O well for the sailor lad,
   That he sings in his boat on the bay!

And the stately ships go on
   To their haven under the hill;
But O for the touch of a vanished hand,
   And the sound of a voice that is still!

Break, break, break,
   At the foot of thy crags, O Sea!
But the tender grace of a day that is dead
   Will never come back to me.

Alfred Lord Tennyson

MEETING AT NIGHT

The gray sea and the long black land;
And the yellow half-moon large and low;
And the startled little waves that leap
In fiery ringlets from their sleep,
As I gain the cove with pushing prow,
And quench its speed in the slushy sand.

Then a mile of warm sea-scented beach;
Three fields to cross till a farm appears;
A tap at the pane, the quick sharp scratch
And blue spirt of a lighted match,
And a voice less loud, through its joys and fears,
Than the two hearts beating each to each!

Robert Browning

MY LOST YOUTH

Often I think of the beautiful town
That is seated by the sea;
Often in thought go up and down
The pleasant streets of that dear old town,
   And my youth comes back to me.
      And a verse of a Lapland song
      Is haunting my memory still:
      "A boy's will is the wind's will,
And the thoughts of youth are long, long thoughts."

I can see the shadowy lines of its trees,
   And catch, in sudden gleams,
The sheen of the far-surrounding seas,
And islands that were the Hesperides
   Of all my boyish dreams.
      And the burden of that old song,
      It murmurs and whispers still:
      "A boy's will is the wind's will,
And the thoughts of youth are long, long thoughts."

I remember the black wharves and the slips,
   And the sea-tides tossing free;
And Spanish sailors with bearded lips,
And the beauty and mystery of the ships,
   And the magic of the sea.
      And the voice of that wayward song
      Is singing and saying still:
      "A boy's will is the wind's will,
And the thoughts of youth are long, long thoughts."

I remember the bulwarks by the shore
   And the fort upon the hill;
The sunrise gun, with its hollow roar,
The drumbeat repeated o'er and o'er,
   And the bugle wild and shrill.
      And the music of that old song
      Throbs in my memory still:
      "A boy's will is the wind's will,
And the thoughts of youth are long, long thoughts."

I remember the sea-fight far away,
   How it thundered o'er the tide!
And the dead captains, as they lay
In their graves, o'erlooking the tranquil bay
   Where they in battle died.
      And the sound of that mournful song
      Goes through me with a thrill:
      "A boy's will is the wind's will,
And the thoughts of youth are long, long thoughts."

I can see the breezy dome of groves,
   The shadows of Deering's Woods;
And the friendships old and the early loves
Come back with a Sabbath sound, as of doves
   In quiet neighborhoods.
      And the verse of that sweet old song,
      It flutters and murmurs still:
      "A boy's will is the wind's will,
And the thoughts of youth are long, long thoughts."

I remember the gleams and glooms that dart
   Across the school-boy's brain;

The song and the silence in the heart,
That in part are prophecies, and in part
   Are longings wild and vain.
     And the voice of that fitful song
     Sings on, and is never still:
     "A boy's will is the wind's will,
And the thoughts of youth are long, long thoughts."

There are things of which I may not speak;
   There are dreams that cannot die;
There are thoughts that make the strong heart weak,
And bring a pallor into the cheek,
   And a mist before the eye.
     And the words of that fatal song
     Come over me like a chill:
     "A boy's will is the wind's will,
And the thoughts of youth are long, long thoughts."

Strange to me now are the forms I meet
   When I visit the dear old town;
But the native air is pure and sweet,
And the trees that o'ershadow each well-known street,
   As they balance up and down,
     Are singing the beautiful song,
     Are sighing and whispering still:
     "A boy's will is the wind's will,
And the thoughts of youth are long, long thoughts."

And Deering's Woods are fresh and fair,
   And with joy that is almost pain
My heart goes back to wander there,
And among the dreams of the days that were,

I find my lost youth again.
And the strange and beautiful song,
The groves are repeating it still:
"A boy's will is the wind's will,
And the thoughts of youth are long, long thoughts."
Henry Wadsworth Longfellow

PRAYER TO PERSEPHONE

Be to her, Persephone,
All the things I might not be;
Take her head upon your knee.
She that was so proud and wild,
Flippant, arrogant, and free,
She that had no need of me,
Is a little lonely child
Lost in Hell — Persephone,
Take her head upon your knee;
Say to her, "My dear, my dear,
It is not so dreadful here."
Edna St. Vincent Millay

AFTER A DOLMETSCH CONCERT

Out of the conquered Past
    Unravishable Beauty;
Hearts that are dew and dust
    Rebuking the dream of Death;
Flower o' the clay down-cast
    Triumphant in Earth's aroma;
Strings that were strained in rust
    A-tremble with Music's breath!

Wine that was spilt in haste
    Arising in fumes more precious;
Garlands that fell forgot
    Rooting to wondrous bloom;
Youth that would flow to waste
    Pausing in pool-green valleys —
And Passion that lasted not
    Surviving the voiceless Tomb!

Arthur Upson

READING ALOUD

Once we read Tennyson aloud
    In our great fireside chair;
Between the lines my lips could touch
    Her April-scented hair.

How very fond I was, to think
    The printed poems fair,
When close within my arms I held
    A living lyric there!

Christopher Morley

MY OLD KENTUCKY HOME

The sun shines bright in the old Kentucky home;
    'Tis summer, the darkeys are gay;
The corn-top's ripe, and the meadow's in the bloom,
    While the birds make music all the day.
The young folks roll on the little cabin floor,
    All merry, all happy and bright;
By-'n'-by hard times comes a-knocking at the door: —
    Then my old Kentucky home, good-night!

Weep no more, my lady,
    O, weep no more today!
We will sing one song for the old Kentucky home,
    For the old Kentucky home, far away.

They hunt no more for the possum and the coon,
    On the meadow, the hill, and the shore;
They sing no more by the glimmer of the moon,
    On the bench by the old cabin door.
The day goes by like a shadow o'er the heart,
    With sorrow, where all was delight;
The time has come when the darkeys have to part: —
    Then my old Kentucky home, good-night!

The head must bow, and the back will have to bend,
    Wherever the darkey may go;
A few more days, and the trouble all will end,
    In the field where the sugar-canes grow.
A few more days for to tote the weary load —
    No matter, 'twill never be light;
A few more days till we totter on the road: —
    Then my old Kentucky home, good-night!

Weep no more, my lady,
    O, weep no more today!
We will sing one song for the old Kentucky home,
    For the old Kentucky home, far away.
                              Stephen Collins Foster

GIVE ALL TO LOVE

Give all to love;
Obey thy heart;

Friends, kindred, days,
Estate, good-fame,
Plans, credit, and the Muse —
Nothing refuse.

'Tis a brave master;
Let it have scope:
Follow it utterly,
Hope beyond hope:
High and more high
It dives into noon,
With wing unspent,
Untold intent;
But it is a god,
Knows its own path
And the outlets of the sky.

It was never for the mean;
It requireth courage stout.
Souls above doubt,
Valor unbending,
It will reward —
They shall return
More than they were,
And ever ascending.

Leave all for love;
Yet, hear me, yet,
One word more thy heart behoved,
One pulse more of firm endeavor —
Keep thee today,
Tomorrow, forever,

Free as an Arab
Of thy beloved.

Cling with life to the maid;
But when the surprise,
First vague shadow of surmise
Flits across her bosom young,
Of a joy apart from thee,
Free be she, fancy-free;
Nor thou detain her vesture's hem,
Nor the palest rose she flung
From her summer diadem.

Though thou loved her as thyself,
As a self of purer clay,
Though her parting dims the day,
Stealing grace from all alive;
Heartily know,
When half-gods go,
The gods arrive.

Ralph Waldo Emerson

THE OLD FAMILIAR FACES

I have had playmates, I have had companions,
In my days of childhood, in my joyful schooldays —
All, all are gone, the old familiar faces.

I have been laughing, I have been carousing,
Drinking late, sitting late, with my bosom cronies —
All, all are gone, the old familiar faces.

I loved a Love once, fairest among women:
Closed are her doors on me, I must not see her —
All, all are gone, the old familiar faces.

I have a friend, a kinder friend has no man:
Like an ingrate, I left my friend abruptly;
Left him, to muse on the old familiar faces.

Ghost-like, I paced round the haunts of my childhood.
Earth seemed a desert I was bound to traverse,
Seeking to find the old familiar faces.

Friend of my bosom, thou more than a brother,
Why wert not thou born in my father's dwelling?
So might we talk of the old familiar faces —

How some they have died, and some they have left me,
And some are taken from me; all are departed —
All, all are gone, the old familiar faces.

Charles Lamb

THE LIGHT OF OTHER DAYS

Oft in the stilly night,
    Ere slumber's chain has bound me,
Fond Memory brings the light
    Of other days around me:
      The smiles, the tears
      Of boyhood's years,
The words of love then spoken;
      The eyes that shone
      Now dimm'd and gone,
The cheerful hearts now broken!

Thus in the stilly night
  Ere slumber's chain has bound me,
Sad Memory brings the light
  Of other days around me.

When I remember all
  The friends so link'd together
I've seen around me fall
  Like leaves in wintry weather,
    I feel like one
    Who treads alone
Some banquet hall deserted,
    Whose lights are fled,
    Whose garlands dead,
And all but he departed!
Thus in the stilly night
  Ere slumber's chain has bound me,
Sad Memory brings the light
  Of other days around me.

Thomas Moore

LOVE'S SECRET

Never seek to tell thy love,
  Love that never told can be;
For the gentle wind doth move
  Silently, invisibly.

I told my love, I told my love,
  I told her all my heart,
Trembling, cold, in ghastly fears.
  Ah! she did depart!

Soon after she was gone from me,
   A traveler came by,
Silently, invisibly:
   He took her with a sigh.

                   William Blake

PAST AND PRESENT

I remember, I remember
The house where I was born,
The little window where the sun
Came peeping in at morn;
He never came a wink too soon
Nor brought too long a day;
But now, I often wish the night
Had borne my breath away.

I remember, I remember
The roses, red and white,
The violets, and the lily cups —
Those flowers made of light!
The lilacs where the robin built,
And where my brother set
The laburnum on his birthday —
The tree is living yet.

I remember, I remember
Where I was used to swing,
And thought the air must rush as fresh
To swallows on the wing;
My spirit flew in feathers then
That is so heavy now,
And summer pools could hardly cool
The fever on my brow.

I remember, I remember,
The fir trees dark and high;
I used to think their slender tops
Were close against the sky:
It was a childish ignorance,
But now 'tis little joy
To know I'm farther off from Heaven
Than when I was a boy.

Thomas Hood

SONG

Why so pale and wan, fond lover?
   Prithee, why so pale?
Will, when looking well can't move her,
   Looking ill prevail?
   Prithee, why so pale?

Why so dull and mute, young sinner?
   Prithee, why so mute?
Will, when speaking well can't win her,
   Saying nothing do't?
   Prithee, why so mute?

Quit, quit, for shame, this will not move:
   This cannot take her.
If of herself she will not love,
   Nothing can make her:
   The devil take her!

Sir John Suckling

TO CELIA

Drink to me only with thine eyes,
   And I will pledge with mine;
Or leave a kiss but in the cup,
   And I'll not look for wine.
The thirst that from the soul doth rise
   Doth ask a drink divine;
But might I of Jove's nectar sup,
   I would not change for thine.

I sent thee late a rosy wreath,
   Not so much honoring thee
As giving it a hope that there
   It could not withered be;
But thou thereon didst only breathe
   And sent'st it back to me;
Since when it grows, and smells, I swear,
   Not of itself but thee!

Ben Jonson

"NOT MARBLE, NOR THE GILDED MONUMENTS"

The praisers of women in their proud and beautiful poems
Naming the grave mouth and the hair and the eyes
Boasted those they loved should be forever remembered
These were lies

The words sound but the face in the Istrian sun is forgotten
The poet speaks but to her dead ears no more
The sleek throat is gone and the breast that was troubled to
     listen
Shadow from door

Therefore I will not praise your knees nor your fine walking
Telling you men shall remember your name as long
As lips move or breath is spent or the iron of English
Rings from a tongue

I shall say you were young and your arms straight and your
      mouth scarlet
I shall say you will die and none will remember you
Your arms change and none remember the swish of your
      garments
Nor the click of your shoe

Not with my hand's strength not with difficult labor
Springing the obstinate words to the bones of your breast
And the stubborn line to your young stride and the breath to
      your breathing
And the beat to your haste

Shall I prevail on the hearts of unborn men to remember
(What is a dead girl but a shadowy ghost
Or a dead man's voice but a distant and vain affirmation
Like dream words most)

Therefore I will not speak of the undying glory of women
I will say you were young and straight and your skin fair
And you stood in the door and the sun was a shadow of leaves
      on your shoulders
And a leaf on your hair

I will not speak of the famous beauty of dead women
I will say the shape of a leaf lay once on your hair
Till the world ends and the eyes are out and the mouths
      broken
Look! It is there!

Archibald MacLeish

MUSIC I HEARD

Music I heard with you was more than music,
And bread I broke with you was more than bread
Now that I am without you, all is desolate,
All that was once so beautiful is dead.

Your hands once touched this table and this silver,
And I have seen your fingers hold this glass.
These things do not remember you, beloved:
And yet your touch upon them will not pass.

For it was in my heart you moved among them,
And blessed them with your hands and with your eyes.
And in my heart they will remember always:
They knew you once, O beautiful and wise!

Conrad Aiken

LOVE IS A TERRIBLE THING

I went out to the farthest meadow,
I lay down in the deepest shadow;

And I said unto the earth, "Hold me,"
And unto the night, "O enfold me,"

And unto the wind petulantly
I cried, "You know not, for you are free!"

And I begged the little leaves to lean
Low and together for a safe screen;

Then to the stars I told my tale:
"That is my home-light, there in the vale,

"And O, I know that I shall return,
But let me lie first mid the unfeeling fern.

"For there is a flame that has blown too near,
And there is a name that has grown too dear,
And there is a fear"...

And to the still hills and cool earth and far sky I made moan,
"The heart in my bosom is not my own!

"O would I were free as the wind on wing;
Love is a terrible thing!"

Grace Fallow Norton

THE CHAPLET

When I came home at evening
    With flowers in my hand,
And on my head a chaplet
    From an enchanted land,
Not one of those that pass'd me
    Appear'd to understand.

They thought that like the others
    I wore a hat, and went
As prosy on the sidewalk
    As one collecting rent —
They knew not who had kissed me
    Nor all the matter meant.

Witter Bynner

GRENSTONE RIVER

Things you heard that blessed be
You shall tell to men like me:

What you heard my lover say
In the golden yesterday,
Leaving me a childish heart,
Glad to revel, quick to start.

And though she awhile is gone
And I come today alone,
'Tis the self-same whisper slips
Through your ripple from her lips.

Long shall she and I be dead,
While you whisper what she said;
You, when I no word can give her,
Shall forever whisper, river:

Things you heard that blessed be,
Telling them to men like me.

Witter Bynner

EVENING SONG

Look off, dear Love, across the sallow sands,
　　And mark yon meeting of the sun and sea,
How long they kiss in sight of all the lands.
　　Ah! longer, longer, we!

Now in the sea's red vintage melts the sun,
　　As Egypt's pearl dissolved in rosy wine,

And Cleopatra night drinks all.   'Tis done,
  Love, lay thy hand in mine.

Come forth, sweet stars, and comfort heaven's heart;
  Glimmer, ye waves, round else unlighted sands.
O night!   Divorce our sun and sky apart,
  Never our lips, our hands.

Sidney Lanier

MEMORY

My mind lets go a thousand things,
Like dates of wars and deaths of kings,
And yet recalls the very hour —
'Twas noon by yonder village tower,
And on the last blue noon in May —
The wind came briskly up this way,
Crisping the brook beside the road;
Then, pausing here, set down its load
Of pine-scents, and shook listlessly
Two petals from that wild-rose tree.

Thomas Bailey Aldrich

REMEMBERING

You said so little that I had to guess
  The thoughts that lay behind your steady eyes,
But men who say a great deal more leave less
  To be remembered when their names arise.

Alice Hartich

A LITTLE WHILE I FAIN WOULD LINGER YET

A little while (my life is almost set!)
    I fain would pause along the downward way,
    Musing an hour in this sad sunset ray,
While, Sweet! our eyes with tender tears are wet:
A little hour I fain would linger yet.

A little while I fain would linger yet,
    All for love's sake, for love that cannot tire;
    Though fervid youth be dead, with youth's desire,
And hope has faded to a vain regret,
A little while I fain would linger yet.

A little while I fain would linger here:
    Behold! who knows what strange, mysterious bars
    'Twixt souls that love may rise in other stars?
Nor can love deem the face of death is fair;
A little while I fain would linger here.

A little while I yearn to hold thee fast,
    Hand locked in hand, and loyal heart to heart;
    (O pitying Christ! those woeful words, "We part!")
So ere the darkness fall, the light be past,
A little while I fain would hold thee fast.

A little while, when light and twilight meet —
    Behind, our broken years; before, the deep
    Weird wonder of the last unfathomed sleep —
A little while I still would clasp thee, Sweet,
A little while, when night and twilight meet.

A little while I fain would linger here;
  Behold! who knows what soul-dividing bars
  Earth's faithful loves may part in other stars?
Nor can love deem the face of death is fair:
A little while I still would linger here.

                      Paul Hamilton Hayne

I SHALL NOT BE AFRAID

I shall not be afraid any more,
Either by night or day;
What would it profit me to be afraid
With you away?

Now I am brave. In the dark night alone
All through the house I go,
Locking the doors and making windows fast
When sharp winds blow.

For there is only sorrow in my heart;
There is no room for fear,
But how I wish I were afraid again,
My dear, my dear!

                      Aline Kilmer

Footloose for Far Places

REVEILLE

Wake: the silver dusk returning
  Up the beach of darkness brims,
And the ship of sunrise burning
  Strands upon the eastern rims.

Wake: the vaulted shadow shatters,
  Trampled to the floor it spanned.
And the tent of night in tatters
  Straws the sky-pavilioned land.

Up, lad, up, 'tis late for lying:
  Hear the drums of morning play;
Hark, the empty highways crying
  "Who'll beyond the hills away?"

Towns and countries woo together,
  Forelands beacon, belfries call;
Never lad that trod on leather
  Lived to feast his heart with all.

Up, lad: thews that lie and cumber
  Sunlit pallets never thrive;
Morns abed and daylight slumber
  Were not meant for man alive.

Clay lies still, but blood's a rover:
  Breath's a ware that will not keep.
Up, lad: when the journey's over
  There'll be time enough to sleep.

                              A. E. Housman

THE VAGABOND

Give to me the life I love,
Let the lave go by me,
Give the jolly heaven above,
And the byway nigh me,
Bed in the bush with stars to see,
Bread to dip in the river,
There's the life for a man like me,
There's the life forever.

Let the blow fall soon or late,
Let what will be o'er me,
Give the face of earth around,
And the road before me.
Wealth I seek not, hope nor love,
Nor a friend to know me;
All I seek, the heaven above
And the road below me.

Or let Autumn fall on me,
Where afield I linger,
Silencing the bird on tree,
Biting the blue finger,
White as meal the frosty field,
Warm the fireside haven,
Not to Autumn will I yield,
Not to Winter even.

Let the blow fall soon or late,
Let what will be o'er me;
Give the face of earth around,
And the road before me.
Wealth I ask not, hope nor love,
Nor a friend to know me,
All I ask, the heaven above
And the road below me!

Robert Louis Stevenson

SEA–FEVER

I must go down to the seas again, to the lonely sea and the
      sky,
And all I ask is a tall ship and a star to steer her by,
And the wheel's kick and the wind's song and the white
      sail's shaking,
And a gray mist on the sea's face and a gray dawn breaking.

I must go down to the seas again, for the call of the running
      tide
Is a wild call and a clear call that may not be denied;
And all I ask is a windy day with the white clouds flying,
And the flung spray and the blown spume, and the sea-gulls
      crying.

I must go down to the seas again to the vagrant gypsy life,
To the gull's way and the whale's way where the wind's like a
      whetted knife;
And all I ask is a merry yarn from a laughing fellow-rover,
And quiet sleep and a sweet dream when the long trick's over.

John Masefield

CALLAO

She's running up for Callao in the blue Pacific weather,
She's running free for Callao on a clean and even keel,
With the ripples chuckling 'round her run and a dainty little
feather
Of foam beneath her figure-head and a ribbon at her heel.

So Tina, snap your castanets —
Tina, Tina —
And Tina, tune your old guitar and sing your gayest
ditty.
For a clipper's bound for Callao, Callao, Callao,
With a reefer boy that loves you so —
Tina, my pretty.

She's rippling on for Callao to a croon of sapphire water,
She's bowling on for Callao with kites and stunsails spread,
With a wail of sea-birds in her tracks and a porpoise to
escort her,
The Cordillera's snows a-shine like pearly clouds ahead.

So, Tina, pick your reddest rose,
Tina, Tina —
And, Tina, wear your brightest shawl to catch a sailor's
money.
For a clipper's bound for Callao, Callao, Callao,
With a reefer boy who loves you so —
Tina, my honey.

Crosbie Garstin

ROMANCE

I will make you brooches and toys for your delight
Of bird-song at morning and star-shine at night.
I will make a palace fit for you and me
Of green days in forests and blue days at sea.

I will make my kitchen, and you shall keep your room,
Where white flows the river and bright blows the broom,
And you shall wash your linen and keep your body white
In rainfall at morning and dewfall at night.

And this shall be for music when no one else is near,
The fine song for singing, the rare song to hear!
That only I remember, that only you admire,
Of the broad road that stretches and the roadside fire.

Robert Louis Stevenson

SOUTH STREET

As I came down to the long street by the water, the sea-ships
       drooped their masts like ladies bowing,
Curtseying friendly in a manner olden,
Shrouds and sails in silken sunlight flowing,
Gleaming and shimmering from silverie into golden,
With the sea-winds through the sunlit spaces blowing.

As I came down to South Street by the glimmering, tossing
      water, the sweet wind blew, oh, softly, sweetly blew
O'er the lean, black docks piled high with curious bales,
Odorous casks, and bundles of foreign goods,
And all the long ships, with their fair, tall sails,
Lading the winey air with the spice of alien woods.

As I came down by the winding streets to the wondrous
    green sea-water, the sounds along the water-front were
    tuned to fine accord;
I heard the racket of the halliards slapping,
Along the bare poles stabbing up aloft;
I saw loose men, their garments ever flapping,
Lounging a-row along each wooden stair:
Their untamed faces in the golden sun were soft,
But their hard, bright eyes were wild, and in the sun's soft
    flare
Nothing they saw but sounding seas and the crush of the
    ravening wind;
Nothing but furious struggle with toil that never would end.
The call of mine ancient sea was clamoring through their
    blood;
Ah, they all felt that call, but nothing they understood,
As I came down by the winding streets to South Street by
    the water.

As I came down to South Street by the soft sea water,
I saw long ships, their mast-heads ever bowing:
Sweet slender maids in clinging gowns of golden,
Curtseying stately in a fashion olden
Bowing sweetly — each a king's fair daughter —
To me, their millionth, millionth lover,
I, the seventh son of the old sea-rover,
As I came down to South Street by the myriad moving
    water.
                                   Francis E. Falkenbury

CARGOES

Quinquireme of Nineveh from distant Ophir,
Rowing home to haven in sunny Palestine,
With a cargo of ivory,
And apes and peacocks,
Sandalwood, cedarwood, and sweet white wine.

Stately Spanish galleon coming from the Isthmus,
Dipping through the Tropics by the palm-green shores,
With a cargo of diamonds,
Emeralds, amethysts,
Topazes, and cinnamon, and gold moidores.

Dirty British coaster with a salt-caked smoke stack,
Butting through the Channel in the mad March days,
With a cargo of Tyne coal,
Road-rails, pig-lead,
Firewood, iron-ware, and cheap tin trays.

John Masefield

THE OLD SHIPS

I have seen old ships sail like swans asleep
Beyond the village which men still call Tyre,
With leaden age o'ercargoed, dipping deep
For Famagusta and the hidden sun
That rings black Cyprus with a lake of fire;
And all those ships were certainly so old
Who knows how oft with squat and noisy gun,
Questing brown slaves or Syrian oranges,
The pirates Genoese

Hell raked them till they rolled
Blood, water, fruit and corpses up the hold.
But now through friendly seas they softly run,
Painted the mid-sea blue or shore-sea green,
Still patterned with the vine and grapes in gold.

But I have seen
Pointing her shapely shadows from the dawn
An image tumbled on a rose-swept bay
A drowsy ship of some yet older day;
And, wonder's breath indrawn,
Thought I — who knows — who knows — but in that same
(Fished up beyond Aeaea, patched up new
— Stern painted brighter blue —)
That talkative, bald-headed seaman came
(Twelve patient comrades sweating at the oar)
From Troy's doom-crimson shore,
And with great lies about his wooden horse
Set the crew laughing, and forgot his course.

It was so old a ship — who knows, who knows?
— And yet so beautiful, I watched in vain
To see the mast burst open with a rose,
And the whole deck put on its leaves again.

James Elroy Flecker

HILLS

I never loved your plains! —
Your gentle valleys,
Your drowsy country lanes
And pleachèd alleys.

I want my hills! — the trail
  That scorns the hollow.
Up, up the ragged shale
  Where few will follow.

Up, over wooded crest
  And mossy boulder
With strong thigh, heaving chest,
  And swinging shoulder.

So let me hold my way,
  By nothing halted,
Until, at close of day,
  I stand, exalted,

High on my hills of dream —
  Dear hills that know me!
And then, how fair will seem
  The lands below me.

How pure, at vesper-time,
  The far bells chiming!
God, give me hills to climb,
  And strength for climbing!

Arthur Guiterman

A WANDERER'S SONG

A wind's in the heart of me, a fire's in my heels,
I am tired of brick and stone and rumbling wagon-wheels;
I hunger for the sea's edge, the limits of the land,
Where the wild old Atlantic is shouting on the sand.

Oh I'll be going, leaving the noises of the street,
To where a lifting foresail-foot is yanking at the sheet;
To a windy, tossing anchorage where yawls and ketches ride,
Oh I'll be going, going, until I meet the tide.

And first I'll hear the sea-wind, the mewing of the gulls,
The clucking, sucking of the sea about the rusty hulls,
The songs at the capstan in the hooker warping out,
And then the heart of me'll know I'm there or thereabout.

Oh I am tired of brick and stone, the heart of me is sick,
For windy green, unquiet sea, the realm of Moby Dick;
And I'll be going, going, from the roaring of the wheels,
For a wind's in the heart of me, a fire's in my heels.

John Masefield

LOVE IN THE WINDS

When I am standing on a mountain crest,
Or hold the tiller in the dashing spray,
My love of you leaps foaming in my breast,
Shouts with the winds and sweeps to their foray;
My heart bounds with the horses of the sea,
And plunges in the wild ride of the night,
Flaunts in the teeth of tempest the large glee
That rides out Fate and welcomes gods to fight.
Ho, love, I laugh aloud for love of you,
Glad that our love is fellow to rough weather —
No fretful orchid hothoused from the dew,
But hale and hardy as the highland heather,
Rejoicing in the wind that stings and thrills,
Comrade of ocean, playmate of the hills.

Richard Hovey

MAGIC

Within my hand I hold
A piece of lichen-spotted stone —
Each fleck red-gold —
And with closed eyes I hear the moan
Of solemn winds round naked crags
Of Colorado's mountains.   The snow
Lies deep about me.   Gray and old
Hags of cedars, gaunt and bare,
With streaming, tangled hair,
Snarl endlessly.   White-winged and proud,
With stately step and queenly air,
A glittering, cool and silent cloud
    Upon me sails.
    The wind wails,
And from the cañon stern and steep
I hear the furious waters leap.

Hamlin Garland

THE GIPSY TRAIL

The white moth to the closing bine,
  The bee to the opening clover,
And the gipsy blood to the gipsy blood
  Ever the wide world over.

Ever the wide world over, lass,
  Ever the trail held true,
Over the world and under the world,
  And back at the last to you.

Out of the dark of the gorgio camp,
  Out of the grime and the gray

(Morning waits at the end of the world),
  Gipsy, come away!

The wild boar to the sun-dried swamp,
  The red crane to her reed,
And the Romany lass to the Romany lad
  By the tie of a roving breed.

The pied snake to the rifted rock,
  The buck to the stony plain,
And the Romany lass to the Romany lad,
  And both to the road again.

Both to the road again, again!
  Out on a clean sea-track —
Follow the cross of the gipsy trail
  Over the world and back!

Follow the Romany patteran
  North where the blue bergs sail,
And the bows are gray with the frozen spray,
  And the masts are shod with mail.

Follow the Romany patteran
  Sheer to the Austral Light,
Where the besom of God is the wild South wind
  Sweeping the sea-floors white.

Follow the Romany patteran
  West to the sinking sun,
Till the junk-sails lift through the houseless drift,
  And the east and the west are one.

Follow the Romany patteran
   East where the silence broods
By a purple wave on an opal beach
   In the hush of the Mahim woods.

The wild hawk to the wind-swept sky,
   The deer to the wholesome wold,
And the heart of a man to the heart of a maid,
   As it was in the days of old.

The heart of a man to the heart of a maid —
   Light of my tents, be fleet.
Morning waits at the end of the world,
   And the world is all at our feet!

Rudyard Kipling

THE GYPSY GIRL

"Come, try your skill, kind gentlemen,
A penny for three tries!"
Some threw and lost, some threw and won
A ten-a-penny prize.

She was a tawny gypsy girl,
A girl of twenty years,
I liked her for the lumps of gold
That jingled from her ears;

I liked the flaring yellow scarf
Bound loose about her throat,
I liked her showy purple gown
And flashy velvet coat.

A man came up, too loose of tongue,
And said no good to her;
She did not blush as Saxons do,
Or turn upon the cur;

She fawned and whined, "Sweet gentleman,
A penny for three tries!"
— But oh, the den of wild things in
The darkness of her eyes!

Ralph Hodgson

GHOSTS OF INDIANS

Indian-footed move the mists
From the corner of the lake,
Silent, sinuous and bent;
And their trailing feathers shake,
Tremble to forgotten leapings,
While with lingerings and creepings
Down they lean again to slake
The dead thirst of parching mouths,
Lean their pale mouths in the lake.

Indian-footed move the mists
That were hiding in the pine,
But upon the oval lake
In a bent and ghostly line
Lean and drink for better sleeping. . . .
Then they turn again and — creeping
Gliding as with fur and fins —
Disappear through woods and water
On a thousand moccasins.

Witter Bynner

SCHOOL

His seat was by a window.   So he dreamed.
How could he study while the sunlight gleamed
In small, sweet shapes, like wild things tame enough
To dart to him and touch his hands for love?
While there were profiles carved in every cloud
To mark as grim or ludicrous or proud,
And agile shadowings to writhe and crawl
Like ghostly spiders up and down the wall,
He could not help but turn their way to look.
His eyes, that would not follow down his book
The muddy trudgings of deliberate words,
Reflected blue and silver flights of birds.
You would not think there was so much to trace
Of wonderment on just a window space.
But once, when a frail scrap of paper moon
Enchanted him from ten o'clock till noon,
They moved him to the middle of the room.
He learned his lesson then for very gloom,
Until, came glowing to a near-by chair,
A little girl with sunset in her hair.
His soul recolored.   The forlorn dreams came
To warm themselves once more at this new flame.
He pushed aside the dusty Greek.   He had
A different way to read the Iliad.
While through cold ashes others groped to learn,
He lit the towers of Troy and saw them burn.

Winifred Welles

CLIMB

My shoes fall on the housetop that is so far beneath me,
I have hung my hat forever on the sharp church spire.
Now what shall seem the hill but a moment of surmounting,
The height but a place to dream of something higher.

Wings? Oh not for me, I need no other pinions
Than the beating of my heart within my breast;
Wings are for the dreamer with a bird-like longing,
Whose dreams come home at eventide to nest.

The timid folk beseech me, the wise ones warn me,
They say that I shall never grow to stand so high;
But I climb among the hills of cloud and follow vanished
    lightning,
I shall stand knee-deep in thunder with my head against the
    sky.

Tiptoe at last, upon a pinnacle of sunset,
I shall greet the death-like evening with laughter from afar,
Nor tremble in the darkness nor shun the windy midnight,
For by the evening I shall be a star.

Winifred Welles

THE ROAD

Because our lives are cowardly and sly,
Because we do not dare to take or give,
Because we scowl and pass each other by,
We do not live; we do not dare to live.

We dive, each man, into his secret house,
And bolt the door, and listen in affright,
Each timid man beside a timid spouse,
With timid children huddled out of sight.

Kissing in secret, fighting secretly!
We crawl and hide like vermin in a hole,
Under the bravery of sun and sky,
We flash our meannesses of face and soul.

Let us go out and walk upon the road,
And quit for evermore the brick-built den,
And lock and key, the hidden, shy abode
That separates us from our fellow-men.

And by contagion of the sun we may
Catch at a spark from that primeval fire,
And learn that we are better than our clay,
And equal to the peaks of our desire.
                              James Stephens

EL PONIENTE

Beneath the train the miles are folded by;
High and still higher through the vibrant air
We mount and climb.   Silence and brazen glare;
Desert and sage-brush; cactus, alkali,
Tiny, low-growing flowers brilliant, dry;
A vanishing coyote, lean and spare,
Lopes slowly homeward with a backward stare
To jig-saw hills cut sharp against the sky.
In the hard turquoise rides a copper sun.

Old hope comes thronging with an urge, a zest;
Beside the window gliding wires run,
Binding two oceans.   Argosy and quest!
Old dreams remembered to be dreamed and *done!*
It is young air we breathe.   This is the west!

Ruth Comfort Mitchell

TACKING SHIP OFF SHORE

The weather-leech of the topsail shivers,
The bowlines strain, and the lee-shrouds slacken,
The braces are taut, the lithe boom quivers,
And the waves with the coming squall-cloud blacken.

Open one point on the weather-bow,
Is the lighthouse tall on Fire Island Head?
There's a shade of doubt on the captain's brow,
And the pilot watches the heaving lead.

I stand at the wheel, and with eager eye,
To sea and to sky and to shore I gaze,
Till the muttered order of *"Full and by!"*
Is suddenly changed for *"Full for stays!"*

The ship bends lower before the breeze,
As her broadside fair to the blast she lays;
And she swifter springs to the rising seas,
As the pilot calls, *"Stand by for stays!"*

It is silence all, as each in his place,
With the gathered coil in his hardened hands,
By tack and bowline, by sheet and brace,
Waiting the watchword impatient stands.

And the light on Fire Island Head draws near
As, trumpet-winged, the pilot's shout
From his post on the bowsprit's heel I hear,
With the welcome call of "*Ready!   About!*"

No time to spare!   It is touch and go;
And the captain growls, "Down, helm! hard down!"
As my weight on the whirling spokes I throw,
While heaven grows black with the storm-cloud's frown.

High o'er the knight-heads flies the spray,
As we meet the shock of the plunging sea;
And my shoulder stiff to the wheel I lay,
As I answer, "*Ay, ay, sir!   Ha-a-rd a lee!*"

With the swerving leap of a startled steed
The ship flies fast in the eye of the wind,
The dangerous shoals on the lee recede,
And the headland white we have left behind.

The topsails flutter, the jibs collapse,
And belly and tug at the groaning cleats;
The spanker slats, and the mainsail flaps;
And thunders the order, "*Tacks and sheets!*"

'Mid the rattle of blocks and the tramp of the crew,
Hisses the rain of the rushing squall:
The sails are aback from clew to clew,
And now is the moment for, "Mainsail, haul!"

And the heavy yards, like a baby's toy,
By fifty strong arms are swiftly swung:

She holds her way, and I look with joy
For the first white spray o'er the bulwarks flung.

"*Let go, and haul!*" 'Tis the last command,
And the head-sails fill to the blast once more:
Astern and to leeward lies the land,
With its breakers white on the shingly shore.

What matters the reef, or the rain, or the squall?
I steady the helm for the open sea;
The first mate clamors, "Belay there, all!"
And the captain's breath once more comes free.

And so off shore let the good ship fly;
Little care I how the gusts may blow,
In my fo'castle bunk, in a jacket dry,
Eight bells have struck and my watch is below.

Walter Mitchell

THE TRAVEL BUREAU

All day she sits behind a bright brass rail
   Planning proud journeyings in terms that bring
   Far places near; high-colored words that sing,
"The Taj Mahal at Agra," "Kashmir's Vale,"
Spanning wide spaces with her clear detail,
   "Sevilla or Fiesole in spring,
   Through the fiords in June." Her words take wing.
She is the minstrel of the great out-trail.

At half-past five she puts her maps away,
   Pins on a gray, meek hat, and braves the sleet,

A timid eye on traffic.   Dully gray
The house that harbors her in a gray street,
The close, sequestered, colorless retreat
Where she was born, where she will always stay.
Ruth Comfort Mitchell

THE OLD BAYOU

The rosy egret, Sunset,
Wings up the moss-gray skies;
And creeping underclouds, the Dusk,
    A burning beetle, dies.
Round cypress, oak, and willow
    A raucous music cries,
And from the water, dark beneath,
    The mist's white shadows rise,
And glimmering down the bayou
    With starlight-twinkling eyes,
The Twilight oars her blue canoe
    Pale-prowed with fireflies.
Her owlet-call the Darkness
    Utters in vague surmise;
Then with a sibilant voice afar
    The bayou Hush replies.
Now Night the cricket hinges
    Of her old doorway tries,
And stealing through the House of Dreams
    Sleep to the silence sighs.
Wide to the dark one window
    She flings, and from it flies
A moth — the round, white, wandering Moon,
    Whose ghostly image lies

Upon the bayou's bosom
  In strangely shimmering wise —
A phantom barque with a phantom maid,
  Who a phantom paddle plies.

Madison Cawein

SARDINIA FROM A LINER

It stood at bay in its own dark sea,
And gnashed its jagged rocks at me.

Over it thunders lurked in their wrack,
Lightning and windy waves drew back.

It wore its hills with a tribal pride,
Corsica cowered at its side.

A brigand island with brawny hips,
Scowling at sky and sea and ships —

But its purple wallets were filled, I knew,
With potent grapes for a potent brew,
With olive and myrtle and roses too.

Leonora Speyer

From "DE GUSTIBUS"

What I love best in all the world
Is a castle, precipice-encurled,
In a gash of the wind-grieved Apennine.
Or look for me, old fellow of mine,
(If I get my head from out the mouth

O' the grave, and loose my spirit's bands,
And come again to the land of lands) —
In a sea-side house to the farther South,
Where the baked cicala dies of drouth,
And one sharp tree — 'tis a cypress — stands,
By the many hundred years red-rusted,
Rough iron-spiked, ripe fruit-o'ercrusted,
My sentinel to guard the sands
To the water's edge.   For, what expands
Before the house, but the great opaque
Blue breadth of sea without a break?
While, in the house, forever crumbles
Some fragment of the frescoed walls,
From blisters where a scorpion sprawls.
A girl bare-footed brings, and tumbles
Down on the pavement, green-flesh melons,
And says there's news today — the king
Was shot at, touched in the liver-wing,
Goes with his Bourbon arm in a sling:
— She hopes they have not caught the felons.
Italy, my Italy!
Queen Mary's saying serves for me —
                    (When fortune's malice
                    Lost her Calais)
Open my heart and you will see
Graved inside of it, "Italy."
Such lovers old are I and she:
So it always was, so shall ever be!

Robert Browning

THE OLD HOUSES OF FLANDERS

The old houses of Flanders,
They watch by the high cathedrals;
They over-top the high town-halls;
They have eyes, mournful, tolerant and sardonic, for the
    ways of men
In the high, white, tiled gables.

The rain and the night have settled down on Flanders;
It is all wet darkness; you can see nothing.

Then those old eyes, mournful, tolerant and sardonic,
Look at great, sudden, red lights,
Look upon the shades of the cathedrals;
And the golden rods of the illuminated rain,
For a second . . .

And those old eyes,
Very old eyes that have watched the ways of men for
    generations,
Close forever.

The high, white shoulders of the gables
Slouch together for a consultation,
Slant drunkenly over in the lea of the flaming cathedrals.
They are no more, the old houses of Flanders.
                          Ford Madox Ford

OLD NÜRNBERG

You mellow minstrel of a town,
So suave and weather-warmed and brown,

So red and blue and unafraid
Of colors Titian might have made,
Carmine and cobalt scarce belong
In sturdy staves of German song,
Which as you sing, you dare bedeck
With cadenced tints of peacock's neck!

You make and sing, as you have done
Through centuries of shade and sun,
A naïve music that beguiles,
Of porcelain spires and peach-bloom tiles,
And at your brownest you reveal
A message exquisitely real —
Dark topaz eaves of some old inn,
Or house-front like a violin.

Was amber most your mood, when he,
The Master, marked your minstrelsy,
Or did you dream in azure smoke
And hide your colors 'neath a cloak?
Had your least tower been less fair,
Less like a voice across the air,
Or any dome less gold and blue,
Would he have stayed for love of you?

To him whom you enthralled so long,
You were the singer and the song:
Within your streets the tawny tone
Of ancient houses, most your own,
Was like an Aria he heard,
Bold rhythm mated to proud word,
And balcony or carven door
Struck chords he may have missed before.

Can you recall what undertones
Of mirth along your cobblestones
Allured him, or what far-flung spells
From lanes of legendary bells?
Somehow your beauty let him hear
Forgotten voices singing clear:
Somehow you made your meaning plain,
That Herr Hans Sachs might live again.

The Master long ago has gone,
But like his music, you sing on,
In colors clear and magical —
Emerald, coral, cardinal.
    ... I pray you, guard your antique grace,
The fountain in your market place,
Your doves, your bells — and belfries too —
And that brown-amber smile of you!

Grace Hazard Conkling

THE PAINTED DESERT

THE NAVAJO

Lean and tall and stringy are the Navajo,
Workers in silver and turquoise, herders of flocks,
Their sheep and goats cover the hills like scattered rocks.
They wear velvet shirts, they are proud, they go
Through the sage, upright on thin bright horses,
Their speech is low,
At their necks they gather the black smooth cataract of their
    locks,
Quick are their eyes and bright as the eyes of a fox.
You may pass close by their encampments and never know.

In Walpi

There is an eagle screaming from a roof
In Walpi, a black eagle with pale eyes.
The kitchen smoke
Morning and evening rises in pale columns
About him.   At noon the heat beats down
Upon his head and lies like fire on his shoulders.
He never sees the Indians below him,
His captors, all day, his look goes out
Across the striped reds of the painted desert,
All day he looks far off to cloud-hung mesas,
All day he screams.

Ceremonial Hunt

As the racing circle closed in like a lasso
Of running dogs and horses, as the sage was swept,
Out of the turmoil suddenly upward leapt
A jack-rabbit's fawn and jet, with its great soft eye
And fantastic ears outlined against the sky,
Hanging in life a strange moment, then falling back
From that remote beautiful leap to the teeth of the pack,
And the trampling hoofs and the Indians' thin halloo.

Elizabeth J. Coatsworth

A LONDON THOROUGHFARE TWO A.M.

They have watered the street,
It shines in the glare of lamps,
Cold, white lamps,
And lies

Like a slow-moving river,
Barred with silver and black.
Cabs go down it,
One,
And then another.
Between them I hear the shuffling of feet,
Tramps doze on the window-ledges,
Night walkers pass along the sidewalks.
The city is squalid and sinister,
With the silver-barred street in the midst,
Slow-moving,
A river leading nowhere.

Opposite my window,
The moon cuts,
Clear and round,
Through the plum-colored night.
She cannot light the city;
It is too bright.
It has white lamps,
And glitters coldly.

I stand in the window and watch the moon.
She is thin and lusterless,
But I love her.
I know the moon,
And this is an alien city.

Amy Lowell

NOVEMBER BLUE

O heavenly color, London town
Has blurred it from her skies;
And, hooded in an earthly brown,

Unheaven'd the city lies.
No longer standard-like this hue
Above the broad road flies;
Nor does the narrow street the blue
Wear, slender pennon-wise.

But when the gold and silver lamps
Color the London dew,
And, misted by the winter damps,
The shops shine bright anew —
Blue comes to earth, it walks the street,
It dyes the wide air through;
A mimic sky about their feet,
The throng go crowned with blue.

Alice Meynell

TO THE SCHOONER CASCO

DEAR TO R.L.S.

(Remodeled for the fishing-trade of the Pacific Coast)

Has he forsaken heaven quite
    Where is no sail nor any sea,
And for the sake of lost delight
    Evaded immortality,
To feel the wind that sets you free,
    And tempt you to a wide blue flight
Where any trailing dawn may be
    Deep-fringed with breakers bursting white?

Would he exchange all Paradise
    For islands arabesqued with morn,
In your slim shape the magic lies,

And to such honor were you born.
For him shall peace grow less forlorn,
  Who has the sea-light in his eyes,
And hears Orion's hunting-horn
  Cry challenged down the blazing skies?

Now men forget what dawns you knew,
  What painted sunsets flaring far:
For these calm coasts they destine you,
  Nor think whose Silver Ship you are.
Oh leaping bow and thrilling spar
  And canvas bright against the blue,
Your Skipper steers you for a star!
  Obey him as you used to do.

So shall you tread again the floor
  Uncharted you were wont to roam,
And flee in ecstasy before
  The squalls that fail to drive you home:
Shall hear his laughter as of yore,
  When the cloud breaks, the green waves comb
And make his spirit glad once more
  With flagons of enchanted foam!

But when the ocean's azure swoon
  Glasses some isle of memories,
Steal thither softly, to maroon
  Your willful master, if he please!
Slip in by night behind the trees
  Of its star-paven deep lagoon,
And drift across the Pleiades
  To anchor in the floating moon.

                    Grace Hazard Conkling

REQUIEM

Under the wide and starry sky,
Dig the grave and let me lie.
Glad did I live and gladly die,
   And I laid me down with a will.

This be the verse you grave for me:
Here he lies where he longed to be,
Home is the sailor, home from sea,
   And the hunter home from the hill.

                     Robert Louis Stevenson

Men and Women in Literature and Fable

ON FIRST LOOKING INTO CHAPMAN'S HOMER

Much have I traveled in the realms of gold,
    And many goodly states and kingdoms seen;
    Round many western islands have I been
Which bards in fealty to Apollo hold.
Oft of one wide expanse had I been told
    That deep-browed Homer ruled as his demesne:
    Yet did I never breathe its pure serene
Till I heard Chapman speak out loud and bold:
Then felt I like some watcher of the skies
    When a new planet swims into his ken;
Or like stout Cortez, when with eagle eyes
    He stared at the Pacific — and all his men
Looked at each other with a wild surmise —
    Silent, upon a peak in Darien.

John Keats

MESSIRE GEOFFREY CHAUCER TO HIS EDITOR

Right-worthie Clerk of ever-readie Pen
Whose Toil it is to weigh ye Wordes of Men,
Beholde a Little Thynge whiche I have writ
Full fittingly & with some Dele of wit
(As I doe think), which, an it pleases thee,
I pray thee, printe ye same right suddenlie.

Bot, gif it plese thee not, I crie thee Grace,
Let not thine Office Lad my Work deface
With anie Mark at all: — noe, let him not
My Parchment wrongwise fold, nor stamp nor blot,
Since I have scribed it fair with Peyne and Cost
And wolde not have my Labour wholly lost.
And doe not hold ye Writing over-long;
Some wiser Clerk, good hap, may like my song.

                                    Arthur Guiterman

SHAKESPEARE READS THE KING JAMES VERSION

(ANNO DOMINI, 1611)

"Now, by our Lady, here is master speech!
I swear such language is beyond my reach,
Though I (quoth Ben) have skill to marshal words
And make them peal like trumpets, lute like birds.
But here is marvel passing Ben or me,
Our Lord come down to earth, in verity.

"Old Tyndale wrought full well, and I have read
These long, long years his Book by board and bed
And blessed him for it; but this Book of James
Writes up in gold the hundred gloried names
Of them who took from Hebrew or from Greek
The Word of God or of his Jesus meek.

"I'll to the tavern, o'er a stoup of wine
Con once again this Treasure, line by line;
The old, dear Gospel I have loved full well

So fashioned, it shall cast a faery spell
And pluck a heedless world anew from Hell!"

Richard Burton

IS THIS THE LARK!

Is this the lark
Lord Shakespeare heard
Out of the dark
Of Dawn!   Is this the bird
That stirred
Lord Shakespeare's heart!

Is this the bird whose wing,
Whose rapturous antheming,
Rose up, soared radiant, became
Sharp flame
To Shelley listening
And made him sing,
Throbbing alone, aloof, feveredly apart,
His profuse strains of unpremeditated art!

To think that I should hear him now
Telling that single fiery rift of heaven a wild lark comes!...
The fresh cool scent of earth yearns at the plow;
In short keen rapid flurries the woodpecker drums....
To think that I should hear that mad thing sliding
Along a smoking opal ladder!
Hear that inevitable deluge of music riding
Into the sun, richer now — fainter now — madder!
To think that I should hear and know
The song that Shelley heard, and Shakespeare, long ago!

Joseph Auslander

YOU, ANDREW MARVELL

And here face down beneath the sun,
And here upon earth's noonward height,
To feel the always coming on,
The always rising of the night.

To feel creep up the curving east
The earthly chill of dusk and slow
Upon those under lands the vast
And ever-climbing shadow grow,

And strange at Ecbatan the trees
Take leaf by leaf the evening, strange,
The flooding dark about their knees,
The mountains over Persia change,

And now at Kermanshah the gate,
Dark, empty, and the withered grass,
And through the twilight now the late
Few travelers in the westward pass.

And Baghdad darken and the bridge
Across the silent river gone,
And through Arabia the edge
Of evening widen and steal on,

And deepen on Palmyra's street
The wheel rut in the ruined stone,
And Lebanon fade out and Crete
High through the clouds and overblown,

And over Sicily the air
Still flashing with the landward gulls,
And loom and slowly disappear
The sails above the shadowy hulls,

And Spain go under and the shore
Of Africa, the gilded sand,
And evening vanish and no more
The low pale light across that land,

Nor now the long light on the sea —
And here face downward in the sun
To feel how swift, how secretly,
The shadow of the night comes on. . . .

Archibald MacLeish

ON A PORTRAIT OF DR. SAMUEL JOHNSON, LL.D.

This is the Doctor Johnson of the "Prayers" —
   That great, tormented, craggy man, who poured
His sloth, his lovingkindness, and his cares
   In agonized petitions to the Lord.

O rough, pure, stubborn, troubled soul: for whom
   A smile of special tenderness men keep —
Who prayed for strength "to regulate my room,"
   And "preservation from immoderate sleep." . . .

If life brought Doctor Johnson to his knees
It may bring others also, if you please —
Bachelors of Arts . . .
         And LL.D's.

Christopher Morley

MEMORABILIA

Ah, did you once see Shelley plain,
   And did he stop and speak to you,
And did you speak to him again?
   How strange it seems and new!

But you were living before that,
   And also you were living after;
And the memory I started at —
   My starting moves your laughter!

I crossed a moor, with a name of its own
   And a certain use in the world no doubt,
Yet a hand's-breadth of it shines alone
   'Mid the blank miles round about!

For there I picked up on the heather
   And there I put inside my breast
A moulted feather, an eagle-feather!
   Well, I forget the rest.

                        Robert Browning

JOHN KEATS

(DIED, ROME, FEBRUARY 23, 1821)

Pontifical, that night in alien Rome,
   Strode "easeful Death" before the gates of morn.
   His gaunt arm's sweep — wherewith the veil was torn,
One Bright Star flashing stedfast in the "gloam" —
   "Charmed magic casements opening on the foam

Of perilous seas in faery lands forlorn";
And over these, by "viewless wings" upborne,
The world-sick English lad was wafted home.

Be sure Kind Death, whom he had sung so oft,
    Not here would let the floods of music fail.
Eternal song surged 'round him, blending soft
    With voices of his fellows, crying "Hail!"
But over all one clear note soared aloft —
The ecstatic singing of a Nightingale.

Thomas Augustine Daly

EMILY DICKINSON

Inclosed within a hedge
Of privet, doubts and nays,
A burning spinster paced
Her clipped New England days.

While pretty singers droned
A local, nasal hymn,
She raised a timeless voice;
It reached the spatial rim.

She never saw a moor,
She never saw the sea,
Yet from a hilltop in her heart
She scanned Infinity.

Melville Cane

RUPERT BROOKE

Once in my garret — you being far away
Tramping the hills and breathing upland air,

Or so I fancied — brooding in my chair,
I watched the London sunshine feeble and gray
Dapple my desk, too tired to labor more,
When, looking up, I saw you standing there
Although I'd caught no footstep on the stair,
Like sudden April at my open door.

Though now beyond earth's farthest hills you fare,
Song-crowned, immortal, sometimes it seems to me
That, if I listen very quietly,
Perhaps I'll hear a light foot on the stair
And see you, standing with your angel air,
Fresh from the uplands of eternity.

Wilfrid Wilson Gibson

From THE POETS

We who were prophets and priest-men
For the Kings of the East and the Eastmen,
The bugles of God to the beast-men,
His terrible seal on our brow —
Physicians of music and makers
Of language and law and the breakers
Of battle, strength-lifters, heart-shakers —
We are nice poets now.

And we sip cups of tea, nibble crumpets,
And we celebrate ninnies and strumpets,
While the rust bites the throat of the trumpets
And the ram's horn hangs on the wall;
And the fifes of the lord are polluted
With melodies tickled and tooted

Out of the stops that once fluted
Tall silver songs for King Saul.
.   .   .   .

Joseph Auslander

ULYSSES IN AUTUMN

I who knew Circe have come back
   To sink a furrow in the loam;
Left twilights billowing and black
   For the soft glow of home:
To hear instead of a guttural sea
The needles of Penelope.

Still in my heart the Trojan sack
   Hisses and Helen's beauty goes
Glimmering .... And I have come back
   To drink the stale cup of repose —
I who knew Circe and the wine
That turns men grunting into swine.

Can I forget Achilles?   Fly
   For ever from Calypso's guile?
The roaring red pit of that Eye
   Drown in some domestic smile?
Cluck at a sweaty plow who led
The white-flanked stallions of Diomed?

No, for these nerves are iron yet,
   And in these veins, this caverned breast
Echoes the howling parapet;
   The trumpets will not let me rest ....

Think you Odysseus drowses so
Who still can bend the terrible bow!

The lotos voices call my blood
   Implacable and rumorous:
All night there drums a ghostly thud
   Of feet . . . O young Telemachus,
Plead with your mother to release
My spirit fevered for the Fleece!

The trees are straining in the storm,
   Spattering gold; and from the sea
The old tang creeps between the warm
   Breath of her lovely flesh and me:
Each dank leaf dripping down in fire
Fuels the dream of Troy and Tyre.

I know it will be some little thing
   Like wild geese in a streaming wedge
Severely beautiful; a string
   Of bird-prints on the water's edge
That suddenly shall crack galley whips
And hurl me headlong to the ships!

Joseph Auslander

THE ODYSSEY

As one that for a weary space has lain
Lulled by the song of Circe and her wine
In gardens near the pale of Proserpine,
Where that Ææan isle forgets the Main,
And only the low lutes of love complain,

And only shadows of wan lovers pine,
As such an one were glad to know the brine
Salt on his lips, and the large air again —
So gladly, from the songs of modern speech
Men turn, and see the stars, and feel the free
Shrill wind beyond the close of heavy flowers,
And through the music of the languid hours,
They hear like ocean on a western beach
The surge and thunder of the Odyssey.

Andrew Lang

ELAINE

Oh, come again to Astolat!
    I will not ask you to be kind.
And you may go when you will go,
    And I will stay behind.

I will not say how dear you are,
    Or ask you if you hold me dear,
Or trouble you with things for you
    The way I did last year.

So still the orchard, Lancelot,
    So very still the lake shall be,
You could not guess — though you should guess —
    What is become of me.

So wide shall be the garden-walk,
    The garden-seat so very wide,
You needs must think — if you should think —
    The lily maid had died.

Save that, a little way away,
I'd watch you for a little while,
To see you speak, the way you speak,
And smile — if you should smile.

Edna St. Vincent Millay

MEDUSA

I had come to the house, in a cave of trees,
Facing a sheer sky.
Everything moved — a bell hung ready to strike,
Sun and reflection wheeled by.

When the bare eyes were before me
And the hissing hair,
Held up at a window, seen through a door.
The stiff bald eyes, the serpents on the forehead
Formed in the air.

This is a dead scene forever now.
Nothing will ever stir.
The end will never brighten it more than this,
Nor the rain blur.

The water will always fall, and will not fall,
And the tipped bell make no sound.
The grass will always be growing for hay
Deep on the ground.

And I shall stand here like a shadow
Under the great balanced day,
My eyes on the yellow dust that was lifting in the wind,
And does not drift away.

Louise Bogan

DON QUIXOTE

Dearest of all the heroes!   Peerless knight
Whose follies sprang from such a generous blood!
Young, young must be the heart that in thy fight
Beholds no trace of its own servitude.
Young, or else darkened, is the eye that sees
No image of its own fate in thy quest.
The windmills and the swine — by such as these
Is shaped the doom of those we love the best.
Belovèd knight! La Mancha's windows gleam,
Across the plain time makes so chill and gray,
With thy light only.   Still thy flambeaux stream
In pomp of one who on his destined day
Put up his spear, his kindly pennon furled,
And died of the unworthiness of the world.

Arthur Davison Ficke

Study Helps

NOTES

COLUMBUS

Gates of Hercules: opposite rocks at the entrance of the Mediterranean Sea, one in Spain and the other in Africa; supposed, until modern times, to mark the end of the world.

QUIVIRA

Francisco Coronado: Francisco Vasquez de Coronado (1500–1545), a Spanish explorer, who in 1541, prompted by lying tales, set out from Mexico on a two-thousand mile expedition in search of Quivira, described as fabulously wealthy.

Gonfalon: the standard or flag.

Aragon and Castile: the two kingdoms in Spain which united at the marriage of Ferdinand and Isabella.

Sonora: a state in northwestern Mexico.

Missal: a book of service for the Mass.

Fray: Fra, a Friar or religious Brother.

Zuñi: an Indian tribe inhabiting New Mexico.

Granada: a province in southern Spain.

Fraught: filled.

Christian: the hero of *Pilgrim's Progress* by John Bunyan.

Cohort: band of warriors.

PICKETT'S CHARGE

On July 3, 1863, General George E. Pickett, with 15,000 Confederates, charged the Union lines at Gettysburg.

Fasces: a bundle of rods containing an axe.

CRAVEN

On August 5, 1864, Admiral David G. Farragut with a

Federal fleet of four iron monitors, some wooden ships, and several gunboats won a decisive victory over the Confederate gunboats in Mobile Bay. Craven commanded one of Farragut's monitors, the *Tecumseh.* It was destroyed by torpedoes, Craven meeting the heroic death here recorded.

Sidney: Sir Philip Sidney, wounded at Zutphen in the Netherlands, 1586, refused a cup of water in favor of a dying soldier, with the remark: "Thy need is greater than mine."

Nelson: the British naval hero, who was several times wounded in action before he met his death at the Battle of Trafalgar in 1805. His last hours were passed in stoic suffering with other dying men in the cockpit of his flagship, the *Victory.*

Paladins: knights, originally the twelve peers of Charlemagne the Great.

INCIDENT OF THE FRENCH CAMP

Ratisbon: (now Regensburg), located on the Danube River, sixty-five miles north of Munich.

Lannes: one of Napoleon's trusted marshals, who distinguished himself at Marengo, Austerlitz, Jena, Montebello, and other battles in various Napoleonic campaigns.

Vans: wings.

THE HIGHWAYMAN

Stable-wicket: stable door.

Ostler: hostler, groom.

THE MAN HUNT

Brush: thicket.

Bay: deep-toned cry of a dog.

Clave: clove, split.

Laired: trapped in his hiding-place.

Quarry: an animal or person hunted.

Gun-butt: the blunt end of the gun.

GENERAL WILLIAM BOOTH ENTERS INTO HEAVEN

General William Booth was for many years the leader of the Salvation Army.

THE RAVEN

Poe himself declared that the raven is "emblematical of mournful and never-ending remembrance."

Lenore: no real person is intended.

Pallas: Greek goddess of wisdom.

Seraphim: angels.

Nepenthe: drug to ease pain.

Balm in Gilead: cure for grief.

Aidenn: Eden.

Plutonian: Pluto ruled over the lower world. The word here suggests the darkness of death.

THE CONGO

Leopold's ghost: Leopold, King of Belgium, who treated the Negroes in the Congo with great cruelty.

Mumbo-Jumbo: an imaginary creature who terrified the African blacks.

Juba: a dance, accompanied by clapping, patting the knees and thighs, stamping, and singing.

Ebony: heavy and durable wood, most highly prized when its color is a lustrous black.

Agate: a precious stone.

Shotes: young hogs.

Jacob and the golden stairs: in the dream recorded in the Bible, Jacob saw angels ascending and descending a ladder.

Apostles: the twelve disciples of Jesus sent forth to preach the gospel.

THE SACK OF OLD PANAMA

The episode described in this poem is authentic. Sir Henry Morgan (1635–88) was famous for his cruelty, his daring, and his greed. After a stormy career as a buccaneer, he became lieutenant-governor of Jamaica.

Port Royal: a town on the coast of Jamaica in the West Indies.

Don: a title granted to Spanish gentlemen.

Porto Bello: a village in Panama, captured in 1739.

Hang every master that can't show his papers: if he were not a pirate, every ship captain (master) would have his sailing papers in order.

Buccaneering: piratical adventure.

Linnet: finch.

Thomas Sir Modyford: English governor of Panama.

Baubles: trinkets, here jewels.

THE GLORY TRAIL

Mogollons: plateau in Central Arizona.

Yearling: an animal one year old.

Maverick: an unbranded animal.

THE COWBOY'S LAMENT

Laredo: a city in Texas.

EVE

Cobra: serpent.

Blasphemous: irreverent.

THE HAUNTED PALACE

This poem appears in *The Fall of the House of Usher*, perhaps the best of Poe's prose tales.

Porphyrogene: born to the purple; that is, legitimately royal.

KUBLA KHAN

A tailor called at Coleridge's lodgings while the latter was engaged in the composition of these verses. With the interruption vanished the dream that was the basis of the poet's inspiration. *Kubla Khan* was left as it stands, an unfinished masterpiece.

Dulcimer: an ancient instrument whose strings were struck with light hammers.

AND YET FOOLS SAY
Robots: mechanical automata that obediently do the work of human beings.

THE AUTOMOBILE
Umbrageous: shady.
Coverts: sheltered places.
Volant: flying.
Amphibian: an animal living both on land and in the water.
Plato: the greatest of the Greek philosophers, (427?–347 B.C.)
Paracelsus: a Swiss alchemist and philosopher (1493–1541) who sought to extend the powers of the human race.

RADIO (Lindsey)
Falconry: training falcons or hawks.

THE SONG OF THE PRESS
Typos: short for *typographers*, printers.
Platen: the flat part of the printing press which brings the paper against the type.
Brabble: noisy chatter.
While the little poky fogies are a-hauling off to hit: in the time it takes smaller, out-dated machines to get started.

I LIKE TO SEE IT LAP THE MILES
Boanerges (see Mark 3:17): sons of thunder.

THE FLYERS
Elysian: pertaining to Elysium, where, according to the Greeks, souls dwelt in happiness after death. Hence, heavenly.
Keel: here, the bottom of the airship.
Icarus: a character in Greek mythology. To escape from Crete with his father, Icarus invented wings which he attached to himself by means of wax. He flew so high, however, that the sun melted the wax, and he fell into the sea and was drowned.
Caravels: small vessels.

Lima: the capital of Peru.

Omsk: a city in Russia.

Bombay: important city in India.

Moiled: worked hard.

Indenture: apprenticeship, vocation.

CLOUDS

Dinosaur: an extinct reptile.

Mastodon: an extinct elephant.

Moon-faint mottlings: dim shadows intermingled.

LINDBERGH: A Ballad

Viking: the Vikings were Northmen who roamed the sea as pirates in ancient times.

Cambered: curved.

Spirit: Lindbergh's plane was called *The Spirit of St. Louis.*

Le Bourget: the landing field in France.

GOETHALS, THE PROPHET-ENGINEER

Colonel George Washington Goethals labored for seven years (1907–1914) to construct the Panama Canal.

Dithyrambs: originally poetry written in honor of Dionysus, the Greek god of wine. Hence, any poetry written in wild, irregular strain.

Balboa: the Spanish adventurer who discovered the Pacific in 1512.

Magellan: the Portuguese navigator who sailed around South America.

Need poleward warp and veer: make the hard passage around Cape Horn.

PITTSBURGH

Ingots: blocks of steel.

Staccato: shrill, disconnected whistling.

LINES WRITTEN AFTER THE DISCOVERY BY THE AUTHOR OF THE GERM OF YELLOW FEVER

On August 21, 1897, Ronald Ross, a British scientist, experimenting with mosquitoes, isolated the malaria parasite.

AMERICA
Disavouched: disowned.
Younkers: youths.

THE RIVETER
Truss: bars fastened together to form a framework.

THE STEAM SHOVEL
Lairs: crouches.
Behemoth: an enormous animal described in the Book of Job.
Grendel: the monster in *Beowulf*, an old English epic, who devoured the king's men as they slept.
Couchant: crouching, but with head held up.
Ruck: common people.

CALIBAN IN THE COAL MINES
Caliban: the savage and well-nigh soulless slave in Shakespeare's *Tempest*.

THE BARREL ORGAN
The City: London.
Symphony: here used to suggest the harmony of God or Nature to which the earth revolves by day and night.
La Traviata: a popular opera by the Italian composer, Verdi.
Il Trovatore: another of Verdi's well-known operas.
Kew: Kew, seven miles from London, is famous for its botanical gardens.
Linnet: finch.
Throstle: thrush.
Troubadour: one of a class of lyrical poets who flourished from the eleventh to the end of the thirteenth century, chiefly in France and Italy. In this case, however, the reference is to Verdi.
Verdi: Guiseppe Fortunino Francesco Verdi (1813–1901) the most celebrated of Italy's operatic composers.

Piccadilly: a famous London street about a mile long, lined by shops, clubs, and houses.

A che la morte: words taken from a popular air in Verdi's *Il Trovatore.*

Hansom: a two-wheeled covered cab with a driver's seat behind, the reins coming up over the top.

Isis: Upper Thames River in England.

"THE TROUBADOR OF EZE"

Eze: Village, Alpes Maritimes, France.

THE BELLS

Runic: characteristic of runes, poetry written by the ancient Anglo-Saxons and Scandinavians.

Tintinnabulation: the tinkling or jingling sound of bells.

Euphony: a pleasing harmony of sound.

Palpitating: throbbing.

Monody: a mournful song; a dirge.

Ghouls: imaginary evil beings who rob graves and devour corpses.

Paean: a hymn or solemn song addressed to Apollo or to other Greek deities.

THE MAN WITH THE HOE

The poem first appeared in the San Francisco *Examiner* of January 15, 1899, and instantly won world-wide fame.

Seraphim: angels.

Plato: a great philosopher (427 347 B.C.)

Pleiades: small stars in the constellation Taurus, six of which are visible to ordinary sight.

LONDON SNOW

Paul's: St. Paul's Cathedral in London.

THE GREAT LOVER

Inenarrable: indescribable.

A LADY

Harpsichord: a forerunner of the piano, used from the 16th to the 18th centuries.

UNCLE ANANIAS

Ananias, a follower of the Apostles, was killed in punishment for lying.   In our day the name is applied to any liar.
Benedight: blessed.

SYMPHONY PATHÉTIQUE

The sixth symphony of Tschaikowsky.
Pegasus: a winged horse in Greek mythology; a symbol of the inspired imagination.

OF A CHILD THAT HAD FEVER

Eros: Cupid.
Feverfew: plant used for relieving fever; febrifuge.
Dispassion: apathy, lack of passion.
Attaint: stain, disgrace.

SMELLS

Gramarye: magic.

FACTORY WINDOWS ARE ALWAYS BROKEN

Yahoo: a term taken from Swift's *Gulliver's Travels,* a brute in human form; here, brutal, vicious.
Something is rotten — I think in Denmark: See Shakespeare, *Hamlet,* Act I, Sc. iv.

THE BRUTE

Brae: (Scotch) hillside.
Overplus: surplus.

THE BALLAD OF THE OYSTERMAN

Leander swam the Hellespont: in Greek mythology, the lover who each night swam the Hellespont to visit Hero. When he died by drowning, Hero threw herself into the sea.

YOU ARE OLD, FATHER WILLIAM

This is a parody on a poem written by the English Poet Laureate, Robert Southey.

THE YARN OF THE *NANCY BELL*

Bo'sun: (boatswain) an officer in charge of the forward deck.

Gig: a light boat reserved for the captain's use.
Quid: a quid of tobacco.

PLAIN LANGUAGE FROM TRUTHFUL JAMES
Bill Nye: an American humorist, contemporary with Bret Harte.
Right Bower: the knave of the trump suit.

THE JESTER CONDEMNED TO DEATH
Seraglio: harem
Occult: mysterious.

THE JACKDAW OF RHEIMS
Cope: an ecclesiastical mantle or cloak.
Rochet: a tight-sleeved linen robe worn by bishops.
Flawns: pancakes.
Ewer: a large water jug.
Twigged: noticed.
Prigged: stolen.

THE VIZIER'S APOLOGY
Pilaff: pilau, rice boiled with meat, fowl or fish; an Oriental dish.
Pilasters: rectangular columns.

THE LEGEND OF THE FIRST CAM-U-EL
Apologue: a tale which conveys a moral lesson.
Glutinous: sticky, gluey.

THE SYCOPHANTIC FOX AND THE GULLIBLE RAVEN
Gullible: easily deceived.
Umbrageous: shady.
J'admire ton beau plumage: French words meaning: I admire your beautiful feathers.
Persiflage: joking.
Adelina Patti: a famous operatic soprano of the last half of the nineteenth century.
Götterdämmerung: an opera by Richard Wagner.

THE PURPLE COW

Cinq Ans Après: Five years later.

DOCTOR FELL

Thomas Brown had been threatened with expulsion from Christ Church College, Oxford, by the Dean, Dr. John Fell, who promised to forgive him if he would translate impromptu Martial's 32nd epigram, which he did as given in these lines.

THE OWL-CRITIC

Audubon and *Burroughs:* John James Audubon and John Burroughs, two great American authorities on birds.

MIA CARLOTTA

Mash: flirting.

Nobby: stylish.

GOOD-BYE

Sophist schools: the Sophists were Greek philosophers who were more interested in fame and money than in truth.

Man in the bush: Man does not need splendid temples to find God; he may meet him in the humble countryside. Abraham, according to the Bible story, heard the voice of the Lord "in the bush."

FOR A' THAT

Guinea: a British gold coin, worth about five dollars.

Gowd: gold.

Hoddin gray: coarse woolen cloth.

Birkie: a young dandy.

Coof: fool.

Fa': try.

Gree: prize.

MIRACLES

Pismire: ant.

Chef-d'oeuvre: masterpiece.

THE WORLD IS TOO MUCH WITH US

Proteus: in Greek mythology, a Greek sea god who could change shape at will.

Triton: a Greek demigod of the sea whose shell trumpet was used to agitate or calm the waves.

ODE ON A GRECIAN URN

Sylvan: rural; pertaining to forests and trees.

Tempe: a beautiful valley in Thessaly, Greece, dear to Apollo.

Timbrels: tambourines.

Far above: read, *far above all breathing human passion.*

Brede: design.

Pastoral: a work of art depicting country life.

TO NIGHT

Hesperus: the evening star.

IMMIGRANTS

Powhatan: Indian chief famous for his encounter with Captain John Smith.

EACH IN HIS OWN TONGUE

Saurian: lizard.

Rood: cross.

QUATORZAIN

The title means a poem of fourteen lines; a sonnet, or closely resembling it in structure.

IN HARBOR

Leeward: in the direction toward which the wind blows.

Surcease: here used as a verb, to end.

WORTH MAKES THE MAN

Prunella: a kind of woolen material sometimes used in making shoes.

"TIME, YOU OLD GIPSY MAN"

Caravan: a covered wagon.

Jennet: a small Spanish horse.

May: mayflowers.

FAME

Keats: John Keats, the great English poet, died in Rome in 1821. The scene of this poem is laid in Rome.

Baedeker's: Baedeker's Guide Book.
Vast Inane: the uninformed.

THE EAGLE AND THE MOLE
Stoic: showing indifference to pleasure or pain.
Inviolate: secure from violation, unspoiled by the company of others.

POLONIUS' ADVICE TO LAERTES
Character: write, engrave.
Unproportioned: unbalanced, extreme.
Vulgar: unrefined; boorish.
Grapple: attach, unite.
Dull thy palm: cheapen yourself
Censure: criticism.
Husbandry: thrift.

FLOWER IN THE CRANNIED WALL
Crannied: showing crevices or chinks.

A BALLAD OF TREES AND THE MASTER
Clean forspent: entirely exhausted.

DAYS
Hypocritic: deceitful.
Pleachèd: interwoven, as with branches, hedges.
Fillet: band worn across the forehead.

THE MERRY GUIDE
The Merry Guide: Hermes, or Mercury, messenger of the gods, with winged cap and sandals.
Thymy wold: moor covered with thyme, an herb of the mint family.
Weald: wold, wild country.
Serpent-circled wand: the caduceus, distinguishing emblem of Hermes.

VERMONT
Trillium: plant of the lily family.
Olympian: god-like.

ELLEN HANGING CLOTHES
Flags: iris, or fleurs-de-lis.

KENTUCKY MOUNTAINEER
Bitterns: birds of the heron family.
Shoe-makes: sumacs.

HOME-THOUGHTS, FROM ABROAD
Written in Italy, where Browning resided for many years.

THE BAREFOOT BOY
Apples of Hesperides: golden apples presented to Hera, queen of heaven, on her marriage to Zeus.

JUNE
Elmor's light: St. Elmo's fire, a flame of light sometimes seen in stormy weather on church spires or tall masts of ships. St. Elmo is the sailor's patron saint.
Siren-like: in Greek mythology the sea nymphs, called sirens, by their singing lured to destruction the sailors who approached their island.

THE DAFFODILS
Milky Way: bright band of myriads of stars circling the heavens, which may be seen on a clear night.
Jocund: merry.

ODE TO A NIGHTINGALE
Lethe: in classical mythology, a river whose waters produced forgetfulness in the drinker.
Dryad: a Greek nymph.
Flora: Latin goddess of flowers and gardens.
Provençal: pertaining to Provence, the name given in the Middle Ages to the country in Southern France.
Hippocrene: originally a fountain on Mount Helicon, famous for its power to inspire the drinker; here used for wine.
Bacchus: God of wine.
Pards: leopards.
Fays: fairies.

Ruth: the heroine of the Book of Ruth in the Old Testament, who married Boaz and was deeply devoted to her mother-in-law, Naomi.

AN ABANDONED TOW-PATH

Tow-path: a path traveled by men or animals in towing boats.

Dalliance: loitering, useless waiting.

Elfin brass: wind instruments played by elves.

Requiem: musical service for the dead.

Locks: inclosures between two gates used to raise and lower boats in a body of water.

SILVER

Shoon: shoes.

Cote: dovecote, a small house raised above the ground, used by doves.

THE CIRCUS-POSTERED BARN

Circus-postered: Advertisements of the circus nailed on the walls of the barn.

Smoking: steam rising from the hot damp bodies of the horses.

GARGANTUA

Gargantua was a huge voracious giant in a book entitled *Gargantua,* written by the French satirist, Rabelais.

Cobalt: deep blue.

Shire: district or county.

Byres: buildings on a farm.

Blatant: noisy.

Sequester: conceal.

OREAD

The title comes from the Greek signifying *mountain nymph.*

SONG OF THE CHATTAHOOCHEE

Lanier believed that the highest effects of poetry are produced by the musical arrangement of words. Observe how in this poem, through skillful handling of rhythm, rhyme, and tone-color, he succeeds in capturing the spirit of the river. Note the use of the first person pronoun. It is the Chattahoochee itself which is speaking.

Habersham and *Hall* are counties in northeastern Georgia. Rising in Habersham County, the Chattahoochee River winds through Hall County, crosses the plains and empties into the Gulf of Mexico.

Main: the ocean, or any wide expanse of water.

ODE TO THE WEST WIND
Mænad: in Greek mythology a bacchante or nymph who served Dionysus, the god of wine.
Baiæ: a place in Campania, Italy.

TO AUTUMN
Sallows: willows.

THE SOLITARY REAPER
Hebrides: islands west of Scotland.
Numbers: verses.

RIVER SKATER
Convolute: circles on circles.
Foliated: rolled, coiled.

THE SNOW-STORM
Parian: marble, from the marble quarries of Paros in the Ægean Sea.
Maugre: in spite of.

WINTER REVERY
Libational rhythms: methodical beats.

THE DOG
Swink: toil.
Swither: fear.
Narwhal: an Arctic sea mammal.
Wallaby: small kangaroo.
Splay-foot: flat, turned-out feet.

AN ALLEY CAT
Antiphonal: chanting their responses as an anthem is sung in church.
Rameses the Third: an Egyptian monarch reigning about 1300 B.C.

TO A MOUSE
Brattle: hurry.
Pattle: hand-stick for cleaning the plow.
Daimen icker: an ear of corn now and then.
Thrave: 24 sheaves.
Big: build.
Snell: bitter.
But: without.
Hald: holding.
Thole: endure.
Cranreuch: hoar-frost.
Lane: thyself alone.
Agley: awry.

THE SPIDER
Euclid: a Greek mathematician (c. 300 B.C.) whose chief work *Elements*, was the introduction to the study of geometry.

THE FISH-HAWK
Gyres: gyrations.

TO A WATERFOWL
Fowler: bird hunter.

LINCOLN, THE MAN OF THE PEOPLE
Norn Mother: in Norse mythology, the Norns were the Fates.
Matterhorn: the lofty mountain in the Alps between Italy and Switzerland.

THE EAGLE THAT IS FORGOTTEN
Lindsay greatly loved the Governor of Illinois, John P. Altgeld, who showed a marked sympathy for the masses.

UNREST
   Titan: in Greek mythology, one of the giants who fought against the Olympian gods.

THE FALCONER OF GOD
   Falcon: a species of hawk especially trained to pursue and attack wild fowl or game.   It usually plunges down on its prey from above.
   Heron: a bird, resembling a crane, formerly much hunted with falcons.

INVICTUS
   Fell: cruel.
   Horror of the Shade: dark presence of death.
   Strait: narrow.
   Scroll: the book kept in heaven.

AT MAGNOLIA CEMETERY
   This poem was written in 1867 in commemoration of the Confederate dead in Magnolia Cemetery, Charleston.   Timrod himself died in the same year, a victim of tuberculosis, whose ravages had been aggravated by financial losses sustained in the War Between the States.

ULYSSES
   Ulysses was the hero of Homer's Odyssey, here depicted in advanced age.
   Mete and *dole:* administers the law.
   Lees: the sediment at the bottom of a glass of wine.
   Hyades: a group of stars whose rising at sunset warned the ancient Greeks of the coming of the rainy season.
   Furrows: the waves.
   Happy Isles: Elysium, the heaven of Greek heroes, located on the western part of the earth, near the ocean.
   Achilles: the fabled Greek warrior, hero of Homer's *Iliad.*

SAY NOT THE STRUGGLE NOUGHT AVAILETH
   Dupes: a dupe is one deceived by false promises.   Our

hopes are often thus victimized in the course of our lives.
Main: ocean.

CROSSING THE BAR
Tennyson wrote this poem shortly before his death.
Bar: literally, a bank of sand or other matter at the mouth
of a river or harbor, obstructing navigation. The term, however, is used metaphorically in the poem. Tennyson was in
his eighty-first year when he wrote these verses; he knew
that he would soon cross the bar into the life beyond death.

CAESAR REMEMBERS
Cæsar: Julius Cæsar (100–44 B.C.), great Roman general.
Chilterns: chalky stretches in England.

I HEARD A SOLDIER
Veldt: unwooded land in South Africa.

GRASS
Austerlitz, Waterloo: famous battles in the Napoleonic
Wars.
Ypres, Verdun: outstanding battles in the World War.

THE MAN HE KILLED
Nipperkin: a receptacle capable of holding about a half pint
of liquor.
Traps: personal belongings (colloquial.)
Half-a-crown: in England a coin worth $2\frac{1}{2}$ shillings, or
about 60 cents.

THE ANTHEM FOR DOOMED YOUTH
Orisons: prayers.

AFTER BLENHEIM
Blenheim, a village of Bavaria, Germany, was the scene
of a decisive victory by the English and Austrians over
French and Bavarian forces. The battle took place on
August 13, 1704. The Austrians were commanded by Prince
Eugene and the English by the famous Duke of Marlborough.

NEW ENGLAND
Soilure: soiling.

SONNET by Elinor Wylie
This is the fourth in a series of sonnets entitled *Wild Peaches*. It is often referred to as the *Puritan Sonnet*.

HOW DO I LOVE THEE?
Addressed by Mrs. Browning to her husband, the poet Robert Browning.

OZYMANDIAS
The figure of Ozymandias is wholly imaginary.

ENGLAND, 1802
Altar, sword, pen: metaphor for church, army, literature.

"SCORN NOT THE SONNET"
Petrarch (1304–1374): a famous Italian sonneteer, who wrote to and of his beloved Laura.

Torquato Tasso: a celebrated Italian poet of the 16th century.

Camoëns: a Portuguese poet who lived in the 16th century.

Dante (1265–1321): famous for his *Divine Comedy*.

Edmund Spenser: a contemporary of Shakespeare, achieved fame with the *Faerie Queene*.

Milton (1608–1674): famous for his *Paradise Lost*, wrote but few sonnets, most of them, however, masterly.

ON HIS BLINDNESS
At the age of forty-four Milton became blind, partly because of the abuse of his eyes in study and writing. His services to Cromwell's government, for which he was the Latin secretary, was also a contributory factor.

Fondly: foolishly.

Yoke: burden.

Post: travel with haste.

ALL THAT'S PAST
Amaranth: an imaginary flower which never dies.

FOR A DEAD LADY

Saturn: in Greek mythology, father of Zeus.   He was the god of the seedtime and the harvest.

A DREAM

Told: counted out, over.

"TEARS, IDLE TEARS"

This lyric is one of those found in Tennyson's *The Princess.*

PRAYER TO PERSEPHONE

Persephone, the wife of Pluto, was, in Greek mythology, the queen of the lower world.

AFTER A DOLMETSCH CONCERT

Arnold Dolmetsch, a contemporary musician, is well known for playing old music on the musical instruments of other days.

MY OLD KENTUCKY HOME

This is one of the most famous songs of America's popular song writer, rivalling *Old Folks At Home* in the esteem of music lovers.   For most of his songs Foster composed both words and music.

Coon: colloquial for raccoon.

TO CELIA

Jove's nectar: nectar was the drink of the gods.   Jove is Jupiter, the greatest of the Roman gods.

"NOT MARBLE NOR THE GILDED MONUMENTS"

Istrian: pertaining to Istria, formerly a region in the Austrian Empire along the Adriatic.

A LITTLE WHILE I FAIN WOULD LINGER YET

This poem was written toward the close of Hayne's life. His fortune and his health lost in the War Between the States, in which he served as a Colonel in the Confederate Army, Hayne eventually returned to Atlanta, Georgia, to put up a brave fight against poverty and illness.

I Shall Not Be Afraid
Aline Kilmer is the wife of the poet Joyce Kilmer, who was killed in the World War.

The Vagabond
Lave: the others, the rest (Scotch dialect).

Sea Fever
Trick: (nautical dialect) period of service for which a seaman signs up.

Callao
Callao is a Spanish town in Peru.
Kites: light sails, high up, used in gentle winds.

Cargoes
Quinquireme: in ancient times a galley with five tiers of oars.
Ophir: unknown country mentioned in the Bible.
Moidore: an obsolete Portuguese gold coin.

The Old Ships
Famagusta: a seaport of Cyprus.
Aeaea: a small island off the coast of Italy supposed to have been inhabited by Circe. (Now Monte Circello).

A Wanderer's Song
Sheet: rope or chain attached to sails for extending them or hauling them in.
Hooker: a two masted vessel.
Warping: pulling along by a rope to a fixed point.
Moby Dick: the great white whale described in the book *Moby Dick*, by Herman Melville.

The Gipsy Trail
Gorgio: one who is not a gipsy.
Romany: gipsy.
Patteran: a small pile of leaves or grass left by gipsies as a sign to other gipsies of the road taken.
Austral: southern.

THE OLD BAYOU
Egret: heron.

OLD NÜRNBERG
Titian: the great Italian artist of the 16th century, favored rich effects in red, green, yellow, and blue.
The Master: Hans Sachs (1494–1576), born at Nürnberg, wrote over four thousand *Meisterlieder.* Sachs was the head of the Meistersinger school at Nürnberg.

TO THE SCHOONER CASCO
It was in the *Casco* that Robert Louis Stevenson left San Francisco on his journey to Tahiti, Honolulu, and Samoa, which last place was to be his home until his death in 1894.

REQUIEM
Stevenson lies buried, as he desired, on the summit of the peak Vaea on the island of Samoa.

ON FIRST LOOKING INTO CHAPMAN'S HOMER
Chapman's translation of Homer's *Iliad* and *Odyssey* into English verse is dated 1616.
Cortez: this, as you may have noted, is an error. It was Balboa who discovered the Pacific.

MESSIRE GEOFFREY CHAUCER TO HIS EDITOR
Written in imitation of Chaucer's style.
An: if.
Gif: if.

SHAKESPEARE READS THE KING JAMES VERSION
By the time the King James version of the Scriptures appeared in 1611, Shakespeare had written all his plays. They contain many hundred references to the Bible, which he therefore must have read in the earlier Tyndale translation.
Quoth Ben: says Ben Jonson, Shakespeare's friend and fellow-dramatist.

Old Tyndale: The English martyr who translated much of the Bible which appeared in 1539.

YOU, ANDREW MARVELL

The reference is to a poem by the English poet, Andrew Marvel, who was a contemporary of John Milton. In this poem Marvel spoke of the flight of time in the phrase:

"But at my back I always hear
Time's winged chariot hurrying near."

With these lines to ponder on, a modern poet here gives us a remarkable picture of the shadow of night moving across the different countries of the world, as the earth turns.

Ecbatan: now Hamadan, a town in Persia.

Kermanshah: also in Persia.

Palmyra: a ruined city in Syria.

ON A PORTRAIT OF DR. JOHNSON, LL. D.

Dr. Samuel Johnson (1709–1784), the subject of Boswell's famous biography.

JOHN KEATS

Easeful Death: quoted from Keats's *To a Nightingale.*

Bright Star: a reference to the sonnet beginning: "Bright Star, would I were steadfast as thou art!"

Charmed magic casements: quoted from *To a Nightingale,* as is also the phrase *viewless wings.*

EMILY DICKINSON

"I never saw a moor
I never saw the sea."

quoted from Emily Dickinson's poem *Chartless.*

ELAINE

Astolat: the home of Elaine, who fell in love with Lancelot of the Lake. See *Lancelot and Elaine,* a well-known idyll in Tennyson's *Idylls of the King.*

MEDUSA

Medusa was one of three Gorgons found in Greek mythology. Her hair was made of snakes whose glance turned all beholders to stone.

DON QUIXOTE

The Windmills: referring to Don Quixote's celebrated tilt with them as though they were living creatures.

La Mancha: the dwelling-place of Don Quixote, his full title being *Don Quixote de la Mancha.*

General Questions

STORIES BRAVE AND STRANGE

1. What do the titles tell you about the poems? Do you think you can invent better titles for some of the poems?

2. Each of the poems in this section tells a story. Which of them is the most interesting? The most exciting? The most true to life? The most imaginative? In each case give reasons.

3. Do any of these poems have something besides a story to offer the reader? That is, do they impart a moral lesson or some otherwise valuable truth? Do they furnish a vivid description of some scene or person? Select the poems which have this extra value and be prepared to explain it in each case to the satisfaction of the class.

4. How many of the poems in this division are based on historical incidents? Look up an account of these incidents in a history and tell, with reasons, whether you prefer the poet's or historian's treatment of them.

5. Pick out the poems composed in the ballad form. What advantages are there in this form so far as these poems are concerned?

6. Selecting your favorite poem in this group, comment on the following items concerning it:

(a) Are the meter and rhyme scheme suited to the spirit and thought of the poem?

(b) What words or phrases are particularly effective? Do they appeal to the senses? Do they stimulate the imagination?

(c) Does the poem lead you to recall an incident in your own life or one you have read about in books?

(d) Is it worth memorizing, in whole or in part? Why?

MODERN MARVELS

1. What poem in this section captures best the spirit of the machine? Why?

2. How many sonnets are there in this section? Do they share any thought or mood in common? Can you explain why their authors chose the sonnet form?

3. Which poem gives you the deepest sense of the wonders of modern science? Why?

4. Carl Sandburg's *Under a Telephone Pole* and *Smoke and Steel* are written in free verse. Give your reasons for believing the free verse form is or is not suited to the poems.

5. Examine the three free verse poems of MacKnight Black. Is he as successful in the use of free verse as Carl Sandburg?

6. Compare Harriet Monroe's and Therese Lindsey's poems on *Radio*. What is your own viewpoint on the subject?

7. Select your favorite poem in this section. Come to class prepared to discuss one or more of the following:
   (a) The meter, and rhyme-scheme (if any)
   (b) Vivid pictures
   (c) Theme or mood
   (d) Striking or beautiful diction
   (e) Best lines or passage

THE WORKADAY WORLD AND ITS PEOPLE

1. Some of the poems in this section describe the pride or happiness in the heart of the average American. Make a list of such poems and justify the pride or happiness felt.

2. Other poems, on the contrary, point to certain evils in the lot of the working man in the United States. List such poems and give your own views on the problems thus brought to light.

3. Compare *America* by Stephen Vincent Benét with *I Am an American* by Elias Lieberman.

4. Select the poems which tell a story. Is the story element the most important aspect of such poems? Clearly explain the value and purpose of the story in the poems you select for discussion.

5. What common mood or theme do you find in the poems of this section? Support your analysis by reference to a sufficient number of poems.

6. Comment on the pleasures of city life as described in various poems.

7. Compare *Pioneers, O Pioneers* and *Chicago*. In what sense may the latter be regarded as the natural descendant of the former?

8. Discuss the use of onomatopoeia in Poe's *The Bells*. In what other poems in the section may onomatopoeia be found?

9. Why is *The Man with the Hoe* one of the most popular poems of our generation?

THE FUNNY SIDE

1. Humor is said to be serious at bottom. Discuss the poems in this section in which the underlying meaning is serious.

2. Analyze the poems in this section in which humor is increased by the skillful use of rhythm and rhyme.

3. What poems depend for their effect wholly upon clever devices? Can such poems be regarded as masterpieces?

4. Select the poems whose humor is based on exaggeration. Is the exaggeration in each case justified?

5. Is *Ravin's of Piute Poet Poe* a worthy parody on *The Raven*? What qualities must an effective parody possess?

6. Analyze the humor of Guy Wetmore Carryl and Arthur

Guiterman.   How much of it depends on clever rhythm, rhyme, imagination, or brilliant diction?

7. Account for the popularity of *The Purple Cow* by Gelett Burgess.

8. Find the poems with a satirical purpose.   To what extent is the satire successful?

9. Discuss the use of dialect in several of the poems.

10. Which is your favorite poem in this section?   Why?

THE WELL OF WISDOM

1. Many poems in this section have the brevity and compactness of the epigram; for example, Markham's *Outwitted*. Find other examples of the epigram, and discuss their value to the reader.

2. Study the several poems by Ralph Waldo Emerson to be found in this section.   Why are they characteristic of this great thinker?

3. *To Night* by Joseph Blanco White is by some critics ranked among the greatest sonnets in the language.   Why?

4. Which poem in this section surpasses all others in its imaginative power?   Which shows the most vivid use of figures of speech?

5. Compare the two selections taken from the Bible. What elements of poetry do they possess in common?   As regards form, may they be considered examples of free verse?

6. Do you agree with the thought in *Miracles* by Whitman?   Why?

7. Referring to Wordsworth's *The World Is Too Much with Us*, can a like criticism be levelled at the present generation?   Compare this poem, in theme and spirit, with *Voluntaries* by Emerson.

8. What is an ode?   Why is Keats's *Ode on a Grecian Urn* "perhaps the most perfect poem in English"?

9. Would Stephen Crane's poems appear to better advantage if written in meter and rhyme? Why?

10. Find the poems which contain a hidden meaning; for example, *I Saw a Man*. Is the hidden or symbolic meaning in each case less or more important than the literal or obvious one?

UNDER THE OPEN SKY

1. Which poems give you the keenest sense of the joys of the great outdoors?

2. Poets are often inclined to read their own moods into the landscape. Show the effects of such moods on poems found in this section.

3. Which poem in the section exhibits the most skillful use of rhythm? Which contains the most vivid imagery? Which, the deepest or sincerest emotion? Which, the most striking use of onomatopoeia?

4. Are there any poems which might serve as inspirations for paintings? What paintings are called to mind by any of the poems in this section?

5. Does Lowell's *A Day in June* deserve its long-standing popularity? Why? Compare it, in point of theme and feeling, with *The Daffodils* by Wordsworth.

6. What light does the *Ode to a Nightingale* and *To Autumn* throw on the personality of John Keats?

7. Nature may have valuable lessons to impart to man. Do you agree? Compare, in this connection, Wordsworth's *Daffodils* and Frost's *Mending Wall*.

8. Why does Walter de la Mare favor the letter *s* in *Silver*?

9. Describe the poetry of Robert Frost, as represented in this section. Is it as lyrical as that of Keats or Wordsworth, for example? Study *The Sound of Trees*. Give reasons whether or not this poem deserves the name of poetry.

10. In the same way, analyze the merits of Riley's *When the Frost Is on the Punkin'*.

ALL MANNER OF CREATURES

1. Scan all the unusual words in *The Dog* by Don Marquis. Which, in your opinion, are particularly appropriate? Why?

2. How well do the three poems on the dog capture the spirit of the subject? Can you think of other poems that might well find a place in this section? Read them to the class.

3. Which of the three poems on the cat is the most effective? Why?

4. Find all the evidence in *Four Little Foxes* indicating that its author is a lover of animals. What other poems in this section show an equal sympathy for beasts?

5. Comment on the figures of speech in *Crystal Moment*.

6. Discuss the accuracy of the descriptions in *The Hedgehog*, *Chipmunk*, and *The Spider*. Would you prefer a scientist's account of these creatures?

7. Why is Tennyson's *The Eagle* famous?

8. Some critics have suggested that the last stanza of *To a Waterfowl* should have been omitted. Do you agree with them?

CHALLENGE TO COURAGE

1. Compare *Lincoln, the Man of the People* with *O, Captain! My Captain!* Which is more affecting? Which reveals more of the character of Lincoln?

2. Comment on the figures of speech in *Lincoln, the Man of the People*. Do they increase the effectiveness of the poem?

3. What is the mood of Lindsay in *The Eagle That Is Forgotten*? Find another poem in this section with a similar mood.

4. What theme is common to *Do You Fear the Wind?*, *Courage*, and *The Kings*?

5. *The Falconer of God* affords an effective example of the allegory. Explain to the class how the allegory is sustained from beginning to end in the structure, content, and diction of the poem.

6. Do you agree with Henley's triumphant conclusion in *Invictus*?

> "I am the master of my fate:
> I am the captain of my soul."

8. Some critics consider *Ulysses* the noblest (and perhaps the greatest) of Tennyson's poems. Give your own judgment after careful consideration of the meter, thought, mood, figures of speech, and diction. What are its most quotable lines? Is the blank verse in which it is cast an advantage to the poem? Why?

MAN AND WARFARE

1. Study closely the seventh stanza of *Caesar Remembers*. Do you think this stanza develops the personal viewpoint of the author? Why?

2. Is the quatrain form in this poem successfully employed? Is it better employed in *I Heard a Soldier*?

3. In *Back*, what is the attitude of the speaker toward war?

4. What common mood or theme is found in the poems of this section?

5. What does grass symbolize in Carl Sandburg's poem?

6. Do you care for the form of Emory's *be still*? Analyze the form, and show whether or not it can be justified. Be sure that you have clear ideas as to the relation between form and content in poetry.

7. Comment on the effectiveness of the picture in the last six lines of *The Conscript*. Where have you seen this picture before?

8. Discuss the use of onomatopoeia and alliteration in the *Anthem for Doomed Youth*.

9. Does *After Blenheim* help you to see the futility of war? Was such the purpose of Southey in writing the poem? Justify your view by reference to the poem.

REMARKABLE SONNETS

1. Separate the sonnets in this section into the two outstanding types: Italian and Shakespearean. Which group appeals to you more?

2. Does the sonnet form sometimes make the thought more difficult to understand? Why? Illustrate your views by reference to specific poems in this section.

3. Which of these sonnets is the most lyrical? Which the most profound? Which presents the most vivid pictures? Which seems the most sincere? In each case justify your opinions.

4. Do you think Arnold's praise of Shakespeare exaggerated? Defend or attack the eulogy of the poet.

5. What characteristics in common are revealed by Wordsworth's *England, 1802* and Milton's *On His Blindness*?

6. After reading "*Scorn Not the Sonnet,*" have you still doubts as to the value of the sonnet as a poetic form?

7. Learn by heart the most memorable lines in at least four sonnets included in this section. Justify your choice of lines in each case.

LOVE AND MEMORY

1. Why is Eugene Field's *Little Boy Blue* a popular poem? Is it, perhaps, too sentimental?

2. What great lesson is to be learned from Stephen Phillips's *A Dream*? Is the lesson expressed or implied? Do you

think that a poem is better for leaving the lesson to be inferred by the reader? Why?

3. Is the poem *Memory* true to the laws of the mind? Before you answer, think of the things in your past life that stand out most vividly.

4. Notice the sense of motion in Browning's *Meeting at Night*. How does Browning obtain this effect?

5. Comment on the effectiveness of the refrain in *My Lost Youth*. What is the value of the refrain in lyric poetry?

6. Do you agree with the underlying idea in *Give All To Love*? Is this idea characteristic of Emerson? Read Emerson's essay, *Self-Reliance*.

7. Read Charles Lamb's *Dream-Children*. Does it help you to understand the poet who wrote *The Old Familiar Faces*?

8. Select the best known lines of the poems in this section and criticize their merits as poetry.

9. Analyze the form of "*Not Marble Nor the Gilded Monuments*." Is the form well adapted to the purpose of the writer?

10. Which poem in this section exemplifies the highest virtues of meter, rhyme, imagination, figures of speech, thought, emotion, diction?

FOOTLOOSE FOR FAR PLACES

1. What pictures do you see in *Reveillé* by A. E. Housman? What figures of speech help the poet to make these pictures vivid?

2. Analyze the several poems by Robert Louis Stevenson in this section. Do they seem to come naturally from the author of *Treasure Island*, *Kidnapped*, and other romances?

3. Discuss the rhythm of *Sea-Fever* by Masefield. At a public reading of this poem Masefield timed the phrases so

as to convey the sense of waves rising and falling. Try to read the poem to the class with this in mind.

4. Discuss the several poems dealing with the sea. In what ways do their authors attempt to convey the magic of the sea? What part do rhythm, sense, words, pictures, figures of speech, and other poetic factors play in the poems in question?

5. Select your favorite poem in this section, and memorize the best lines.

6. Compare *The Old House of Flanders* and *Old Nürnberg* with respect to form and content. Which, in your opinion, is the better poem? Why?

MEN AND WOMEN IN LITERATURE AND FABLE

1. Have you ever felt (even if in lesser degree) the sense of enchanted adventurousness shown by Keats in *On First Looking into Chapman's Homer*? Tell the class what book it was that so enchanted you, and ask for similar revelations from your fellow-students.

2. Give a two-minute account of the life and work of the following poets who appear as subjects of the verses in this section: John Keats, William Shakespeare, Samuel Johnson, Emily Dickinson, Rupert Brooke. Is the poet in each case faithful to the facts you have discovered?

3. Similarly, tell enough about each of the following to make the poet's work entirely clear to the class. (Ask your teacher or the librarian for the sources to be used for the needed information.)

The Odyssey	Elaine	Don Quixote
Ulysses	Medusa	Hamlet
Menelaus	Paris	Achilles
Penelope	Circe	Proserpine

4. Read Shakespeare's song on the lark (*Cymbeline*, Act II, Scene 3), also Shelley's *To a Skylark*. Do they merit the admiration evident in Auslander's *Is This the Lark*?

5. "Beauty is truth, truth Beauty," said Keats. How can this statement be applied to MacLeish's *You, Andrew Marvell*?

6. Select your favorite poem in this section. It will probably deal with a favorite author. If this proves to be the case, explain why the author happens to be a favorite one.

7. What lines in *Memorabilia* speak eloquently of Browning's love for Shelley? Was Browning in any way influenced by Shelley?

8. Select all the poems by Auslander included in this volume. Comment on their poetic merits.

Special Assignments

STORIES BRAVE AND STRANGE

1. Compare Columbus in Joaquin Miller's poem with a pioneer in the field of science like Pasteur.

2. Compare Stephen Vincent Benét's *Pickett's Charge* with Tennyson's *Charge of the Light Brigade.* Which poem do you prefer, and why?

3. Do you believe that the hero in *The Highwayman* was a noble character? Did he deserve the death he met?

4. Ask the librarian how to obtain information on the life and work of Edgar Allan Poe. Come to class ready to explain why and how Poe came to write *The Raven.*

5. Compare *The Congo* by Lindsay and *Go Down, Death* by Johnson. Which of the two seems to be more faithful to the spirit of the Negro race?

6. Read John A. Lomax's *Cowboy Songs and Other Frontier Ballads.* Select two or three favorites for reading to the class.

7. Organize a committee to select and read aloud favorite poems from the works of Vachel Lindsay, Alfred Noyes, Robert Browning, and Walter de la Mare.

8. In your poetry scrapbook, reserve a section for narrative poems in which from time to time you may paste interesting works clipped from magazines and newspapers.

9. Write a story-poem of your own, based on personal experience or on some stirring historical incident.

MODERN MARVELS

1. Come to class prepared to read poems on modern marvels not included in this section.

2. Imitate the *The Santa Fé Trail* of Vachel Lindsay in a poem of your own. Times Square, New York, will serve as inspiration; or State Street, Chicago; or Main Street anywhere in the United States. Try to suggest the myriad-voiced sound of the traffic and the sense of the nation in motion.

3. If the school orchestra is available for the purpose, let it play the French composer Honegger's *Pacific 231*. This will enable the class to understand, in terms of music, what Lindsay was trying to put into words in the *Santa Fé Trail*.

4. Carry further the dual thought in Daniel Whitehead Hickey's *Machines*. Is Nature opposed to the machine? Is it more beautiful? Can it make men happier?

In answering this question, be sure to apply your knowledge of art, music, biology, physics, chemistry, and history.

5. Is there any poetry to be found in factory towns? (See *Pittsburgh* by James Oppenheim.)

6. Do you think that the coming of the machine has made man less or more sensitive to beauty? State your views fully.

7. Add to your scrapbook by including poems dealing with modern marvels. At some appropriate time read them to the class, giving your reasons for liking them.

8. Read *Factories* by Margaret Widdemer, *The Man with the Hoe* by Edwin Markham. Do they seem to possess any point in common with regard to their criticism of our machine civilization? Compare them with *Smoke and Steel* by Carl Sandburg.

THE WORKADAY WORLD AND ITS PEOPLE

1. Ask your art teacher to show you a reproduction of Millet's *The Man with the Hoe*. What other painters have been inspired in their work by sympathy for the poor?

2. Are the facts of American history in accord with the details supplied by Stephen Vincent Benét in *America*?

3. Write a poem about a snowplow, a tractor, or a similar machine. Imitate the form and spirit of *The Steam Shovel* if you like.

4. In what sense may *Caliban in the Coal Mines* and *The Man with the Hoe* be regarded as companion pieces?

5. Let a committee organize a symposium on modern poetry. Pupils will read one or more poems by each of the following: Edna St. Vincent Millay, Carl Sandburg, Alfred Noyes, Edwin Markham, John V. A. Weaver, Christopher Morley, Rupert Brooke, Amy Lowell, Vachel Lindsay, William Vaughn Moody.

6. Which of the ten poets listed in the preceding exercise belong together? Give your reasons for so grouping them.

7. Sarah N. Cleghorn's four-line *The Golf Links* is considered a great poem. Why?

8. Choose your favorite poem. Comment on the excellences of form and content which have impressed you.

9. Add to your scrapbook poems dealing with the workaday world and its people.

10. If a victrola is available, play the record of Tschaikowsky's *Symphonie Pathétique*. Does Ruth Comfort Mitchell do justice to it in her poem?

THE FUNNY SIDE

1. Come to class ready to read the most humorous verses in your favorite Gilbert and Sullivan operetta.

2. Organize a committee for the purpose of reading a poem in each of the following dialects: Scotch, Yiddish, Italian, Irish, Negro, Yankee. Be sure that the content of such poems is of high quality.

3. Write a limerick of your own. Imitate, if you like, one of those printed in this section.

4. Make the distinction between humor and wit. Find

the poems in this section which illustrate the difference between the two.

5. What other humorous poems by Oliver Wendell Holmes are well known? Read them to the class.

6. Play a record of a favorite selection in a Gilbert and Sullivan operetta. Does Sullivan's music harmonize with Gilbert's poetry? In what respects?

7. Add to your scrapbook humorous verses taken from magazines and newspapers.

8. For Contribution Day have humorous verses recited from the works of Carolyn Wells, Arthur Guiterman, Franklin P. Adams, Hilaire Belloc, Richard Barham, James Whitcomb Riley, Eugene Field, and others.

THE WELL OF WISDOM

1. After some research in the life and works of Robert Burns, give a talk before the class explaining, among other things, why *For A' That* is a characteristic poem.

2. Go to a museum to see a Greek urn. If no museum is conveniently accessible, ask your art teacher to show you a photographic or similar reproduction of a Greek urn. Is Keats's *Ode* wholly to be attributed to the beauty of such an urn?

3. What is a lyric? How many poems in this section fall under this head? Do you prefer lyrical poetry to other types; for example, narrative? Which type is more appealing to you?

4. Imitate *If* by Kipling or Polonius's *Advice to Laertes* by Shakespeare. Adapt the content of either poem to suit your own ideas.

5. Set a committee to work in a search for epigrams which will have a direct bearing on pupil problems. When these are read on an appointed day, let the class evaluate them for form and content.

6. Come to class prepared to report on the life and poetry of William Wordsworth, Emily Dickinson, Stephen Crane, or Elinor Wylie.

7. Add to your scrapbook poems which, because of their wisdom and truth, have a special significance to you.

UNDER THE OPEN SKY

1. Write a lyric based on your love of some tree, flower, brook, hill, or similar natural object. Try to be sincere in mood; aim for melody in the sound of the verses; do not fear to be too personal or self-revealing. Perhaps Edna St. Vincent Millay's and Sara Teasdale's lyrics are worth studying before you undertake your task.

2. Add to your scrapbook poems dealing with the many moods of Nature.

3. What examples of didactic poetry can you find in this section? Does didactic poetry merit high ranking?

4. What poems in this section may be improved by condensation? Defend the revision you would suggest.

5. Organize a symposium on the general topic: The Poet and Nature. Let pupils come to class prepared to give critical readings of the works of Wordsworth, Frost, Keats, Lowell, Housman, and others.

6. Play selections from Beethoven's Sixth Symphony (Pastoral) on the victrola. What poem or poems most closely approach this symphony in theme and spirit?

7. Find the best ten lines of poetry in this section (they need not be consecutive). Justify your choice and defend your standards.

8. Memorize your favorite poem in this section.

9. Look up the theories of Poe, Wordsworth, Arnold, and others, with respect to the nature of poetry. Does any one of these theories meet with your approval?

ALL MANNER OF CREATURES

1. Organize a committee to prepare an anthology of poems dealing with animals. Include creatures omitted from this section. The poems must be scientifically accurate, of course; and they should meet the highest standards as regards rhythm, rhyme, figures of speech, diction, imagination, and so on. The most gifted artists in the class should be asked to contribute appropriate illustrations, and the volume should be circulated for home reading for the remainder of the term.

2. Read R. P. T. Coffin's account of the origin of *Crystal Moment.* This is to be found in *Fifty Poets,* edited by W. R. Benét. Compare this account with Dorothy Wordsworth's explanation of the source of *The Daffodils.*

3. Are the aims of the poet and of the scientist conflicting, overlapping, or totally unrelated? Illustrate by reference to the poems in this section.

4. Why is *Tiger* characteristic of its author?

5. Write a poem on *your* dog, cat, canary, or goldfish. Or better still, write two poems; one in humorous and one in serious vein.

6. Add to your scrapbook poems on All Manner of Creatures.

CHALLENGE TO COURAGE

1. Write a poem about a great man or leader. Be sure to choose an appropriate meter and stanza form. Compare *Lincoln, The Man of the People, O Captain! My Captain!* and *Ulysses.*

2. Does American history confirm the eulogy bestowed on Lincoln by Whitman and Markham?

3. Bring to class a series of poems on the theme of courage.

Select them from the best poets. What new ideas on this subject do they seem to present to you?

4. Memorize your favorite poem in this section, making sure that you can explain to the class why it is worth memorizing.

5. Add to your scrapbook poems that challenge courage.

6. *Courage* by Karle Wilson Baker is an epigram. Can you compose an epigram of your own on this subject?

MAN AND WARFARE

1. Read the following poems to the class:
   Sir Walter Scott's *Soldier, Rest! Thy Warfare O'er*
   Robert Burns's *Bannockburn*
   Robert Browning's *Cavalier Tunes*
   Alfred Lord Tennyson's *Charge of the Light Brigade*
What attitude toward war have these poems in common? How do they differ from the poems in this section? Which group of poems is to be preferred? Why?

2. Find other poems sharing the point of view of the poems in this section.

3. Ask your art teacher for picture postcards of Christ as painted by various artists of the Renaissance. Pass them around the class before the reading of Gibson's *The Conscript*.

4. Consult the newspapers for stories of current warfare. Write a poem in the spirit of Hardy, Sassoon, Southey, or Gibson concerning some modern war.

5. Add to your scrapbook poems dealing with war.

6. What musical composers have written martial elegies? Play a record of such an elegy, if a victrola is available, before reading *The Anthem for Doomed Youth* to the class.

REMARKABLE SONNETS

1. Masefield's sonnet is difficult to grasp unless it is carefully analyzed. Let a pupil who has mastered its thought explain how he did so, answering questions put to him by the members of the class.

3. You will understand *New England* better if you will try to *picture* it in terms of New England *people* and their activities. For "Conscience always has the rocking chair," what picture would you supply?

4. Make a collection of favorite sonnets. If every member of the class will do the same, it is possible to compile a Book of Favorite Sonnets, to be illustrated by the artists in the group and circulated for home reading.

5. Edwin Arlington Robinson, Edna St. Vincent Millay, and John Masefield are three noted sonneteers of our day. Find a few representative sonnets by each of them, and read them to the class, with critical comment. End by indicating, with reasons, the poet you enjoy most.

6. Selecting an adequate number of both older and recent sonnets, for illustrative reading, trace the history of the sonnet, indicating its origins, its scope, and its importance in the history of poetry. Do not hesitate to include writers not represented in this section; for example, Spenser and Rossetti.

7. Have capable pupils review various sonnet cycles; for example, Shakespeare's, Rossetti's, Millay's. Only a few sonnets in each cycle need to be read and interpreted for the benefit of the class.

8. Write a sonnet in Italian or Shakespearean style. Choose a significant theme: one which will stimulate you to speak freely and feelingly.

9. Add to your scrapbook sonnets clipped from magazines and newspapers.

LOVE AND MEMORY

1. Explain to the class what a lyric is. How do you account for the predominance of lyrics in the poems of this section?

2. If any pupil in the class has the necessary talent, let him put one or more of the poems to music. Let the class help him to select the most suitable poems. What qualities should such poems exhibit?

3. Play some musical lyrics on the victrola. What poems in this section can advantageously be introduced by music of this kind?

4. Conduct a symposium on the English and American lyric. Have pupil volunteers read, and report on representative lyrics of Shakespeare, Lovelace, Burns, Keats, Browning, Tennyson, Poe, Masefield, Teasdale, Millay, and others.

5. It is doubtful whether the English lyric has ever surpassed Tennyson's *Break, Break, Break* for sheer beauty of melody and haunting beauty of mood. Do you agree?

6. Write a lyric of your own based on some significant experience.

7. Add to your scrapbook poems dealing with love and memory.

8. Memorize your favorite poem in this section.

FOOTLOOSE FOR FAR PLACES

1. Read to the class other verses by Robert Louis Stevenson with a view to establishing the latter's versatility and range as a poet.

2. Let some pupil read *Dauber*, Masefield's celebrated sea-poem, and report on it to the class, reciting significant passages. Let another pupil give an account of Masefield's life

and work. *Sea-Fever*, *Cargoes*, and *A Wanderer's Song* should be discussed in the light of the additional information thus supplied.

3. Write a poem on the sea or any far-away place that lures your fancy. Be sure to put your longing into your verses.

4. Rewrite the last stanza of *Cargoes*, substituting an appropriate American vessel for the "dirty British coaster."

5. Compare *Magic* by Hamlin Garland with *The Shell* by James Stephens.

6. Richard Wagner painted an interesting picture of Old Nürnberg in his opera, *Die Meistersinger von Nürnberg*. Play a selection from this opera on the victrola before reading Grace Hazard Conkling's *Old Nürnberg* to the class.

7. Add to your scrapbook poems dealing with far places.

8. Look up all the nautical terms in *Tacking Ship Off Shore*. If you know something about ships, perhaps you will be able to tell the class whether these terms have been accurately used. Walter Mitchell, the author of this sea-poem, was a clergyman.

9. Read Robert Louis Stevenson's *In the South Seas*, *Experiences on the Casco* (1888), and the *Equator* (1889). Other members of the class might look up a good Life of Stevenson and report on the Samoan period. The poem *To the Schooner Casco* will then be better understood.

MEN AND WOMEN IN LITERATURE AND FABLE

1. Write a poem in the manner of Arthur Guiterman addressed to the editor of your school magazine. Read the Prologue to Chaucer's *Canterbury Tales* for help with the vocabulary.

2. Select pages from Chapman's *Odyssey* and *Iliad* for

class reading. What are the meters used? Would you use them today?

3. Read specimen pages from the King James version of the Bible. Why is this work great literature? What are the great poems to be found in it? Read such verses for class appreciation.

4. Have a committee discuss the friendship of Samuel Johnson and James Boswell. Read to the class those pages in Boswell's biography which will throw light on Christopher Morley's poem.

5. Write a poem on the poet who has affected you most deeply. Perhaps you may prefer not to imitate any of the poems in this section. The matter is so personal that imitation seems unwarranted.

6. Read half a dozen of Emily Dickinson's poems to the class before taking up the study of Melville Cane's poem.

7. Compare Rupert Brooke's *The Soldier* with the poem by Wilfrid Gibson.

8. Add to your scrapbook poems dealing with characters in literature and fable.

9. Play on the victrola some appropriate air to precede the reading of Auslander's *Is This the Lark?* What selection will you play? How does it harmonize with the spirit of the poem?

10. Ask your teacher or the librarian to let you see picture postcards or other illustrative material connected with the poets and characters portrayed in this section.

Supplementary Reading

STORIES BRAVE AND STRANGE

RALPH PAINE, *Blackbeard Buccaneer*
JOHN MASEFIELD, *On the Spanish Main*
RAFAEL SABATINI, *Captain Blood*
F. J. DARTON, *Wonder Book of Old Romance*
HOWARD PYLE, *Men of Iron*
CHELSEA FRASER, *Heroes of the Air*
CHELSEA FRASER, *Heroes of the Sea*
CHELSEA FRASER, *Heroes of the Wilds*
GEORGE W. TETER, *One Hundred Narrative Poems*
JOHN LOMAX, *Cowboy Songs and Other Frontier Ballads*
JOHN LOMAX, *Cowboy Songs and Songs of the Cattle Trail*
CARL SANDBURG, *American Songbag*
FRANCIS B. GUMMERE, *Old English Ballads*
T. W. HIGGINSON, *Book of American Explorers*
STEPHEN VINCENT BENÉT, *John Brown's Body*

MODERN MARVELS

CARL SANDBURG, *Chicago Poems*
CARL SANDBURG, *Smoke and Steel*
CARL SANDBURG, *Good Morning, America*
WILLIAM HURD HILLYER, *Songs of the Steel Age*
WILFRID GIBSON, *Daily Bread*
CHARLES LINDBERGH, *We*
PAUL DE KRUIF, *Hunger Fighters*
PAUL DE KRUIF, *Microbe Hunters*
PAUL DE KRUIF, *Men against Death*
MICHAEL PUPIN, *From Immigrant to Inventor*

SINCLAIR LEWIS, *Arrowsmith*
FLOYD DARROW, *Masters of Science and Invention*
HENDRIK VAN LOON, *Story of Mankind*

THE WORKADAY WORLD AND ITS PEOPLE

WILFRID WILSON GIBSON, *Collected Poems*
LOUIS UNTERMEYER, *Selected Poems and Parodies*
CARL SANDBURG, *Chicago Poems*
ALFRED NOYES, *Collected Poems*
PAUL ENGLE, *American Song*
JOHN V. A. WEAVER, *In American*
EDWIN MARKHAM, *Man with the Hoe and other Poems*
JAMES STEPHENS, *Collected Poems*
LANGSTON HUGHES, *The Weary Blues*
AMY LOWELL, *Selected Poems*
PAUL L. DUNBAR, *Folks from Dixie*
EDWARD STEINER, *From Alien to Citizen*
MARY ANTIN, *The Promised Land*
JANE ADDAMS, *Twenty Years at Hull House*
HAMLIN GARLAND, *A Daughter of the Middle Border*
HAMLIN GARLAND, *A Son of the Middle Border*
CHARLES AND MARY BEARD, *The Rise of American Civilization*

THE FUNNY SIDE

CAROLYN WELLS, *Idle Idyls*
RICHARD BARHAM, *Ingoldsby Legends*
CHARLES E. CARRYL, *The Admiral's Caravan*
ARTHUR GUITERMAN, *The Laughing Muse*
FRANKLIN P. ADAMS, *So Much Velvet*
THOMAS A. DALY, *Canzoni, Carmina*
PAUL LAURENCE DUNBAR, *Lyric of Love and Laughter*

Eugene Field, *Poems*
James Whitcomb Riley, *The Ole Swimmin' Hole*

THE WELL OF WISDOM

Amy Lowell, *Life of Keats*
Stephen Crane, *The Black Riders, War Is Kind*
New and Old Testament, especially the Psalms
R. W. Emerson, *Essays*
Alfred Lord Tennyson, *In Memoriam*
William Wordsworth, *Collected Poems*
Robert Burns, *Selected Poems*, especially those in *Golden Treasury*
Emily Dickinson, *Complete Poems*
Anthologies: *An Anthology of American Poetry* by Alfred Kreymborg
   The Book of American and English Poetry by Edwin Markham
   An American Anthology by E. C. Stedman
   The Golden Treasury by F. T. Palgrave
   The Oxford Book of English Verse

UNDER THE OPEN SKY

F. T. Palgrave, *Golden Treasury* (especially for poems by Keats and Wordsworth)
Robert Browning, *Selected Poems*
Sara Teasdale, *Flame and Shadow, Dark of the Moon*
Emily Dickinson, *Collected Poems*
Walter de la Mare, *The Listeners*
Adelaide Crapsey, *Verse*
Hilda Doolittle (H. D.), *Collected Poems*
W. H. Davies, *Autobiography of a Super-Tramp*
James Stephens, *Collected Poems*

AMY LOWELL, *Selected Poems*
BLISS CARMAN, *Songs from Vagabondia*
EDNA ST. VINCENT MILLAY, *Renascence, Second April*
HENRY D. THOREAU, *Walden*
ROBERT L. STEVENSON, *Travels with a Donkey*
CHARLES J. FINGER, *Adventures under Sapphire Skies*

ALL MANNER OF CREATURES

WILL JAMES, *Smoky*
ALFRED OLLIVANT, *Bob, Son of Battle*
C. W. GRAY, *Dawgs*
JACK LONDON, *Call of the Wild*
A. E. TERHUNE, *Lad, A Dog*
E. H. BAYNES, *Animal Heroes of the Great War*
HENRI FABRE, *Life of the Spider*
MAURICE MAETERLINCK, *Life of the Bee*
R. L. DITMARS, *Wild Animals I Have Known*
R. L. DITMARS, *Trails of a Naturalist's Quest*
ROBERT HEGNER, *Parade of the Animal Kingdom*

CHALLENGE TO COURAGE

DON MARQUIS, *Dreams and Dust*
WILLIAM R. BENÉT, *The Falconer of God and Other Poems*
VACHEL LINDSAY, *Collected Poems*
W. E. HENLEY, *London Voluntaries*
RICHARD HOVEY, *Collected Poems*
ROBERT L. STEVENSON, *Collected Poems*
CARL SANDBURG, *Abe Lincoln, the Prairie Years*
JOHN DRINKWATER, *Abraham Lincoln* (a play)
I. M. TARBELL, *The Life of Abraham Lincoln*
EDGAR LEE MASTERS, *Vachel Lindsay*
HAMLIN GARLAND, *A Son of the Middle Border*

MAN AND WARFARE

THOMAS HARDY, *Chosen Poems*
WILFRID W. GIBSON, *Collected Poems*
SIEGFRIED SASSOON, *Counter Attack, Satirical Poems*
WILFRED OWEN, *Poems*
MARIA ERICH REMARQUE, *All Quiet on the Western Front*
HENRI BARBUSSE, *Under Fire*

LOVE AND MEMORY

WALTER DE LA MARE, *The Listeners*
W. B. YEATS, *Collected Poems*
A. E. HOUSMAN, *A Shropshire Lad, Last Poems*
F. T. PALGRAVE, *The Golden Treasury*
F. I. CARPENTER, *English Lyrical Poetry*
AUSLANDER AND HILL, *The Winged Horse*
The Oxford Book of English Verse
E. A. ROBINSON, *Collected Poems*
EUGENE FIELD, *Western Verse*
ALFRED LORD TENNYSON, *The Princess, In Memoriam*
ROBERT BROWNING, *Collected Poems*
ROBERT BURNS, *Collected Poems*
EDNA ST. VINCENT MILLAY, *Second April, Figs from Thistles*
JOHN MASEFIELD, *Collected Poems*
CHARLES LAMB, *Essays of Elia*
R. W. EMERSON, *Essays*

FOOTLOOSE FOR FAR PLACES

A cycle of poems on the sea and ships: *A Wet Sheet and a Flowing Sea* by Cunningham; *Old Ironsides* by Holmes; *Old Ships* by David Morton; *The Sailor's Consolation* by Dibdin; *The Ballad of the Ivanhoe* by Bill Adams; all in

Poetry of Youth by Edwin Markham.
A. E. HOUSMAN, *A Shropshire Lad, Last Poems*
JOHN MASEFIELD, *Dauber, The Story of a Round House*
CROSBIE GARSTIN, *Ballad of the Royal Ann*
ROBERT LOUIS STEVENSON, *Songs of Travel and Other Verses*
RICHARD HOVEY AND BLISS CARMAN, *Songs from Vagabondia*
JAMES STEPHENS, *Songs from the Clay*
SIR JOHN MANDEVILLE, *Travels*
HARRY A. FRANCK, *A Vagabond Journey Around the World*
HAMLIN GARLAND, *The Camping Tramp*
MARK TWAIN, *A Tramp Abroad*
VICTOR HEISER, *An American Doctor's Odyssey.*

MEN AND WOMEN IN LITERATURE AND FABLE

AMY LOWELL, *Life of John Keats*
GEOFFREY CHAUCER, *Canterbury Tales*
The Bible, King James Version
JOSEPH AUSLANDER, *Cyclops' Eye, Sunrise Trumpets*
JAMES BOSWELL, *Life of Samuel Johnson*
JANE AUSTEN, *Pride and Prejudice, Sense and Sensibility*
G. K. CHESTERTON, *Life of Robert Browning*
EMILY DICKINSON, *Collected Poems*
M. D. BIANCHI, *Life of Emily Dickinson*
HOMER, *The Iliad and the Odyssey*
ALFRED LORD TENNYSON, *Lancelot and Elaine*
MIGUEL DE CERVANTES, *Don Quixote*
JESSIE M. TATLOCK, *Greek and Roman Mythology*

Biographical Notes

FRANKLIN PIERCE ADAMS (1881–   ) is the celebrated columnist, humorist, translator, poet, and literary man-about-town. After a period of journalism in the Mid-West, he came to New York and there conducted his column, *The Conning Tower*, with phenomenal success. He has published numerous volumes, chiefly humorous, among which might be mentioned *The Diary of Our Own Samuel Pepys*, *Weights and Measures* (1917), *The Conning Tower Book* (1926), and *The Melancholy Lute* (1936).

LEONIE ADAMS (1899–   ) was born in Brooklyn, New York, graduated from Barnard, and now lives at Hillburn, N.Y. In *Those Not Elect* and *High Falcon* she has written poetry of rare excellence.

JOSEPH ADDISON (1672–1719). Addison early in life exhibited a literary gift which attracted the attention of famous people in the literary world, among them John Dryden. In 1705, he published his celebrated poem, *The Campaign*. After occupying several high offices of state, he settled down to the career of essayist and dramatist. His contributions to the *Spectator* are famous, as is also his verse-tragedy, *Cato*. He was buried in Westminster Abbey.

CONRAD AIKEN (1889–   ) was born in Savannah, Georgia. Graduating from Harvard, he traveled abroad. He now resides much of the time in England. Well known as a short-story writer, critic, and novelist, Aiken has done equally notable work as a poet. *Priapus and the Pool* (1926) exhibits an authentic lyrical talent.

ZOË AKINS (1886–   ) is well known as a dramatist. Her play, *The Old Maid*, won the Pulitzer Prize in 1936. Her volumes of verse include *Interpretations* (1912) and *The Hills Grow Smaller* (1937).

THOMAS BAILEY ALDRICH (1836–1907) was born in Portsmouth,

New Hampshire.   He achieved a reputation as a writer of short stories and novels.   All the world knows his *Story of a Bad Boy*. In the field of poetry, he is best remembered for a few exquisitely wrought lyrics and light-hearted society verse.

HERVEY ALLEN (1889–   ) was born in Pennsylvania, became a Lieutenant of Infantry on the Mexican border and later served in France.   After a period of teaching, he turned to writing, publishing a biography of Poe, *Israfel*, and a book of war memories, *Toward the Flame*.   His epic novel, *Anthony Adverse*, was phenomenally successful.   In the verse form, he has shown admirable skill in *Carolina Chansons* and several subsequent volumes.

WALTER CONRAD ARENSBERG (1878–   ) is a critic, art connoisseur, and scholar.   He has done much research in the work of Dante, Shakespeare, and Bacon.   His *Poems* appeared in 1914.

MATTHEW ARNOLD (1822–1888) was born in Saleham, England. He was the son of the great schoolmaster and historian, Thomas Arnold.   After graduating from Oxford with high honors, he became an inspector of schools in London.   For ten years he lectured on poetry at Oxford.   He also delivered lectures on literature, ethics, and philosophy in America.   His poetry is predominantly grave, often pessimistic.   The celebrated *Dover Beach* is typical of this mournful strain; more vigorous though perhaps equally melancholy, is the popular *Sohrab and Rustum*.

LEONARD BACON (1887–   ) is a satirist in verse.   Graduating from Yale in 1909, he worked on a rubber plantation, a cotton plantation, and a cattle ranch, and then became instructor in the University of California.   During the World War he was identified with the Air Service.   *Animula Vagula*, *Guinea Fowl*, and *The Legend of Quincibald* are volumes distinctive for Bacon's incisive and brilliant wit.

KARLE WILSON BAKER (1878–   ) has the following books to her credit: *The Birds of Tanglewood*, *Blue Smoke*, *Burning Bush*, and *Dreamers on Horseback*.

RICHARD HARRIS BARHAM (1788–1845), who went under the

nom de plume of Thomas Ingoldsby, was a canon at St. Paul's Cathedral, London. His *Ingoldsby Legends* are humorous metrical tales, masterly in their kind.

HILAIRE BELLOC, JOSEPH HILAIRE PIERRE BELLOC (1870–   ) is an English historian, biographer, essayist, and poet. His volumes of essays include the interesting *First and Last, On Nothing, On Something,* and *On Everything*. He has written biographica' studies of Cromwell and Danton. His verse includes *More Peers* and *New Cautionary Tales*.

LAURA BENÉT is the sister of William Rose Benét and Stephen Vincent Benét. Her published work includes *Basket for a Fair, Goods and Chattels,* and *Noah's Dove*.

STEPHEN VINCENT BENÉT (1898–   ) was born in Bethlehem, Pennsylvania. He is the younger brother of William Rose Benét, the poet, and associate editor of the *Saturday Review of Literature*. He has published several volumes of verse, among them the widely acclaimed *John Brown's Body*. Latterly he has been writing short stories, as witness his excellent collection, *Thirteen O'Clock*.

WILLIAM ROSE BENÉT (1886–   ) was born in Fort Hamilton in the harbor of New York. Graduated from Yale in 1907, he became a publisher's reader, then Associate Editor of the *New York Post's* Literary Review; later still, Associate Editor of *The Saturday Review of Literature*. Benét has published nearly a dozen volumes of verse, of which *Merchants from Cathay* (1913), *The Falconer of God* (1914), and *Man Possessed* (1927) might be cited.

MACKNIGHT BLACK died in 1931. He had a rare gift for describing the complex miracles of our modern machine civilization. This is abundantly evident in his two volumes, *Machinery* (1929) and *Thrust at the Sky and Other Poems*.

WILLIAM BLAKE (1757–1827) is one of the rarest figures in English literature. He was given to visions and hallucinations during the greater part of his life; yet, being an artist, he managed to weave them into his poems, his paintings, and his engravings. He wrote many volumes of poetry, of which *Songs of Innocence* (1789) and *Songs of Experience* (1794) are perhaps the greatest.

In these he immortalized his sublimely innocent and naïve imagination.

Louise Bogan (1897–   ) was born in Maine. After receiving her education in Boston, she traveled to Vienna and New Mexico, and finally took up her residence in New York City. Her first book, *Body of This Death*, appeared in 1923; her second, *Dark Summer*, six years later. She is a careful craftsman preoccupied with the deeper problems of life.

Berton Braley (1882–   ) is an American humorist whose verses are widely read. His books include *Hurdy-Gurdy on Olympus*, *A Banjo at Armageddon*, and *Morgan Sails the Caribbean*.

Robert Bridges (1844–1930) was educated at Eton and Corpus Christi College, Oxford. After studying medicine in London, he became a practicing physician there, but abandoned this profession for poetry. In 1913 he was appointed Poet Laureate.

Rupert Brooke (1887–1915) was born in Rugby, England. He distinguished himself as an amateur athlete, excelling in cricket, football, tennis, and swimming. When the World War broke out, Brooke sailed to take part in the Dardanelles campaign. He died at Skyros. His *Collected Poems*, published shortly after his death, was pathetic testimony of his genius thus tragically curtailed.

Elizabeth Barrett Browning (1806–1861) was born in England, the daughter of the rather severe Mr. Barrett who figures so prominently in the popular play, *The Barretts of Wimpole Street*. An invalid from earliest years, she sought the assuagement of verse. Her work attracted the not yet celebrated poet Robert Browning, who courted her ardently and married her despite parental disapproval. The Barretts and Browning were never entirely reconciled even to the day of Elizabeth's death. Her best work is found in two volumes: *Sonnets from the Portuguese* and *The Cry of the Children*. She unites profound feeling with great beauty of phrase and image.

Robert Browning (1819–1889) was born in London. After a period of travel in his early manhood, he decided to devote his life to poetry. In 1846 he married Elizabeth Barrett. The couple removed to Italy and lived there for fifteen years. Browning's great poems and dramas are often difficult to understand. This is particularly true of *Paracelsus* (1835), *Sordello* (1840), and his chief work, *The Ring and the Book*. In 1881 the Browning Society was founded in his honor. He lies buried in Westminster Abbey.

WILLIAM CULLEN BRYANT (1794–1878) was born in Cummington, Massachusetts. He studied law and was admitted to the bar in 1815. At the age of seventeen he startled his father by composing *Thanatopsis* — the first truly great poem in American literature. Coming to New York a little later, he settled down to journalism and became editor of the *New York Evening Post* — a position which he occupied for many years. Besides his excellent translations of the *Iliad* and the *Odyssey*, he composed many poems, the best of which deal with the many moods of Nature. His lines are grave, dignified, and noble.

HENRY CUYLER BUNNER (1855–1896) was a successful short-story writer. His verse is often delightfully gay and mocking.

GELETT BURGESS (FRANK GELETT) (1866–   ) wrote *The Purple Cow* in 1895 and found himself a public figure. His book, *Are You a Bromide?* attracted almost equal attention. He is a genuine humorist.

ROBERT BURNS (1759–1796) is Scotland's greatest poet. He followed the plow and wrote as he labored, inspired by the verses of Ferguson. In 1786 appeared the famous Kilmarnock edition of *Poems, Chiefly in the Scottish Dialect*, for Burns, while he could write traditional English with expert ease, found his native dialect the only suitable medium for his peculiar insight into the lives of his countrymen. With a consummate lyrical gift, perhaps the most sublime in the whole history of poetry, he added his canny humor and broad understanding of the human soul. The result is imperishable literature.

RICHARD BURTON (1861–   ) is an American critic, lecturer, and poet. His *Poems of Earth's Meaning* (1917) is a significant work.

WITTER BYNNER (1882–   ) began to write under the influence of A. E. Housman.   His *Grenstone Poems* have been much admired. Born in Brooklyn, New York, he was graduated from Harvard in 1902.   He divides his time between New York and the artist colony at Santa Fé.

GEORGE GORDON, LORD BYRON (1788–1824) was born in London.   His father died in the poet's infancy; his mother was an unbalanced, emotional creature who alternately pampered and illtreated her son.   Byron would have been the better had wiser care been bestowed upon him, for he was keenly sensitive, and lame besides.   Byron's actions and writings, from the beginning of his maturity, are those of a rebel and non-conformist.   *Childe Harold's Pilgrimage, Don Juan*, his plays, *Manfred and Cain*, exhibit his passionate love of liberty.   In 1824 he espoused the cause of Greek independence.   At Missolonghi, he fell ill and died, a martyr to his principles.

MELVILLE CANE has published *Behind Dark Spaces* and *January Garden*.

BLISS CARMAN (1861–1929) was born in Fredericton, New Brunswick, in Canada.   After his graduation from Harvard, he settled in the United States.   With Richard Hovey he published the celebrated *Songs from Vagabondia* (1894).

CHARLES EDWARD CARRYL (1842–1920), the father of Guy Wetmore Carryl, wrote many humorous ballads.   These are to be found in *Davy and the Goblin* and *The Admiral's Caravan*.

GUY WETMORE CARRYL (1873–1904) had a successful career as a journalist.   His topsy-turvy wit and his dexterous rhymes are displayed in such volumes as *Fables for the Frivolous* and *Grim Tales Made Gay*.

MADISON CAWEIN (1865–1914) was born in Louisville, Kentucky, where he passed most of his life.   He was educated at the Louisville High School, where he was fortunate enough to have a teacher who encouraged him to write.   Cawein was the untitled poet laureate of his native state whose moods and fields he knew intimately.   His *Collected Poems* are well worth reading.

FREDERICK MORTIMER CLAPP has published *On the Overland and Other Poems* (1916) and *New York and Other Verses* (1918).

BADGER CLARK (1883–   ) was born in Albia, Iowa. He has a peculiar ear for cowboy tunes. His work in such volumes as *Sun and Saddle Leather* and *Grass-Grown Trails* breathes the freedom and the spaciousness of the Dakota hills.

SARAH NORTHCLIFFE CLEGHORN (1876–   ) was born in Norfolk, Virginia, but has lived most of her life in Vermont. Indeed, it may be said that she is the poet of Vermont, her short lyrics giving a poet's life to its landscape and its people.

ARTHUR HUGH CLOUGH (1819–1861) was born in Liverpool, England. He became a tutor at Oxford and afterwards was connected with the Education Office in London. His *Poems* reveal a profound and meditative spirit. Clough's death in Italy inspired his friend Matthew Arnold, to compose the elegy, *Thyrsis*, in his memory.

ELIZABETH COATSWORTH (1893–   ) was born in Buffalo, New York, and now resides at Hingham, Massachusetts. She is a restless traveler and, naturally, her verses are filled with the experiences she has acquired in many lands. There is a fascinating pictorial quality in such volumes from her pen as *Atlas and Beyond* and *Compass Rose*.

ROBERT P. TRISTRAM COFFIN (1892–   ) was born in Maine. He has taught English at Bowdoin College, Maine, and has written novels and biographies with a Maine background. He recently won the Pulitzer Award in poetry.

SAMUEL TAYLOR COLERIDGE (1772–1834) was educated at Christ's Hospital school, in London. A classmate was Charles Lamb. Another close friend was William Wordsworth who collaborated with him in the writing of the celebrated *Lyrical Ballads* (1798). Falling a victim to the opium habit, he saw his poetic powers decline, though his critical faculties remained as keen as ever. Coleridge was one of the most intellectual and imaginative of English poets. His *Ancient Mariner* is, of course, widely read.

PADRAIC COLUM (1881–   ) was born in Longford, Ireland. As a young man he was identified with the Irish National Theater, afterwards named The Abbey Theatre. He came to this country in 1914.   First a dramatist, with successes such as *Broken Soil* and *Thomas Muskerry* to his credit, he has latterly confined his attention to criticism and poetry.   His *Dramatic Poems* and *Creatures* (1927) are excellent works.

GRACE HAZARD CONKLING (1878–   ) was born in New York and, after graduating from Smith College, studied abroad at the University of Heidelberg and in Paris.   Since 1915 she has published many books.   *Afternoons of April* and *Wilderness Songs* are delightfully fresh and whimsical.   She is the mother of Hilda Conkling, a poet in her own right.

FRANCES CORNFORD is the author of *Mountains and Molehills* (1935).

STEPHEN CRANE (1871–1900) is better known as a novelist and short-story writer than as a poet.   *The Red Badge of Courage* and *Men, Women and Boats* are famous examples of his realism in prose. His two volumes of poetry, *The Black Riders* and *War is Kind*, are highly original.   Crane, following in the footsteps of Walt Whitman, made use of unrhymed lines.

ADELAIDE CRAPSEY (1878–1914) was the inventor of the poetic form known as the cinquain — a stanza of five lines containing two, four, six, eight, and two syllables, respectively.   She wrote little, but that little showed rare genius.

COUNTÉE CULLEN (1903–   ) was born in New York City, educated in the public schools there, and graduated from New York University.   In *Color* and *Copper Suns* he revealed a marked poetic talent that immediately attracted critical acclaim.   He is one of the most brilliant of American Negro poets.

THOMAS AUGUSTIN DALY (1861–   ) was born in Philadelphia, Pennsylvania.   Leaving Fordham University in his sophomore year, he became a newspaper reporter.   He has since been connected with various Philadelphia journals.   He is a natural humorist who says many pungent truths with a smile on his lips.   Sometimes the smile can turn into a hearty chortle as it does in works like *Canzoni* and *Carmina*.   He is particularly adept at dialect verse.

WILLIAM HENRY DAVIES (1870–   ) was born at Newport in Monmouthshire, England. He is of Welsh descent. As a youth, he was a vagrant until Bernard Shaw saved him for literature by recognizing his poetic talent. By that time the poet had lost one leg in a railroad accident in Canada. Davies has published a score of volumes. His *Collected Poems: First Series* (1916) and *Collected Poems: Second Series* (1923) contain the best of his work.

WALTER DE LA MARE (1873–   ) is one of England's most brilliant versifiers. His best books are *The Listeners* (1912) and *Collected Poems 1901–1918*. He is especially successful with children's verses, as his volume, *Peacock Pie*, abundantly testifies. His *Memoirs of a Midget* is a distinguished work of prose.

EMILY DICKINSON (1830–1886) was born in Amherst, Massachusetts. She spent her entire life in one house, seldom passing beyond her doorstep. Little did her townsmen know that the mysterious recluse was composing verse that was later to immortalize her name. Her poems, appearing after her death, have won world-wide acclaim. They are for the greater part brief snatches, but hauntingly wise and beautiful. Critics consider her the greatest woman poet this country has produced.

HILDA DOOLITTLE (H. D.) (1886–   ) was born in Bethlehem, Pennsylvania. She is the wife of the British poet and novelist, Richard Aldington. Her work has been largely inspired by the theories of the Imagists. Her *Collected Poems* (1925) exhibit an exquisite craftsmanship and a rare sensitiveness to color and form.

CHARLES L. EDSON was an American columnist who wrote an interesting work, *The Gentle Art of Columning* (1920).

PAUL ELDRIDGE (1888–   ) was born in Philadelphia, Pennsylvania. He was educated in American and European universities. His published works include: *Vanitas, Our Dead Selves, Cobwebs and Cosmos* (verse); *And the Sphinx Spoke, Irony and Pity, One Man Show* (short stories); *The Intruder* (a play); *My First Two Thousand Years, Salome, The Invincible Adam, Prince Pax* (novels in collaboration with G. S. Viereck). His poems in the Chinese manner have been widely praised.

RALPH WALDO EMERSON (1803–1882). Born in Boston, Emerson was educated at the Boston Latin School and matriculated at Harvard in 1817, where he read widely and showed his first promise as a poet. After his graduation from Harvard, he entered the ministry, becoming pastor of the Second Church in Boston, but soon found this position uncongenial. He was temperamentally unwilling to submit to the doctrines of any church or creed. His activities henceforward were confined to lecturing and writing. After a brief sojourn in England, where he began a lifelong friendship with Carlyle, he returned to his native country to gain imperishable fame for his gospel of freedom. "We will walk on our own feet," he said, in his celebrated address, *The American Scholar*, delivered in 1837. "We will work with our own hands," he continued; "we will speak our own minds." This note of individualism and intellectual independence he struck time and again, in prose essay and verse alike. His poetry is not simple. It is packed tight with thought. But it will well repay the student's attention.

WILLIAM CLOSSON EMORY has published *be still* (1929) and a play, *Glory* (1929).

PAUL ENGLE is a young Midwesterner who received his higher education in England. His *American Song* (1934) was a notable volume if only for its deeply felt sense of identification with the American landscape and the American folk. After a period of travel on the continent of Europe, Engle published *Break the Heart's Anger* (1936). The poet's own heart has been stirred by the remediable evils of the contemporary world.

FRANCIS E. FALKENBURY (1882–   ) was born in New York City and graduated from Public School 40, Manhattan. He is now engaged in the furniture business in Hartsdale, N.Y.

ARTHUR DAVISON FICKE (1883–   ) is much interested in foreign countries, especially in China and Japan. In *The Return of Christ* he laid the scene in Holy China. Ficke has lived in New Mexico as well as in New York. He is an authority on Japanese prints. His best book is *Mountain Against Mountain* (1929).

EUGENE FIELD (1850–1895 was born in St. Louis, Missouri. At

the age of twenty-three he became a reporter on the St. Louis *Evening Journal*. The rest of his life was devoted to journalism. He did notable work for the Chicago *Daily Record*. A warm-hearted man, he loved children, and many of his best remembered verses, such as *Little Boy Blue*, reflect this side of his nature. He also composed burlesques which won wide popularity during his lifetime. His *Collected Poems* appeared in 1910.

SARAH BARD FIELD (1882–   ) is the wife of the poet and satirist, Charles Erskine Scott Wood. At least two distinguished works have come from her pen — *The Pale Woman* and *Barabbas*. She writes vividly, with the flaming zeal of a prophet.

JAMES THOMAS FIELDS (1816–1881) was an American poet and editor, famous in his day. His *Poems* appeared in 1854; *Ballads and Other Verses*, in 1881.

JOHN GOULD FLETCHER (1886–   ) was born in Little Rock, Arkansas. A few years after his graduation from Harvard he went to England and has lived there ever since. He has published almost a dozen books of verse, all of them original, powerful, and important. His poem on Lincoln ranks with those on the same subject by Whitman and Markham. His revised *Preludes and Symphonies* should be read and studied for the insight there afforded into the spirit and technique of modern verse.

FORD MADOX FORD (1873–   ) is the grandson of the famous British painter, Ford Madox Brown. He is a poet, novelist, and critic, who excels in all three fields. For some time he was the collaborator of the novelist, Joseph Conrad.

STEPHEN COLLINS FOSTER (1826–1864) was born in Cincinnati, Ohio. He was the author of many popular old songs, including *Old Black Joe*, *My Old Kentucky Home*, and *Old Folks at Home*.

ROBERT FROST (1875–   ) is of New England stock, though born in San Francisco, California. He came East at the age of ten, graduated from the high school at Lawrence, Massachusetts, and entered Dartmouth College. His college career, however, was brief. Sailing for England in 1912, he embarked on a literary career, publishing *A Boy's Will* (1913) and *North of Boston* (1914).

The latter volume made him famous overnight.   Since that epoch-making work, Frost has added to his reputation with each successive book.   He has an unerring power of observation joined to a homely, humorous idiom — indispensable qualities for one who would write truly of New England folk.

HAMLIN GARLAND (1860–1940) was born in Wisconsin, amidst a pioneer country later vividly described in his autobiographical *A Son of the Middle Border*.   He is an excellent novelist and short-story writer.   His verse, while of less commanding quality than his prose, arrests the reader by its obvious sincerity and power.

THEODOSIA PICKERING GARRISON (1874–   ) is in private life Mrs. Frederic James Faulks.   She was born and educated in Newark, New Jersey.   She writes verse and short stories for numerous magazines.

CROSBIE GARSTIN (1887–1930), a British poet and novelist, traveled extensively.   *The Ballad of the Royal Ann*, which appeared in 1922, is evidence of a vigorous poetic gift.

WILFRID WILSON GIBSON (1878–   ) was born in Hexam, England.   He is well known for his sympathies with the working class, as exemplified in such volumes as *The Stonefolds*, *Daily Bread*, and *Neighbours*.

WILLIAM SCHWENK GILBERT (1836–1911) was born in London. He blazed his way to fame with the *Bab Ballads*.   Then followed his collaboration on the celebrated Gilbert and Sullivan operas, for which hc wrote the books.

LORD GORELL, RONALD GORELL BARNES (1884–   ) has published *Days of Destiny*, war poems (1917), and *1904–1936 Poems*.

HORACE GREGORY (1898–   ) is a distinguished American poet. His *Chelsea Rooming House* appeared in 1930, and *No Retreat*, three years later.

LOUISE IMOGEN GUINEY (1861–1920) was born in Boston, Massachusetts.   The last twenty years of her life were spent in England. Her best two volumes, *A Roadside Harp* (1893) and *Patrons* (1897) reveal a grave and vigorous personality.   Though her verses are traditional in theme, they are not seldom inspired.

ARTHUR GUITERMAN (1871–   ), though of American parentage, was born in Vienna, Austria. He came to this country as
a child and has lived in New York ever since except for occasional
pilgrimages to his country home in Vermont. Guiterman's chief
claim to fame is his extraordinarily tuneful and original humorous
verse. In *The Laughing Muse* (1915) and *Ballads of Old New York*
(1920), to mention but two of his fascinating volumes, he displays
his virtuosity as a rhymster and the irresistible drollery of his wit.

THOMAS HARDY (1840–1928) was born in Upper Bockhampton,
near Dorchester, in the "Wessex" district of England which he
made so famous in his novels. He abandoned architecture for
poetry, then turned to the production of novels, all stamped with
the pessimistic realism and irony which characterized the man.
The Mayor of Casterbridge, Tess of the D'Urbervilles and *Jude the
Obscure* are masterly works in this genre. Towards the latter part
of his life he gained an equally distinctive reputation in poetry,
publishing *The Dynasts*, a monumental dramatic epic dealing with
the life of Napoleon, and several volumes of shorter verse. His
Collected Poems are among the classics of contemporary literature.

FRANCIS BRET HARTE (1839–1902) was born in Albany, New
York. At the age of fifteen he went to California, later taught,
clerked, and set type; more important still, he served for a time as
express messenger on stages running in Northern California. In
this fashion he collected at first hand the materials for the powerful
short stories he soon began to write, of which *The Luck of Roaring
Camp* is the best known example. His poems are also of excellent
quality.

ALICE HARTICH was born in Brooklyn, New York. She is a
graduate of the Froebel Academy and of Adelphi College. She
has put verse writing to practical use since her chum's thirteenth
birthday, celebrating in rhyme anniversaries, accidents, luncheons,
promotions, golden weddings, and charity bridges. She is Assistant
to Principal at Public School 3, Brooklyn.

JOHN HAY (1838–1905) was born in Salem, Indiana. He became the secretary of Abraham Lincoln, and after the latter's

death entered on a diplomatic career. Late in life he was named Secretary of State; it was he who was responsible for the so-called Open-Door Policy in China. His *Pike County Ballads* are his chief claim to literary honors.

PAUL HAMILTON HAYNE (1831–1886) was born in Charleston, South Carolina. He was a member of a distinguished family which includes the famous senator from South Carolina who debated with Daniel Webster. Abandoning the law, the young man entered journalism — a career he was obliged to interrupt at the outbreak of the War Between the States. As in the case of Timrod, the war ruined his prospects and all but destroyed his health. His last years were spent in Atlanta, Georgia, where he wrote several volumes of verse.

WILLIAM ERNEST HENLEY (1849–1903) was an invalid most of his life. His *Hospital Verses* recount his experiences in an Edinburgh infirmary. Later on, in London, he wrote *London Voluntaries* (1892) and *Hawthorn and Lavender* (1898). For the greater part of his maturity he was a distinguished and successful journalist.

DANIEL WHITEHEAD HICKEY has published two volumes of verse, *Bright Harbor* (1932) and *Thirteen Sonnets of Georgia* (1933).

FRANK ERNEST HILL (1888–   ) is an American poet, scholar, and critic. He has translated Chaucer's *Canterbury Tales* into modern English. His volume of verse, *Stone Dust*, shows a genuine poetic talent at work. With Joseph Auslander, he wrote *The Winged Horse*.

WILLIAM HURD HILLYER (1880–   ) published *Songs of the Steel Age* in 1907.

RALPH HODGSON (1871–   ) is of English birth. He has been a publisher and lecturer as well as author. His *Poems*, published in 1918, placed him in the front rank of contemporary poets. He has a passionate love of the animal world; many of his verses are anguished outcries against man's inhumanity to bird and beast.

GEORGE SANFORD HOLMES is a Rhode Islander by birth and ancestry, but removed to Denver, Colorado, soon after his graduation from Brown University. For some twenty years he was connected with *The Rocky Mountain News*. He is now stationed in Washington as a correspondent employed by the Scripps-Howard Newspaper alliance. He is an occasional contributor of newspaper and topical verses.

OLIVER WENDELL HOLMES (1809–1894) was born in Cambridge, Massachusetts. He received his education at Andover Academy and at Harvard, where he was a member of the celebrated class of 1829. Embarking on a physician's career, he distinguished himself by zeal and resourcefulness in his chosen profession. From 1847 to 1888 he was a professor of anatomy at Harvard. Holmes's fame rests on his prose works, *The Autocrat of the Breakfast Table* and *The Poet at the Breakfast Table*; and on scattered poems such as *Old Ironsides* and *The Chambered Nautilus*. He wrote many volumes of verse, among which *Songs in Many Keys* and *The Iron Gate* might be mentioned.

THOMAS HOOD (1799–1845) was a gifted journalist, whose puns and witty sallies were famous in their day. His serious poems, however, are not lacking in quality. In fact, such verses as *The Bridge of Sighs* and *The Song of the Shirt* bid fair to endure as long as our literature.

A. E. HOUSMAN (1859–1936) is one of the greatest of modern poets by virtue of his two slender volumes, *A Shropshire Lad* (1896) and *Last Poems* (1922). A scholarly professor of Latin in London, he was an ardent lover of beauty, as his verses abundantly testify. His craftsmanship is flawless; his mood, almost invariably mournful.

LANGSTON HUGHES (1902–   ) was born in Joplin, Missouri. In *The Weary Blues* and *Fine Clothes to the Jew* he has captured the spirit of Negro song. He has had an interesting and varied career as traveler, worker, and teacher. He has a keen fellow-feeling for the lot of the Negro, which he expresses in unforgettably powerful melodies.

ORRICK JOHNS (1887–   ) was born in St. Louis, Missouri. *Black Branches* contains verse of unusual quality.

JAMES WELDON JOHNSON (1871–1938) has done much for Negro

literature in this country.   He is the author of *Fifty Years and Other Poems* and *God's Trombones, Some Negro Sermons in Verse*. His autobiography, *Along This Way*, is a fascinating testament of a vivid and well-spent life.   He edited the interesting *Book of American Negro Poetry*.

JOHN KEATS (1795–1821).   Born the son of a stable-keeper, Keats early in his tragically brief life showed great qualities of mind and heart.   He was apprenticed to a surgeon; and he would himself have pursued this career had it not been for his overmastering love of poetry.   Falling under the influence of Leigh Hunt, he began to compose narrative poems and lyrics unequaled for their imagery and melody.   *Ode on a Grecian Urn*, *Ode to a Nightingale*, and *Ode to Autumn* are only three of the masterpieces which came from his pen.   Unfortunately for English literature, Keats fell a victim to tuberculosis which he contracted on a walking tour to Scotland.   He died in Rome where he had gone in a vain attempt to seek a cure, and lies buried in the Protestant cemetery there.

ALINE KILMER (1888–   ) was born in Norfolk, Virginia. After the death of her husband, Joyce Kilmer, the poet, she became a lecturer and magazine contributor.   *Vigils* (1921) and *The Poor King's Daughter* (1925) are two of her volumes of verse.

JOYCE KILMER (1886–1918) was born in New Brunswick, New Jersey.   He received his higher education at Rutgers and at Columbia.   In 1917 he enlisted in the New York National Guard. He was killed in action overseas, a year later.   *Trees and Other Poems* and *Main Street and Other Poems* are the two outstanding volumes from his pen.

RUDYARD KIPLING (1865–1936) was born in Bombay, India. After working as a newspaper reporter, he went to England, but continued to write on Indian subjects, particularly in his short stories.   *Soldiers Three* and *Plain Tales from the Hills* are examples of his genius as a story-teller.   Little less distinguished is his gift for poetry.   His best work in this field is to be found in his *Inclusive Edition* (1885–1918).   His lines are vigorous and robust; his themes spring from the hard necessities of our times.   His *If*,

Recessional, Gunga Din, and a score of other poems have made a deep impression on the common man.

ALEXANDER KINMAN LAING (1903–   ) is an American poet. *Fool's Errand* (1928) attracted favorable attention.

CHARLES LAMB (1775–1834) is best known as the author of the *Essays of Elia.* He also wrote drama and poetry, not without success.

ANDREW LANG (1844–1912) was better known as a critic and essayist than as a poet. His light verses, however, still retain their charm, notably those in *Rhymes à la Mode* (1884).

SIDNEY LANIER (1842–1881) was born in Macon, Georgia. He graduated from Southern College and, when the War Between the States began, volunteered and was taken prisoner while on service on a blockade runner. The hardships of his imprisonment doubtless shortened his life. Lanier was an accomplished musician, a rare teacher, and withal a born poet. His *Science of English Verse* exhibited the acuteness of his intellect. His poems, as musical and expert as the best by Poe, hold a high place in the esteem of critics.

FRANCIS LEDWIDGE (1891–1917) was another victim of the World War. Born in Slane, Ireland, he showed great promise in his two books, *Songs of the Fields* and *Songs of Peace.*

RICHARD LE GALLIENNE (1866–   ) was born in Liverpool, England. He has gained a considerable reputation as poet, critic, and journalist. He is the father of Eva Le Gallienne, the actress, and latterly has resided in Paris. His volume, *English Poems,* was accorded a favorable reception.

ELIAS LIEBERMAN (1883–   ) has had a notable career in the educational system of New York City. He is now principal of the Thomas Jefferson High School in the Borough of Brooklyn. As a poet, he achieves distinction by the scrupulous quality of his craftsmanship. His prevailing mood is one of compassionate tenderness; but his muse can be hearty and often gay. His poem *I Am an American* has been widely quoted.

VACHEL LINDSAY (1879–1931) was born in Springfield, Illinois.

He was graduated from Springfield High School, and after three years at Hiram College, studied art in Chicago and New York City. Inspired by the mission of the poet, he toured the country, preaching the gospel of beauty, and earning bed and board by selling a pamphlet entitled *Rhymes to be Traded for Bread*. In 1914 he published *The Congo and Other Poems* and became instantly famous. *The Congo*, and previously *General Booth Enters into Heaven*, revealed a new kind of poetry — a poetry compounded of ragtime, deep emotion, and catchy rhythms that appealed to large numbers of people. *Collected Poems* (1923) added to his reputation. His friend, Edgar Lee Masters, has recently written a fascinating life of this brilliant and original poet.

THERESE LINDSEY, MRS. THERESE KAYSER LINDSEY, has written *Blue Norther, Texas Poems* (1928), and *A Tale of the Galveston Storm* (1936).

JOHN A. LOMAX (1872–   ), in collaboration with Alan Lomax, has published *American Ballads and Folk Songs* (1934) and *Negro Folk Songs* (1936).

HENRY WADSWORTH LONGFELLOW (1807–1882) was born in Portland, Maine, the town he described so tenderly in his poem, *My Lost Youth*. His father, a successful lawyer, sent the boy to Bowdoin. Upon his graduation in 1825, Longfellow began to prepare himself for the position of professor of modern languages. He taught at Bowdoin and later at Harvard University. Longfellow's house in Cambridge was the famous old Craigie House, the headquarters of Washington during the siege of Boston. Here the poet wrote many of his celebrated works. His life was singularly happy and prosperous, for he knew only one great tragedy — the death of his wife by burning. The popularity of Longfellow's poetry is incontestable. *The Song of Hiawatha*, *The Courtship of Miles Standish*, and the *Tales of a Wayside Inn* are only three of literally scores of works which have cast a spell upon the reading public.

AMY LOWELL (1874–1925) was born in Brookline, Massachusetts. She came of the distinguished family which has included poets, statesmen, and educators. A literary innovator, she championed the cause of free verse and did much to stimulate public interest in poetry. Her best books, *Sword Blades and Poppy Seed* (1914), *Men, Women and Ghosts* (1916), and *Can Grande's Castle* (1918) reveal her vivid, dynamic personality and her extraordinary eagerness for new images and sensations. She was also an excellent critic and essayist. Her biography of John Keats, which appeared in 1925, is a standard work.

JAMES RUSSELL LOWELL (1819–91) was born in Cambridge, Massachusetts. He was descended from New England stock. After graduation from Harvard and a brief dalliance with the law, he turned to letters and in 1842 issued a book of poems entitled *A Year's Life*. It was *The Biglow Papers* (1846) which gave him a national reputation. Appointed Smith professor of modern languages at Harvard, in 1855, he showed himself a distinguished scholar, without interrupting his literary labors. A steady stream of essays poured from his pen — *Fireside Travels, Among My Books*, and *My Study Windows*. In 1877 he was appointed Minister to Spain and served in that post for three years.

PERCY MACKAYE (1875–) has been intensely interested in community drama and pageants. His *Wakefield, a Folk Masque*, was a successful spectacle; so too were centennial pageants he prepared for St. Louis, New York, and other cities. His *Poems and Plays*, in two volumes, give the reader a good idea of his versatile artistry.

ARCHIBALD MACLEISH (1892–) was born in Illinois, graduated from Yale — oddly enough, for a poet, he played football — and after studying law, visited Paris, where he remained for some time. He has published *Tower of Ivory*, *The Happy Marriage*, *Conquistador*, and has also written drama for the radio. *Conquistador* brought him the Pulitzer Prize in 1933.

EDWIN MARKHAM (1852–1940). Born in Oregon City, Oregon, Edwin Markham began writing poetry when he was a boy herding sheep and cattle on his mother's range on the Coast Mountains of California. Later he served as school superintendent in the same State. In 1899 he became famous overnight with the publication of his great poem, *The Man with the Hoe.* In this poem he protested against injustice and appealed for the rights of the toiling millions in the lower ranks of labor. Almost equally famous is his *Lincoln, the Man of the People,* the prize poem on the Great Emancipator, which its author read at the dedication of the Lincoln Memorial Building at Washington, D.C., in 1922. Edwin Markham is known and loved by millions of Americans. He lives on Staten Island, New York.

DON MARQUIS (1878–1938) was born in Illinois. Arriving in New York, he became one of the leading columnists of the day. His humorous verses appearing in *The Sun* won him a deserved reputation. His play, *The Old Soak,* showed him a master of racy dialogue and shrewd characterization. *Dreams and Dust* and *Poems and Portraits* are two of his better known volumes of verse.

JOHN MASEFIELD (1874–   ) was born in Ledbury, Hertfordshire, England. Taking to the sea early in life, he sailed on many ships. It is recorded of him that, once in America, he worked as a barkeeper and dishwasher in a Greenwich Village saloon. Yonkers also knew him briefly as a worker in a carpet factory. Back in England, at length, he turned to the art of letters, adorning it at once with such powerful productions as *The Widow in the Bye Street* and *Dauber,* both published in 1912. His subsequent works, *Good Friday and Other Poems, Reynard the Fox,* and half a dozen others have placed him in the forefront of British poetry. At the death of Robert Bridges, he became Poet Laureate of England. Masefield's sympathies are strongly on the side of the "scorned — the rejected — the men hemmed in with the spears."

GEORGE MEREDITH (1828–1909) was born in Portsmouth, Hampshire, England. He was sent to school in Germany. Returning to England at the age of sixteen, he was articled to a solicitor in London; but after an inauspicious start in the law, he soon turned to journalism. He was for many years the literary adviser of the London publishers, Chapman and Hall. His literary work falls into two classes: his novels and his poems. Of the first, *The*

Ordeal of Richard Feverel and *The Egoist* are perhaps the most important. In the latter field, his *Poems and Lyrics of the Joy of Earth* and *A Reading of Earth* testify to his powerful mind and a love of nature second only to Wordsworth's in grandeur and profundity.

JOAQUIN MILLER (1841–1913). Cincinnatus Heine Miller, the poet of the West, was born in Indiana. His life was one long adventure; he pursued many vocations and professions, becoming a miner in California, a judge in Oregon, and an editor in New York City. His best poetry is found in the volumes, *Songs of the Sierras* and *Songs of the Desert*.

EDNA ST. VINCENT MILLAY (1892–   ) is one of America's greatest poets. Born in Rockland, Maine, she attended Vassar College. It was at Vassar that she wrote her celebrated poem, *Renascence*. There followed *Figs from Thistles* (1920), *Second April* (1921), *The Harp-Weaver and Other Poems* (1924), and more recently, *The Buck in the Snow* and *Conversations at Midnight*. Miss Millay has been honored with the Pulitzer Prize. In 1927 she contributed the libretto for Deems Taylor's opera, *The King's Henchman*, an instantaneous success. Her work, in the varied moods of poetry, is marked by passages of extraordinary beauty and depth of feeling.

JOHN MILTON (1608–1674) is one of the grandest figures in English poetry. Educated at Cambridge, he early manifested an extraordinary talent, which expressed itself, soon after graduation, in the celebrated poems, *L'Allegro* and *Il Penseroso*. The death of a friend inspired that sublime elegy, *Lycidas*. Entering the service of Cromwell, he suspended his poetic powers for a time; but the fall of the Commonwealth having provided him with the necessary leisure, he set to work again and produced *Paradise Lost*, *Paradise Regained*, and the Biblical play in the Greek manner, *Samson Agonistes*. Milton's sonnets rank among the best in any literature.

WALTER MITCHELL was born in Nantucket, Massachusetts, in 1826. After graduation from Harvard, he entered the ministry and became an editorial contributor to *The Churchman*. He wrote some verse and one distinguished novel, *Bryan Maurice*.

HAROLD MONRO (1879–   ) is a British critic, poet, and anthologist. His *Collected Poems* appeared in 1933.

HARRIET MONROE (1860–1936) was the founder and editor of *The Poetry Magazine*. More than any other editor in America, she encouraged the art of poetry in this country. In fact, she practically devoted her life to it. In *Chosen Poems* (1935) will be found ample evidence of her own creative talent.

MINNIE HITE MOODY (MRS.) is an American author. In 1936 she published *Death is a Little Man*.

WILLIAM VAUGHN MOODY (1869–1910) was born in Spencer, Indiana, and after graduation from Harvard, taught at the University of Chicago. His *Poems and Poetic Dramas* exhibit an ardent and lofty temperament with a rare lyrical gift.

CHRISTOPHER MORLEY (1890–   ) is an American of English parentage. After graduating from Haverford College, he became a journalist in Philadelphia. Soon, however, he settled down to a career as a writer of belles-lettres, novels, and verse. The range of his literary activity is extraordinary. He has written some of the best essays of the age, also several outstanding novels, of which *Where the Blue Begins* and *Thunder on the Left* might be mentioned. His poetry, while less voluminous than his prose, is no less distinguished.

RICHARD KENDALL MUNKITTRICK (1853–1911) was a humorous prose writer and poet well known to Americans in the closing years of the nineteenth century. His best poems are found in *The Acrobatic Muse* and *The Moon Prince and Other Nabobs*.

JOHN G. NEIHARDT (1881–   ) was born in Sharpsburg, Illinois. After a period of study at Nebraska Normal College, he took up his residence among the Omaha Indians, learning their legends and their folkways. *The Song of Hugh Glass*, *The Song of Three Friends*, and *The Song of the Indian Wars* are interesting contributions toward an epic cycle dealing with pioneer life in the West.

SIR HENRY NEWBOLT (1862–   ) was born in Bilston, Staffordshire. In *Admirals All* (1897) he produced a number of rousing narrative poems which became immediately popular.

GRACE FALLOW NORTON (1876–   ) is a poet and translator. Her books of verse include *Roads* and *The Sister of the Wind and Other Poems*.

WILLIAM OLDYS (1696–1761) was a British scholar, bibliographer, and poet.

GEORGE O'NEIL (1898–   ) was born in St. Louis, Missouri. He is a dramatist and novelist of real distinction. His volumes of verse, *The Cobbler in Willow*, *The White Rooster*, and *God-Beguiled*, exhibit an authentic talent.

JAMES OPPENHEIM (1882–1933) was born in St. Paul, Minnesota. After some years in social service, he embarked upon a literary career. His *Songs for the New Age* (1914) and *The Sea* (1923) reveal a profound love of truth and beauty. His verses are often Biblical in their rhythm and grandeur.

WILFRED OWEN (1893–1918) was, like Brooke, a victim of the World War. Born in Oswestry, England, he matriculated at London University, and at the outbreak of hostilities, enlisted in the Artist's Rifles. He was killed in action a few days before the Armistice. His *Poems* (1920) revealed the splendid promise of his art.

DOROTHY PARKER (1893–   ) is an American satirist and short-story writer, famous for her wit. Her volumes of verse include *Laments for the Living* and *Enough Rope*. She has also written an interesting book of short stories, *After Such Pleasures*.

STEPHEN PHILLIPS (1868–1915) was an English poet with a marked dramatic bent. During the years of his supremacy on the stage, he gave an enormous impetus to blank verse drama. *Herod* (1900) and *Ulysses* (1902) were enthusiastically received. His lesser poetry appears to advantage in the volume, entitled *Lyrics and Dramas*, published in 1913.

EDGAR ALLAN POE (1809–1849) was born in Boston, the child of actors, who died while he was yet an infant. He was adopted by John Allan, a prosperous merchant of Richmond, who does not

seem to have sympathized with the boy or to have fully appreci-
ated his genius. It is a fact, however, that Edgar was a law unto
himself, headstrong and intractable. After a period of residence
at the University of Virginia, he ran away to Boston. Later, he
entered West Point and was discharged for insubordination.
After a final estrangement with John Allan, he drifted into journalism, became editor of the *Southern Literary Messenger* and various
other magazines, removed to New York, married Virginia Clemm,
his thirteen-year-old cousin, and lived in his Fordham cottage in
well-nigh hopeless poverty. The death of Virginia was a blow
from which he did not recover. He died in the streets of Baltimore under mysterious circumstances. There is little need to
discuss his poems or to analyze the reason for their world-wide
fame. Poe's work belongs to the ages.

ALEXANDER POPE (1688–1744) is the outstanding figure of the
so-called "classic age" in English poetry. Born and educated in
London, physically unprepossessing, for he was dwarfed and un-
healthy, he was the poet of town life, brilliant, satirical, sometimes
vindictive. His great intellect was well served by his masterly
use of the heroic couplet, as witness his memorable *Essay on Man*
and *Essay on Criticism*. Pope also distinguished himself by trans-
lating Homer's *Iliad*. This poet composed many lines that have
often been quoted. "Hope springs eternal in the human breast,"
is one such quotation; again, "The proper study of Mankind is
Man." No inspiring or exalted artist, he was nevertheless a
supremely witty and careful craftsman.

LIZETTE WOODWORTH REESE (1856–1936) was born in Maryland. She taught English in the Western High School, Baltimore,
and after a long period of service retired in 1921. In her volumes,
A Wayside Lute and *Wild Cherry*, she displayed a quiet yet authentic poetic gift. Her most famous poem, one of the greatest
of recent times, is her sonnet, *Tears*.

LOLA RIDGE was born in Ireland, moved to Australia, and finally
settled down to pursue the poet's craft in this country. She is an
ardent champion of the cause of labor. Her long poem, *The*

Ghetto, is one of the most powerful poems of modern times.   Her *Firehead* is a worthy successor.

JAMES WHITCOMB RILEY (1853–1916) was one of the most popular of American poets.   His chief interest was in the common people, their folkways, their speech, their sentiments.   These he put into tender and humorous verse.   It will be a long time before readers will forget his poems, *When the Frost is on the Punkin, Little Orphant Annie,* and *The Raggedy Man.*   His best known volumes are *The Ole Swimmin' Hole* and *Rhymes of Childhood.*

ELIZABETH MADOX ROBERTS (1886–   ) is a native of Kentucky.   Though often ill, she has written much prose and some verse.   Her novels exhibit an extraordinarily sensitive analyst of human nature.   *Under the Tree* is a significant work in verse.

EDWIN ARLINGTON ROBINSON (1869–1935) was born in Head Tide, Maine.   He attended Harvard for two years, moved to New York, and lived a necessitous existence there for many years.   It is to the credit of Theodore Roosevelt that he helped relieve the poverty of the poet by giving him employment in the New York Customs House.   Robinson's last years were more prosperous, however; he spent his summers at the MacDowell Colony in Peterborough, New Hampshire, and his winters in cherished seclusion in New York.   He was an unusually shy and sensitive person. *Captain Craig, The Man Who Died Twice, Tristram,* and half a dozen other masterly volumes tell the story of Robinson's notable achievement as a poet.   He was perhaps the most subtly analytical and truly discerning of latter-day poets.

RONALD ROSS (1857–1932) was a British physician and bacteriologist.   He was born in Almora, India.   He entered the Indian medical service and by a series of experiments discovered that malaria is spread by mosquitoes.   Besides various medical and scientific works, he wrote *Memoirs* (1923).

CARL SANDBURG (1878–   ) was born of Swedish parents in Galesburg, Illinois.   In early youth he sought a livelihood in various laborious occupations, becoming a porter, truckhandler, dishwasher, harvest hand, and finally a journalist.   He became famous with *Chicago Poems* which appeared in 1916. *Smoke and Steel* and *Good Morning, America* have repeated the theme found in his first volume — his emphasis on the rights of the common man, his robust preoccupation with the argot and the manners of the American folk. Sandburg's chief virtue is this faithful presentation of the common people, in whom he revels with a true democrat's delight. His *Rootabaga Stories* for children and his monumental *Life of Abraham Lincoln* have shown his solid powers as a writer of prose.

Lew Sarett (1888–   ) was born in Chicago and passed his childhood in Michigan and Northern Wisconsin. To pay his way through college, he became a guide among the Chippewas. His early poems were the result of chanting Indian songs. Better than any other contemporary American poet, he knows how to "write an Indian poem with the beat of Indian music." His books include, among others, *Slow Smoke* and *Wings Against the Moon*.

Siegfried Sassoon (1886–   ) was another English poet who served in the World War with distinction. He fought in France and Palestine, winning the Military Cross for heroism. In *The Old Huntsman* (1917), *Counter-Attack* (1918), and *Satirical Poems* (1926) Sassoon displays a variety of gifts, chiefly irony and a lyric anger. He is outspoken against the honors of war and the many brutalities of modern life.

John Godfrey Saxe (1816–1887) was an American satirist and humorous poet. He was the author of *Leisure-day Rhymes* and of *Masquerade and Other Poems*.

Alan Seeger (1888–1916) was born in New York. At the beginning of the World War, he enlisted in the Foreign Legion of France. He died in action on July 4, 1916, near the village of Belloy-en-Santerre. His *Collected Poems* appeared in 1916.

William Shakespeare (1564–1616) is the world's greatest poet and dramatist. Born in Stratford-on-Avon, he early became enamored of the stage, and as soon as opportunity offered, moved to London to take up the precarious career of actor and dramatic hack. In the latter rôle soon outdistancing his rivals, he scored one success after another in comedy, fantasy, and tragedy. There are no greater comedies in the whole range of world literature than *A Midsummer-Night's Dream* and *As You Like It*. Similarly, in the field of tragedy, *Macbeth*, *Hamlet*, *Othello*, and *King Lear* remain unapproached, almost unapproachable. It must not be forgotten that Shakespeare is our greatest poet as well as greatest dramatist. His dramas are filled with unforgettably beautiful lyrical snatches. His *Sonnets* are equally remarkable.

PERCY BYSSHE SHELLEY (1792–1822) was born near Horsham, Sussex. An unhappy boy, scorned by his fellow pupils at Eton, he paid a great price for his original and independent mind. At Oxford he published a work entitled *The Necessity of Atheism* and was promptly expelled. Associating himself with the liberal philosopher and reformer, William Godwin, he produced a series of great poetic works, among them *Prometheus Unbound*, *Revolt of Islam*, and *Hellas*, which deepened a talent already indicated by the earlier *Queen Mab*. Sailing to Italy under a cloud because of the drowning of his first wife, Harriet, he passed there the few remaining years of his ill-starred life. He was drowned in a storm off Leghorn. Some of his shorter poems are the adornment of our literature, as witness *Ode to the West Wind*, *To a Skylark*, and *To Night*.

SIR PHILIP SIDNEY (1554–1586) was a fascinating Elizabethan figure who fought wars and wrote books with equal verve. His death at Zutphen is memorable; it was he who, dying himself, denied himself a cup of water that he might present it to a stricken soldier beside him. His sonnets, included under the title *Astrophel and Stella*, rank with those written by Shakespeare and Spenser. Sidney was also the author of the celebrated critical study, *An Apology for Poetry*, and of the novel, *Arcadia*.

HORACE SMITH (1779–1849) was an English humorist, the celebrated author of *Rejected Addresses*.

ROBERT SOUTHEY (1774–1843) was a prolific English writer who by sheer industry climbed to a high place in the world of letters. He even became the poet laureate, filling the office just before

Wordsworth. While he produced several fine works of prose, notably *The Life of Nelson*, he is remembered today only for three or four short lyrics.

STEPHEN SPENDER is a British poet who has turned from liberalism to the ardent championship of the laboring classes. In *Poems* (1933) and *Vienna* (1934), he reveals his social and political views in vivid and eloquent terms.

LEONORA SPEYER (1873–   ) was born in Washington, D.C. In her girlhood she was a professional violinist. She married Sir Edgar Speyer, a celebrated English musician. Her poetry has a music as individual as her own distinctive personality.

JAMES STEPHENS, born in Dublin in 1882, is one of the most fascinating of present-day writers. His novels, *The Crock of Gold* and *Mary, Mary*, are delightful examples of Celtic wit and imagination at their best. His verse is no less satisfying. His *Collected Poems* (1926) reveal a puckish fancy, not without its moments of pathos and wisdom.

ROBERT LOUIS STEVENSON (1850–1894) was born in Edinburgh, Scotland. After studying law, he was admitted to the bar, but soon found the legal profession uncongenial, especially since he discovered in himself a marked talent for literature. Best known as a novelist and essayist, he could write verse with the best of lyricists. *A Child's Garden of Verses* is a children's classic. *Underwoods* and *Ballads* are also deservedly popular.

JESSE STUART (1907–   ) is a Southerner who leaped to fame with the publication of a volume of sonnets, *Man with a Bull-Tongue Plow*. The book is chiefly remarkable for its understanding of the Southern hill folk, whose idiom and passions it faithfully records. He has also written a volume of short stories, *Head o'-Hollow*, and an autobiography.

SIR JOHN SUCKLING (1609–1642) was a soldier, a member of Parliament, and a great gallant. His verse is witty and often cynical.

ROBERTA T. SWARTZ (1903–   ) was born in Brooklyn, New York. She is a graduate of Mount Holyoke, class of 1925.

JOHN BANNISTER TABB (1845–1909) was born in Amelia County,

Virginia. He was on the Southern side in the War Between the States, serving for a time on a blockade-runner. Ordained as a Catholic priest in 1884, he continued the writing of devotional songs, wherein he excelled. For a long period he was professor of English at St. Charles College, Ellicott City, Maryland.

BERT LESTON TAYLOR (1866–1921) was a Chicago journalist whose daily column won nation-wide attention. His humorous verses inspired many of our contemporary wits and versifiers. In *A Line O' Verse or Two, Line O' Type Lyrics,* and *Motley Measures* he exercises the comic muse with infectious abandon.

SARA TEASDALE (1884–1933) was born in St. Louis, Missouri. *Rivers to the Sea* (1915), *Love Songs* (1917), *Flame and Shadow* (1920), and *Dark of the Moon* (1926) raised her to the front rank of American poets. For sheer melody and haunting beauty of phrase, she has rarely been surpassed in the whole range of the American lyric.

ALFRED LORD TENNYSON (1809–1892) was born in Lincolnshire, England. His father, who was a clergyman, encouraged his literary tastes. He attended Trinity College at Cambridge where he struck up a friendship with Arthur Hallam, in memory of whom he later composed his famous elegy, *In Memoriam.* From early youth he wrote copiously and by 1850 had attained such fame that he was the logical successor to Wordsworth as poet laureate. Thenceforward, he lived a secluded life, chiefly on the Isle of Wight, becoming a celebrated international figure. He died in 1892 and was buried in Westminster Abbey. Among his celebrated works are *Poems* (1842), *The Princess, Maud,* and *Idylls of the King.*

EDWARD THOMAS (1878–1917) was a British poet who fought in the World War and was killed in action at Arras, France. His *Poems* (1917) were produced under the encouragement of his fellow-poet and friend, Robert Frost, while the latter was on a visit in England. Thomas, like Frost, had a great love for the common miracles of daily life.

FRANCIS THOMPSON (1857–1907) was born in Preston, Lancashire. In his youth he was poor to beggary, once being obliged to sell matches in London. Befriended by the Meynells, he soon showed his mettle as a poet, especially with the production of that fine mystic poem, *The Hound of Heaven.*

EUNICE TIETJENS (1884–   ) was born in Chicago, Illinois. For some years she was Associate Editor of *Poetry: A Magazine of Verse.* She has also served as foreign correspondent for the *Daily News* of Chicago. Her *Profiles from China* (1917) is one of her better books.

HENRY TIMROD (1829–1867) was born in Charleston, South Carolina. When the War Between the States broke out, he became a correspondent of a Southern newspaper. Ruined financially when hostilities ceased, and his health undermined, he lingered a few short years before he died of tuberculosis at Columbia. An edition of his poetry appeared posthumously, edited by Paul Hamilton Hayne.

RIDGELY TORRENCE (1875–   ) was born in Xenia, Ohio. He has been associated in an editorial capacity with various magazines, among them *Cosmopolitan* and *The New Republic.* Two volumes of verse have come from his pen — *The House of a Hundred Lights* (1900) and *Hesperides* (1925). He has also written several plays.

HERBERT TRENCH (1865–1923) was an English poet, playwright, and translator.

NANCY BYRD TURNER (1880–   ) has published *Star in a Well* (1935). She has also written prose works on the life of George Washington.

LOUIS UNTERMEYER (1885–   ) is a native of New York City. His best volumes of poetry are *Challenge* (1914) and *Burning Bush* (1928). He is also a distinguished critic, translator, and anthologist. His translation of Heine's poetry exhibits scholar and poet in perfect union. His *Collected Parodies* (1926) displays the lighter qualities of his many-sided talent.

ARTHUR UPSON (1877–1908) has written *The Tides of Spring and Other Poems.*

HENRY VAN DYKE (1852–1933) was born in Pennsylvania and educated at Princeton. For some time he was a clergyman, a calling which he abandoned to become professor of English at Princeton. Besides much serious verse, van Dyke left a considerable volume of interesting essays.

HENRY VAUGHAN (1622–1695) was chiefly interested in religious poetry. He was educated at Oxford and later became a physician. His verse is deeply mystical.

WILLARD AUSTIN WATTLES (1888–   ) has written *Lanterns in Gethsemane: a Series of Biblical and Mystical Poems in regard to the Christ in the Present Crisis*.

JOHN VAN ALSTYN WEAVER (1893–1938) came into notice with his *In American — Poems* (1928). Several subsequent volumes of verse were less successful. He collaborated with George Abbott on a play, *Love 'Em and Leave 'Em*.

WINIFRED WELLES (1893–   ) was born in Norwichtown, Connecticut. She was one of the editors of *The Measure*, a poetry magazine founded by Genevieve Taggard. She has written several delightful volumes of verse, among them *The Hesitant Heart* and *This Delicate Love*.

CAROLYN WELLS is an American humorist, anthologist, novelist, and poet.

JOHN HALL WHEELOCK (1886–   ) was born in Far Rockaway, Long Island. He was graduated from Harvard in 1908 and completed his studies at the Universities of Göttingen and Berlin. He has written many volumes of poetry but his first, *The Human Fantasy*, is perhaps his best.

JOSEPH BLANCO WHITE (1775–1841). This English poet composed one poem, *To Night*, which many critics consider one of the greatest sonnets in the language. His other work has long since been forgotten.

WALT WHITMAN (1819–1892) was born in West Hills, Long Island. After a scanty education, he came to Brooklyn, where for many years he eked out a precarious livelihood by odd jobs as a journalist. For a short time he was the editor of the *Brooklyn Daily Eagle*. In 1855 he published the first edition of *Leaves of Grass* — perhaps the most important single volume of verse in the history of American letters.   It was little esteemed at the time, but with the years came European approval and admiration. Towards the end of his life, Whitman, then an invalid, found himself the object of wide public acclaim.   His admirers came to do him belated homage in the little house at Camden, New Jersey, now an oft-visited shrine.

JOHN G. WHITTIER (1807–1892) was born in Haverhill, Massachusetts, and received a meager education in the district schools. Inspired in his boyhood days by the poetry of Robert Burns, he resolved to become a poet himself.   After writing for various newspapers and engaging in politics, he moved to Amesbury, Massachusetts, where he resided for the remainder of his long life. Meanwhile he kept up a steady production of verse and prose. His Anti-Slavery poems are now forgotten; but his brief lyrical descriptions of country life are still remembered.   Whittier is one of the truest poets of New England; his lines breathe the manly, patient, freedom-loving qualities which pre-eminently marked their author.

MARGARET WIDDEMER was born in Doylestown, Pennsylvania. After graduation from Drexel Institute in 1909, she went into journalism.   She has written many novels and volumes of short stories.   Her best poems are found in *Factories, with Other Lyrics*, published in 1915.

WILLIAM WORDSWORTH (1770–1850).   Born in The Lake Country of England, Wordsworth early displayed that profound love of nature which he immortalized later in his poetry.   As a young man he visited Paris and imbibed the doctrines of the French Revolution.   Returning to England, he made the acquaintance of William Taylor Coleridge, with whom he collaborated on the epoch-making *Lyrical Ballads*.   Wordsworth's great creative period was the first decade of the nineteenth century, during which time he composed his most beautiful and noble verses.   In later life he became as reactionary as hitherto he had been liberal.   In 1843 he was chosen poet laureate.   Wordsworth is the truest and greatest poet of Nature in the whole range of English literature.

He believed that Nature had a refining and spiritualizing influence on mankind, and set forth this belief in a poetic style which for sheer lyric beauty has never been surpassed.

ELINOR WYLIE (1886–1928) was born in Somerville, New Jersey. Her grandfather was Governor of Pennsylvania; her father, solicitor general under Theodore Roosevelt. After a lengthy stay abroad, she took up residence in New York, and in 1924 married William Rose Benét. In *Nets to Catch the Wind* and *Black Armour* she displayed a magnificent poetic sensibility and an exquisite craftsmanship. She also wrote several outstanding novels, among them *Jennifer Lorn* and *The Orphan Angel.*

WILLIAM BUTLER YEATS (1865–1939) was born in Sandymount, Dublin. He was early in life fascinated by the folklore of his native Ireland and when the Irish Literary Revival swept over the country in the latter part of the century, actively identified himself with the movement. In such plays as *The Land of Heart's Desire* he invigorated the Irish Theater. His *The Wind Among the Reeds* contains some of his most memorable verse. He was awarded the Nobel Prize in Literature.

A Poetry Library

FOR THE STUDENT INTERESTED IN THE APPRECIATION
AND WRITING OF VERSE

Pupils working on the General Questions and Special Assignments will find much to interest them in the following volumes:

JOSEPH AUSLANDER, *Letters to Women*
STEPHEN V. BENÉT, *John Brown's Body*
WILLIAM R. BENÉT, *Man Possessed*
MACKNIGHT BLACK, *Machinery*
ANNA H. BRANCH, *Rose of the Wind*
WILLIAM C. BRYANT, *Collected Poems*
HILDA CONKLING, *Poems by a Little Girl*
NATHALIE CRANE, *The Janitor's Boy*
STEPHEN CRANE, *Collected Poems*
EMILY DICKINSON, *Complete Poems*
RALPH W. EMERSON, *Collected Poems*
EUGENE FIELD, *A Little Book of Western Verse*
ROBERT FROST, *Collected Poems*
O. W. HOLMES, *Collected Poems*
RICHARD HOVEY AND BLISS CARMAN, *Songs of Vagabondia*
LANGSTON HUGHES, *The Weary Blues*
ALFRED KREYMBORG, *Less Lonely*
VACHEL LINDSAY, *Collected Poems*
HENRY W. LONGFELLOW, *Collected Poems*
JAMES R. LOWELL, *Collected Poems*
EDWIN MARKHAM, *Collected Poems*
EDNA ST. VINCENT MILLAY, *Second April*
WILLIAM V. MOODY, *Poems and Poetic Dramas*
EDGAR A. POE, *Collected Poems*
E. A. ROBINSON, *Collected Poems*
CARL SANDBURG, *Selected Poems*

SARA TEASDALE, *Flame and Shadow*
LOUIS UNTERMEYER, *The New Adam*
JOHN V. A. WEAVER, *In American*
JOHN G. WHITTIER, *Collected Poems*
C. E. S. WOOD, *The Poet in the Desert*
ELINOR WYLIE, *Collected Poems*

In British poetry, the works of the following poets will repay study in connection with one or another of the projects listed: Bridges, Brooke, R. and E. B. Browning, Byron; Chaucer, Chesterton, Coleridge, Collins, Cowper; de la Mare; Gibson, Gray; Henley, Herrick, Housman; Keats, Kipling; Masefield, Milton, Morris; C. and D. G. Rossetti; Sassoon, Shakespeare, Shelley, Sidney, Southey, Spender, Spenser, Suckling, Swinburne; Tennyson, Thompson; Vaughan; Wordsworth; and Yeats.

The following anthologies will be found to contain material of use to the student in the preparation of class assignments:

CONRAD AIKEN, *Modern American Poets*
JOHN DRINKWATER and
    HENRY SEIDEL CANBY, *Twentieth Century Poetry*
EDWIN MARKHAM, *The Book of Poetry*
ALFRED KREYMBORG, *Lyric America*
HOUSTON PETERSON, *The Book of Sonnet Sequences*
BURTON E. STEVENSON, *The Home Book of Verse*
LOUIS UNTERMEYER, *Modern American Poetry*

Also:

The Oxford Book of English Verse
C. E. ANDREWS and
    M. O. PERCIVAL, *Romantic and Victorian Poetry*
FREDERICK I. CARPENTER, *English Lyrical Poetry*
A. T. QUILLER-COUCH, *The Oxford Book of Victorian Verse*
FRANCIS T. PALGRAVE, *The Golden Treasury*

BOOKS FOR THE STUDENT
INTERESTED IN THE WRITING OF POETRY

Louis Untermeyer, *Modern British Poetry*

For mastering the technique of poetry the following titles are recommended:

Fernald's or Crabbe's *Synonyms*

Roget's *Thesaurus*

Loring's or Walker's *Rhyming Dictionary*

also

F. B. Gummere, *A Handbook of Poetics*

C. F. Johnson, *Forms of English Poetry*

Louis Untermeyer, *Forms of Poetry*

Clement Wood, *The Craft of Poetry*

Books in the history and criticism of poetry that are well worth the student's attention:

Max Eastman, *The Enjoyment of Poetry*

Alfred Kreymborg, *Our Singing Strength*

Amy Lowell, *Tendencies in Modern American Poetry*

John L. Lowes, *Convention and Revolt in Poetry*

Margaret Wilkinson, *New Voices*

To these may be added the magazine *Poetry* and William S. Braithwaite's annual *Anthologies of Magazine Verse*.

Index of First Lines

Index of Titles

Index of Authors